ELECTRICITY AND ELECTRONICS

ELECTRICITY
AND
ELECTRONICS
Saul A. Ritterman
BRONX COMMUNITY COLLEGE

The Macmillan Company, New York
Collier-Macmillan Limited, London

The Macmillan Company
866 Third Avenue, New York, New York 10022

Collier-Macmillan Canada, Ltd., Toronto, Ontario

Library of Congress catalog card number: 77-160076

5-9-74

First Printing

To My Wife, Katharine, and Our Children

Preface

This book is for students working in any technical field that requires some understanding of electricity and electronics. The intent is to offer a cohesive approach to the topics which are covered and at the same time to include a reasonably diverse selection of material. The material presented in each chapter is a logical extension of information contained in preceding chapters. For instance, the concept of conduction leads to Ohm's Law, which in turn leads to multiloop circuits. This structured developmental process is used throughout; the student, through his comprehensive understanding of electronics, will be able to make practical applications of his knowledge.

The first part introduces the principles of electricity and develops these principles to show practical applications. It also provides the groundwork for the study of electronics in Part II. After a study of diodes, power supplies, transistors, and amplifiers, the last four chapters demonstrate how the principles of electricity and electronics are combined into practical control systems. Examples are provided to show how these systems can be used to control, communicate, compute, and measure both electrical and non-electrical qualities.

Each chapter begins with a brief introduction and ends with a summary. The student will find it useful to read this material before delving into the chapter. This approach highlights the important principles in each chapter so that they can be kept in mind during the actual study of the chapter. Key statements appear in boldface type, permitting the student to concentrate on the text rather than devoting time to underlining or otherwise marking the salient points. Examples and illustrative problems are presented whenever new topics and methods are introduced. Numerous questions and problems follow each chapter.

The book can be used for either the full-year or one-term courses. In the former case the instructor can use all chapters in sequence. For those instructors who desire to use this text for their one-semester combined course, the emphasis on the following sections will be useful:

> 1.1 through 1.5; 2.1 through 2.5; 4.1 through 4.3, and 4.5; 5.7, and 5.8; 6.1, 6.4, 6.6, and 6.7; 7.1, 7.2, 7.4, 7.6, and 7.7; 8.1 through 8.6; 9.1 through 9.3; 10.6, 10.8, and 10.9; 11.1 through 11.4, 11.7, and 11.8; 12.1 through 12.5, and 12.7; 14.1, 14.2, 14.6, and 14.7.

This section comprises roughly half the book, and offers reasonably continuous as well as broad coverage. For many instructors this will prove to be the optimum selection for their one-term course but, based on need and experience, other combinations will certainly be more appropriate. In this respect the book is truly flexible.

Acknowledgment

It is impossible to thank everyone who helped me in preparing this book. Many terms of students asking lots of good questions have steered me to the topics that need emphasis. Others have offered suggestions and still others have typed various portions. Among those I should like to mention by name are Professor Frederick J. Berger of Bronx Community College, Professor Peter Stark of Queensborough Community College, and John Beck and Leo Malek, my editors at The Macmillan Company.

S. A. R.

Contents

PART I ELECTRICITY

PART II ELECTRONICS

PART I ELECTRICITY

Chapter 1 Electrical Fundamentals

1.1   Introduction

Since this book is concerned with electricity and electronics we must begin with a definition of electricity: **Electricity is the study of controlled charge movement.** Thus, if charge can be moved from one location to another in a prescribed manner, it is possible to work virtual miracles. A knowledge of electricity and electronics should be based on an understanding of the methods by which electric charge is made available for controlled movement. This chapter is concerned with techniques for moving charge through various materials which have been found to be important.

1.2   Atomic Theory

An accurate understanding of the nature of charge and charge movement requires some understanding of modern atomic theory. We require at least enough familiarity with atomic principles so that the fundamentals of electricity will be clear.

As we look around us, we see different forms of **matter**. Matter may be defined as anything that has mass and occupies space. The complete absence of matter is **vacuum**. In addition to matter and vacuum there is also **energy**, which may be defined as the ability to do work. Energy may be obtained by mechanical, electrical, chemical, thermal, and optical means. Although Einstein has shown that there is a direct relationship between matter and energy, the two are generally thought of as distinct quantities.

A knowledge of the structure of matter is needed to understand electrical charge and its movement. If a piece of matter is divided into smaller and smaller pieces we can (in principle, although not in practice) obtain the smallest possible piece of that particular form of matter. The smallest amount of a substance that still retains the original physical and chemical properties is called a **molecule.** The molecule is in turn made up of **atoms.** Atoms are the basic building blocks of nature. There are 92 different atoms which occur in nature. The simplest element is hydrogen and the most complex natural element is uranium. There is also an increasing number of larger atoms which have been created artificially, such as plutonium, neptunium, berkelium, and so on.

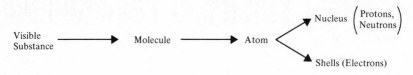

1.1   Subdivisions of matter.

An important characteristic of all atoms is that, regardless of type, they are composed of the same particles. The particles which constitute the atom are smaller than the atom itself and are referred to as subatomic particles. Atoms in the natural state consist of three different subatomic particles: **protons, neutrons,** and **electrons.** Protons and neutrons are in a central core of the atom, called the **atomic nucleus.** Electrons orbit around the nucleus in what are referred to as rings or **shells.** The term **electron shell** is preferable to electron ring since shell indicates the three-dimensional structure of the atom. Forms of matter in order of decreasing mass and size are shown in Fig. 1.1.

Atoms differ only in number of protons, neutrons, and electrons. A carbon atom, for example, contains six protons and six neutrons in the nucleus and six electrons in the shells. A sodium atom has a nucleus which contains 11 protons and 11 neutrons, and the total number of electrons in the shells is 11. A chlorine atom contains 17 protons and 18 neutrons in the nucleus, and 17 electrons in the shells, and so on. Figure 1.2 shows a two-dimensional representation of the carbon atom. Protons and neutrons have approximately the same weight (1.67×10^{-25} grams). The weight of an electron is almost 2000 times less than the proton (approximately 9.1×10^{-28} grams). From an electrical standpoint, of chief concern are the charges of the subatomic particles.

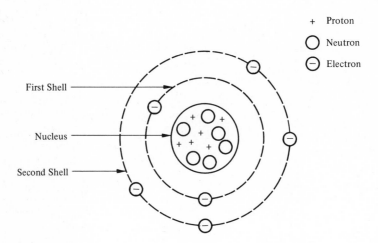

1.2   The carbon atom.

The neutron is electrically neutral. Neutrons are not affected by electrical forces. Protons and electrons are electrically active. This means that protons and electrons will exert forces on other electrons and protons. The proton is said to be positively charged. A proton will be repelled from other positively charged bodies and will be attracted to negatively charged bodies. The electron has a negative charge. That is, electrons and protons have opposite polarity electrical charges. Electrons will be attracted to positively charged bodies and will be repelled from negatively charged bodies. That is, **like charges repel, unlike charges attract.**

Although the proton and electron have very different weights, the magnitude of their electric charge is the same. The charge of a single electron or proton is quite small, and a larger unit of charge is customarily used. The standard unit of charge is the **coulomb.** The coulomb is the combined charge of 6.24×10^{18} electrons or protons. If the charges are electrons we have a negative coulomb and if the charges are protons we have a positive coulomb. In either case the magnitude of the coulomb is the same.

The electrical force with which charges attract or repel each other is described by **Coulomb's law:**

$$F = k \frac{Q_1 Q_2}{d^2}$$ (1.1)

where

    F is the force of attraction or repulsion,

    k is a constant determined by the substance which separates the charges and the units of measurement,

    Q_1 and Q_2 are the charges in coulombs, and

    d is the distance between the charges.

If the polarities of both charges are the same (either both positive or both negative) Eq. 1.1 will have a positive sign. Since like charges repel, a positive sign indicates a force of repulsion. If, on the other hand, Q_1 and Q_2 have opposite polarities Eq. 1.1 will have a negative sign. Since unlike charges attract, a negative sign will indicate a force of attraction.

Equation 1.1 also shows that the force between charges varies inversely as the distance squared. For example, if two charges are separated by a distance and that distance is doubled, the force between the two charges will drop to one quarter of the original value. Similarly, if the distance between the charges is tripled, the force between charges will drop to one ninth of the original value, and so on. This is illustrated in Fig. 1.3.

The electrons (negative charge) in the outer shells of an atom are farther from the nucleus (positive charge) than the electrons in the inner shells. Therefore the force of attraction between the nucleus and the outer-shell electrons is smaller than the force attracting the inner-shell electrons. This is a consequence of the inverse square property of Coulomb's law. In particular, the force between the nucleus and the outermost shell of electrons

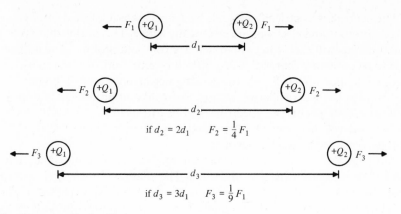

1.3   Illustrating Coulomb's law.

is much smaller than the force attracting any other shell, since the separation is greatest. This means that the easiest electrons to separate from the parent atom are those in the outermost shell.

What we have said is that Coulomb's law indicates that electrons in the outermost shell are least attracted to the positively charged nucleus. Therefore a minimum amount of external energy will be required to remove an electron from the outer shell. According to the laws of modern physics, the energy of electrons can be increased only by specific amounts called **quanta.** If an amount of energy other than a quantum is added nothing will happen. However, if a quantum of energy is added electrons may either change orbits or be emitted from the outermost shell. The amount of external energy required to cause an electron to be emitted is a specific amount, but it depends on the initial energy of the atom. The energy levels of atoms in a piece of matter will vary from atom to atom. Therefore, instead of a specific energy level required for emission of electrons there will be a permissible energy band.

Before any electron is emitted an atom is electrically neutral; that is, there are as many protons as there are electrons so that the total overall charge is zero. After an electron is emitted the parent atom is positively charged, since there is now one less electron than the number of protons. The negatively charged electron which is emitted is called a **free electron**. The word "free" indicates that it is free of the parent atom and may wander about the material. "Free" does not mean that it was obtained without any effort. Rember that a quantum of energy had to be added to remove the electron from the outer shell.

As we go from lighter to heavier atoms, the number of electrons increases by one, as does the number of protons, so that the charge neutrality of atoms is maintained. The manner in which the increase in electrons takes place is important.

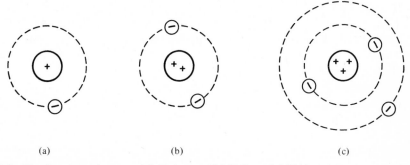

1.4 The first three elements. (**a**) Hydrogen. (**b**) Helium. (**c**) Lithium.

There is a maximum number of electrons that can exist in any shell. The innermost shell can contain a maximum of two electrons. Hydrogen is the lightest element, consisting of a single proton in the nucleus and a single electron. The next heavier element is helium, which has two protons and two electrons. Two electrons is the maximum for the first shell, so the next heavier atom will have two shells of electrons. After helium there is lithium, which has three protons and three electrons. Two electrons are in the inner shell and the remaining electron is in the second shell. This situation is illustrated in Fig. 1.4. The maximum number of electrons in the second shell is eight. Thus the element which has 11 protons and 11 electrons will have

$$
\begin{aligned}
\text{first shell} &= 2 \text{ electrons} \\
\text{second shell} &= 8 \text{ electrons} \\
\text{third shell} &= 1 \text{ electron} \\
\hline
&= 11 \text{ electrons}
\end{aligned}
$$

This particular element is sodium.

Each shell has a maximum number of electrons; the maximum number of shells is seven. The nature of atomic structure is such that atoms attempt to complete electron shells. Since this is generally not the case, the atoms resort to sharing outer-shell electrons with adjacent atoms. This, in fact, is the basis of the chemical bond. Electrons in the outermost shell which take part in the sharing process are called **valence electrons.** For example, we have just seen that sodium has one electron in the third shell. Chlorine has seven electrons in the third shell, and the maximum number in the third shell is eight electrons. If a sodium atom and a chlorine atom share their valence electrons, both achieve a complete third shell. The resulting molecule is sodium chloride (table salt) which interestingly enough has none of the properties of either sodium or chlorine. Apparently there is a good deal involved in sharing valence electrons.

It is also possible for atoms of the same type to share valence electrons. For example, two atoms of hydrogen can share their single electrons to form a complete two-electron shell; this results in a hydrogen molecule. If atoms of the same type share electrons to complete the outermost shell this is called a **covalent** bond.

The spacing between atoms determines the character of the substance. Substances in which atoms are separated by distances which are large compared to the size of the atoms are the gases: hydrogen, oxygen, cooking gas, and so on. Substances in which atoms are closer together but can still "slide" over each other are the liquids: water, oil, acid, and so on. Substances in which atoms are closer together than in liquids are the solids: iron, wood, carbon, and so on. Except for living cells most solids are crystalline in nature. A **crystal** is a substance in which there is an ordered arrangement between the atoms which is repeated throughout the material.

1.3   Conductors

We have seen that atoms are electrically neutral since they contain the same number of electrons as protons. Moreover, charge neutrality is preserved when atoms combine to form molecules. From an electrical standpoint, **atoms are of interest since they are the source of free electrons.** We have already mentioned that energy is required to remove electrons from atomic shells. The energy required to generate these free electrons can be of several forms. Heat and light are two forms of energy which can be used to obtain free electrons. If a substance is heated the electrons in the outermost shell may increase their energy to a level which is sufficient to break the attraction of the nucleus. This concept can be stated in terms of required energy bands. Each shell contains electrons with specific energy bands. The outermost or valence band is the one with the lowest energy. If the correct quantum of energy is added, electrons from the valence band become free electrons. Free electrons are also called conduction-band electrons.

It is not necessary actually to add heat to a substance to obtain free electrons. Any material is always at some temperature above absolute zero, and the thermal energy corresponding to that temperature will be sufficient to generate some free electrons. However, whenever there is a temperature change the number of free electrons must also change. Similarly, changes in light intensity will cause changes in the number of free electrons. Thus the energy dependence of the number of free electrons provides the basis for electronic thermometers and photographic light meters.

Free electrons are always in motion within a material, but these movements are in random directions. As a result the average motion of electrons in any particular direction is zero, as illustrated in Fig. 1.5. Electric **current** is a directed flow of electrical charge. To get a directed flow of charge a force

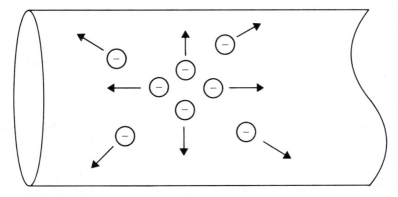

1.5   Random motion of free electrons.

which exploits the nature of charged particles must be used. **The force required to move charges must rely on attraction and repulsion of charges.**

For example, if a sample of material is placed between a positively charged body and a negatively charged body a current will flow, as shown in Fig. 1.6. The rods may be charged by rubbing with materials which will transfer charge. Depending on the composition of the rod and the cloth, it is possible for electrons to leave the rod and enter the cloth. In this case, since some electrons have been removed from the rod, the rod retains a net positive charge. The cloth, on the other hand, now has excess electrons and therefore has become negatively charged. Such a situation arises when a glass rod is rubbed with a silk cloth.

With different materials it is possible for the rubbing to cause electrons to be transferred from the cloth to the rod. In this case the rod becomes negatively charged while the cloth becomes positively charged. Such a situation

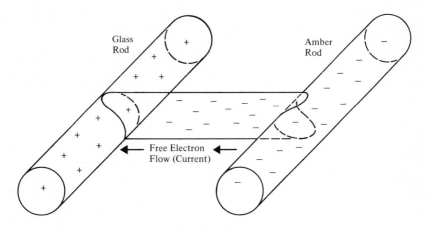

1.6   Direction of current between charged rods.

arises when amber is rubbed with a wool cloth. In fact, the Greek word for amber is electron.

Although a current will flow in a piece of material attached between amber and glass rods which have been rubbed with the proper materials, this is obviously not a practical situation. To maintain the charge the rods would have to be rubbed continuously or else the charges would soon become neutralized.

A **battery** is a practical example of a force based on separation of unlike charges. In a battery, chemical energy rather than friction is used to obtain centers of positive and negative charge. Therefore, when the terminals of a battery are attached to a piece of material the free electrons are repelled from the negative terminal of the battery and attracted by the positive terminal. The creation of a free electron also means that there is now a positively charged atom, because the atom was originally neutral. However, this positively charged atom does not contribute to the total current since it is tightly bound in the crystalline structure.

Notice that the battery or other source of electrical force does not furnish the free electrons. The free electrons are in the material to which the battery is connected. **The battery directs the flow of electrons by using attraction and repulsion.** A somewhat similar situation exists in a water pump. The pump is not the source of water; water is already there. The pump provides the force to move the water. Similarly, a battery may be considered a pump for free electrons.

The unit of current (I) is measured in **amperes** (Amp.). One ampere is a coulomb of charge flowing past a given point in 1 sec.:

$$I = \frac{\text{coulombs}}{\text{second}} = \frac{Q}{t} \qquad (1.2)$$

where t is in seconds.

In addition, milliamperes (mA), which are thousandths of an ampere, and microamperes (uA), which are millionths of an ampere, are convenient units of current.

Electrical force is required to move charge. This is referred to as electromotive force (emf). The unit of electromotive force which directs the charge is the **volt** (V). One volt is the work (in joules) required to move a coulomb:

$$V = \frac{\text{joules}}{\text{coulomb}} = \frac{W}{Q} \qquad (1.3)$$

Example 1.1 illustrates how these units are used.

Example 1.1.

When a 1.5 V battery is connected to a certain piece of material, 9.36×10^{18} electrons flow past a fixed point in 2 sec. Find the current and the work performed by the battery.

Solution Step 1. Determine the number of coulombs.

$$1 \text{ coulomb} = 6.24 \times 10^{18} \text{ electrons}$$

$$\frac{9.36 \times 10^{18}}{6.24 \times 10^{18}} = 1.5 \text{ coulombs}$$

Step 2. Determine the current.

$$I = \frac{Q}{t}$$

$$= \frac{1.5 \text{ coulombs}}{2.0 \text{ sec}}$$

$$= 0.75 \text{ Amps.}$$

Step 3. Determine the work by solving Eq. 1.3 for W and using the proper values:

$$V = \frac{W}{Q}$$

$$W = VQ$$

V was given as 1.5 volts and Q was found to be 1.5 coulombs.

$$W = 1.5 \times 1.5$$

$$W = 2.25 \text{ joules}$$

Three equations have been presented thus far. These are Coulomb's law, the defining equation for current, and the defining equation for voltage. Notice that all three of these equations have one thing in common. Electrical charge (in coulombs) appears as a dimension. In fact, this is the unique characteristic which distinguishes electrical units from mechanical units. The charge Q will appear in every electrical term and will be absent from all mechanical terms. That is, if a unit reduced to its basic dimensions still retains Q, then it is an electrical unit.

Even at the same temperature different materials will have different free-electron densities; that is, the number of free electrons per cubic centimeter will vary from substance to substance. Atoms which have fewer than four valence electrons are better sources of free electrons than atoms which have more than four valence electrons. The free-electron density (electrons per cubic centimeter) determines the electrical property of a material. Materials which have a very large free-electron density permit large currents to flow and are called **conductors.** Materials which have a very small free-electron density permit only small currents to flow and are called **insulators.** Materials with intermediate free-electron densities permit moderate current flow and are called **resistors.** Table 1.1 compares the free-electron densities.

Table 1.1   Free-Electron Densities

Material	Free electrons/cm³
Conductor	$> 10^{21}$
Resistor	$10^{11}-10^{21}$
Insulator	$< 10^{11}$

The difference between conductors, resistors, and insulators is only a difference in quantity. All three types have free electrons. It is a question of "how many" which determines the classification. The field of electronics needs all three types.

Although the electrical property of a material is determined by its free-electron concentration, it is more customary to use the term **resistance.** Thus a very low-resistance material is a conductor. Similarly, a very high-resistance material is an insulator and an intermediate-resistance material is a resistor. Resistance depends on the geometry of a piece of material as well as on free-electron density. A little consideration will show that geometry must affect resistance. If we have two pieces of the same material and one is longer than the other, the longer piece will have the higher resistance. It is true that the longer piece will have more free electrons, but the electrons will have to travel a greater distance in the longer piece. The greater distance will require more work to move the free electrons and therefore resistance increases as length increases. A useful analogy is an automobile trip. More work is expended in moving an automobile on a long trip than on a short trip. Thus the "resistance" of the long trip is greater.

What if we have two pieces of the same material with equal lengths but different cross-sectional areas? Which piece will have the higher resistance? The piece with the larger cross section has more "paths" for the free electrons. If there are more paths, it is easier for free electrons to travel and the resistance will be lower. Therefore a piece of material with a smaller cross section will have a higher resistance. Again an automobile analogy may be helpful. A multilane road is easier to travel since it has more automobile paths. Hence the "resistance" of a multilane road is lower than that of a single-lane road.

We have seen that resistance depends on free-electron density, length, and area. These results may be put in the form of an equation:

$$R = \rho \frac{L}{A} \tag{1.4}$$

where
   R is resistance (the ohm is the unit of resistance),
   ρ is the resistivity (resistivity is a quantity which depends on free-electron density),

L is the length of the piece of material in centimeters, and
A is the cross-sectional area of the material in square centimeters.
Let us determine the dimensions of ρ. To do this Eq. 1.4 is first solved for ρ:

$$\rho = \frac{RA}{L} = \frac{\text{ohms} \times \text{cm}^2}{\text{cm}} = \text{ohm-cm}$$

Notice that the quantity A/L is a geometric term and will have the dimension of length if consistent units are used for A and L. Centimeters are typically used as a length measurement in the field of electronics. The resistivities of some materials of interest are given in Table 1.2. If the resistivity and geometry of a piece of material are known the resistance may be determined as shown in Example 1.2.

Table 1.2 Resistivity of Typical Materials

Material	Resistivity (ohm-cm)
Carbon	3.5×10^{-6}
Copper	1.72×10^{-6}
Glass	1.0×10^{18}
Lead sulfide	1.0

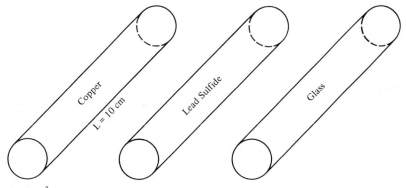

$A = 1 \text{ cm}^2$

1.7 Rods with same dimensions and different resistivities.

Example 1.2.

Rods of copper, lead sulfide, and glass are each 10 cm long and have a cross-sectional area of 1 cm² as shown in Fig. 1.7. Find the resistance of each rod.

Solution Step 1. Since all three rods have the same dimensions, determine the L/A ratio

$$\frac{L}{A} = \frac{10 \text{ cm}}{1 \text{ cm}^2} = \frac{10}{\text{cm}}$$

Step 2. Using Eq. 1.4 we can now insert 10/cm for L/A.

$$R = \rho \frac{L}{A} = \rho \frac{10}{\text{cm}}$$

Step 3. Using the resistivities from Table 1.2 we can now determine the resistance of each rod:

$$R_{\text{copper}} = 1.72 \times 10^{-6} \text{ ohm-cm} \times \frac{10}{\text{cm}} = 1.72 \times 10^{-5} \text{ ohm}$$

$$R_{\text{lead sulfide}} = 1.0 \times 10 = 10 \text{ ohms}$$

$$R_{\text{glass}} = 1.0 \times 10^{18} \times 10 = 10^{19} \text{ ohms}$$

Resistivity, length, and area are factors which are under our control; that is, we can select materials and geometries to give us any value of resistance which we may require. However, Eq. 1.4 does not take into account the effect of temperature on the resistance of a piece of material. While the dimensions of a rod will not change appreciably with moderate temperature changes, the resistivity will change a good deal. This is because resistivity is determined by free-electron density. Since free electrons are a result of thermal energy being added to valence electrons, it is to be expected that free-electron density will vary when temperature changes.

The question is whether resistance increases, decreases, or remains the same as temperature increases. The answer depends on the type of material and in fact all three variations are possible.

In the case of conductors all or almost all of the valence electrons are already free electrons at room temperature. This means that an increase in temperature will not significantly increase the free-electron density. Instead the increase in temperature will increase the energy of the already-existing free electrons. This results in greater random velocities of the free electrons. Since the velocities are higher and random, a battery will be less able to control these higher-energy free electrons. Thus, **an increase in temperature will increase the resistance of a conductor.**

In the case of insulators a temperature increase will have a different effect. Insulators have many valence electrons but very few free electrons. Therefore the effect of a temperature rise will be to increase the free-electron density; that is, the temperature increase will increase the energy of the valence electrons to a level where they become free electrons. Since there are more electrons freed in an insulator, **as temperature increases, the resistance of an insulator decreases.**

At first it may seem odd that the resistance of conductors increases while the resistance of insulators decreases as temperature increases. Resistance depends on resistivity and free electrons determine resistivity. In the case of conductors a temperature rise does not lead to an increase in free-electron density because there are no more valence electrons to be freed. In the case of insulators there are many valence electrons and a temperature rise will free these electrons.

Resistors have free-electron densities which are between those of conductors and insulators. As temperature increases some resistors increase in resistance while others decrease. The determining factor is again the number of and energy of the free electrons. In fact it is possible to combine a resistor whose resistance increases with temperature with a resistor whose resistance decreases with temperature to make a resistor which is not affected by changes in temperature.

We have seen that although resistivity is expressed in ohm-centimeters it is the free-electron density which determines resistivity. Table 1.3 compares conductors, resistors, and insulators in terms of both resistivity and free-electron density.

Table 1.3   Properties of Electronic Materials

Material	Free electron density (electrons/cm^3)	Resistivity (ohm-cm)
Conductor	$>10^{21}$	$<10^{-4}$
Resistor	10^{11}–10^{21}	10^{-4}–10^{12}
Insulator	$<10^{11}$	$>10^{12}$

1.4   Practical Resistors

Resistors are the most common component in electronics. They are made in many sizes and from a variety of materials. Most resistors are of carbon composition; that is, the resistor is made of a mixture of carbon and an organic binder. Usually the organic binder is flour. An insulator is placed around the resistor so that electrical contact will be made only at the lead wires. Carbon composition resistors are available with tolerances of either 5 or 10%.

Wirewound resistors are used when greater accuracy is required. They are made by wrapping turns of a high-resistance wire such as Nichrome around a form. As in the case of the carbon composition resistor, wirewound resistors also have insulating jackets. Even as "simple" an electronic component as a resistor consists of a conductor, an insulator, and a resistor. The external leads are the conductors, the body is the resistor, and the protective jacket is the insulator.

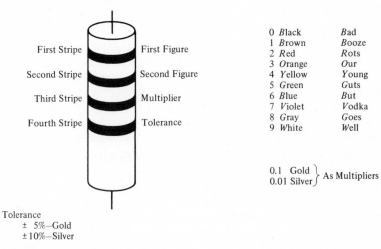

1.8   Carbon composition resistor. *(Courtesy Allen-Bradley Company.)*

First Stripe	First Figure
Second Stripe	Second Figure
Third Stripe	Multiplier
Fourth Stripe	Tolerance

0	*Black*	*Bad*
1	*Brown*	*Booze*
2	*Red*	*Rots*
3	*Orange*	*Our*
4	*Yellow*	*Young*
5	*Green*	*Guts*
6	*Blue*	*But*
7	*Violet*	*Vodka*
8	*Gray*	*Goes*
9	*White*	*Well*

0.1   Gold ⎱
0.01 Silver ⎰ As Multipliers

Tolerance
  ± 5%—Gold
  ±10%—Silver

1.9   Resistor color code.

It is possible to make resistors that have the same size but different resistance. This is accomplished by using materials with different resistivities. In the case of carbon composition resistors the ratio of carbon to flour is varied. In the case of wirewound resistors more turns or different diameter resistance wire is used. Figure 1.8 is a cutaway of a "simple" carbon resistor.

The stripes on the carbon composition resistor are a **color code** which indicates the value of the resistor. There are four stripes. The first stripe represents the first figure, the second stripe the second figure, the third stripe is the multiplier, and the fourth stripe represents the tolerance. Figure 1.9 shows the configuration as well as a mnemonic sentence which has been found helpful in learning the color code. Use of the color code is best illustrated by an example:

Example 1.3.

A resistor is striped yellow, violet, red, and gold. Find the nominal value and the extreme values which are possible.

Solution Step 1. The figures are

$$\text{yellow} = 4 = \text{first figure}$$

$$\text{violet} = 7 = \text{second figure}$$

$$\text{red} = 10^2 = \text{multiplier}$$

The nominal value is 4700 ohms (i.e., 47×10^2 ohms).

Step 2. The gold strip signifies a $\pm 5\%$ tolerance.

$$5\% \text{ of } 4700 = 235 \text{ ohms}$$

Therefore,

$$R_{max} = 4700 + 235 = 4935 \text{ ohms}$$

$$R_{min} = 4700 - 235 = 4465 \text{ ohms}$$

Since the third stripe represents a multiple of 10 it is only possible to have resistors which are multiples of 10 when using the color code. Obviously this means that only a limited number of color-coded resistance values are possible. This is actually an asset rather than a disadvantage. By concentrating on relatively few values of resistance rather than a larger variety costs can be kept down.

Furthermore, the standard values which do exist have been chosen strategically. The standard values in the 10%-tolerance series are obtained by multiplying each previous value by the tenth root of 10 (approximately 1.2) and rounding off. The resulting values are 1.0, 1.2, 1.5, 1.8, 2.2, 2.7, 3.3, 3.9, 4.7, 5.6, 6.8, 8.2, and 10.0 ohms. Any value which is a multiple of 10 of any of these values, up to 22 million ohms, is available as a standard value. The effect of this system is that there is a standard value within 10 % of any resistance we may require. For example, we may need a 90-ohm resistor. Ten percent of 90 ohms is 9 ohms and the 82-ohm standard value is closer than that.

If 10 % is insufficient for our requirements there is also a 5 % series which includes additional values and can place us within 5 % of any desired value. In rare cases greater precison is required and this requires wirewound or some other more accurate type of resistor.

1.5   Semiconductors

In the previous discussion materials that had electrical properties between those of conductors and insulators were called resistors. Resistors might also have been called semiinsulators or semiconductors to indicate properties between insulators and conductors. The term semiinsulator is not used. The term **semiconductor** is reserved for a special class of resistors.

Semiconductors are generally considered to be resistors in which the prime constituent is an element with four valence electrons. Since eight electrons are required to complete the outer shell, semiconductors contain half the required number. Semiconductors are crystalline.

Carbon is an element which has four valence electrons. If a carbon atom forms a covalent bond with four other carbon atoms the outer shell is completed. If this process is performed with four other carbon atoms and then repeated many times a carbon crystal is formed. A carbon crystal is the material which is known as diamond. A diamond, of course, exists in three dimensions, but, for our purpose a two-dimensional representation is sufficient. This is shown in Fig. 1.10. The inner circles represent the carbon nucleus with all the electrons except those in the valence band. The valence electrons (four per atom) are represented by the lines which connect the atoms. Notice that there are eight valence electrons associated with each carbon atom. Four of these are the original valence electrons; the others are those which are shared with adjacent atoms to complete the valence shell. Since only carbon atoms are involved, diamond consists of covalent bonds.

Due to thermal energy some covalent bonds will be broken and a relatively small number of free electrons will exist. Actually diamond is an excellent, although expensive, insulator. As temperature increases more covalent bonds are broken, increasing the free-electron density. At about 2500°F enough covalent bonds have been broken so that the crystal structure cannot support itself and the diamond melts. For reasons that will be explained shortly, diamond is not used as a semiconductor material. The two important elements with four valence electrons which are used to manufacture semiconductors are germanium (Ge) and silicon (Si).

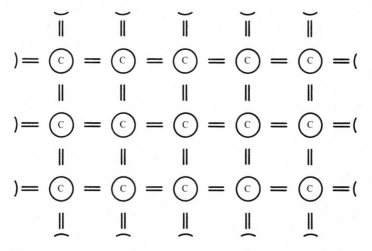

1.10   Diamond crystal in two dimensions.

Pure germanium and silicon are used to make semiconductors. It is interesting to note that there are no other substances which are prepared with such purity and care as are silicon and germanium. The "raw" material for making semiconductors is silicon or germanium which is 99.9% pure. This material is then placed in a quartz container and pulled through a zone refining oven, which is shown in Fig. 1.11. Since the impurities are different from the semiconductor material, the impurities will float in the molten region. As the quartz container is pulled past the heating coils the molten region moves to one end and takes the impurities along to that end. Several passes through the furnace will increase the purity except at the impure end.

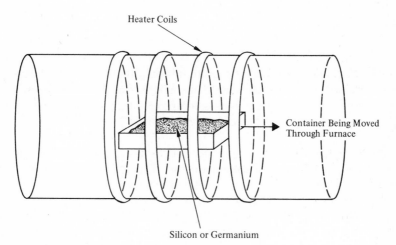

Heater Coils

Container Being Moved
Through Furnace

Silicon or Germanium

1.11   Zone refining oven.

The impure end is cut off, leaving a bar of semiconductor material which is so pure that the impurity level cannot be detected by chemical tests. Instead the purity is determined by an electrical test. Resistivity is measured to determine the level of purity. Pure germanium has a resistivity of 45 ohm-cm and pure silicon, 220,000 ohm-cm. If there are any impurities the resistivity will be lower since there will be more free electrons.

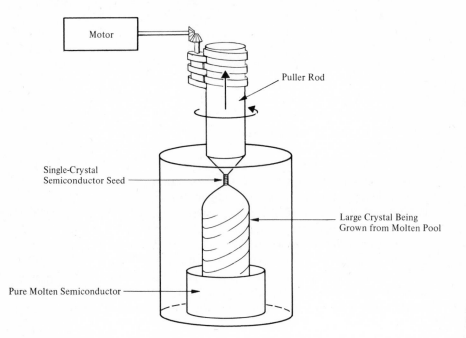

1.12   Crystal puller.

Most electronic applications require not only that the material be ultra-pure, but also that it be in the form of a single crystal. Silicon or germanium which comes out of a zone refiner is composed of many individual crystals which are attached to each other. A single crystal is formed in a crystal puller, which is shown in Fig. 1.12.

A small single crystal of pure semiconductor is attached to a pull rod and inserted into pure molten semiconductor. The rod is slowly withdrawn from the molten material as it is rotated. This results in a single crystal ingot which may be anywhere from 1 to 3 ft long.

A germanium or silicon crystal structure looks like the diamond crystal of Fig. 1.10 except that the carbon atoms are replaced by either silicon or germanium.

1.6   Semiconductor Doping

Although pure silicon or germanium single crystals are required to make semiconductors, the pure form is not used as such. Some elements such as arsenic (As), antimony (Sb), and phosphorus (P) contain five electrons. What happens if an arsenic atom replaces a germanium atom in a germanium crystal? Four of the five arsenic valence electrons replace four germanium electrons. However, the fifth electron from the arsenic atom is still available even though the outer shell is complete. Since there is no bond for this last electron to complete, it exists as a free electron. This is shown in Fig. 1.13. This situation occurs every time an arsenic atom replaces a germanium atom. Therefore, as more and more arsenic atoms replace germanium atoms the crystal will contain more and more free electrons and thus become a better conductor. Notice that the crystal as a whole is still electrically neutral since the arsenic atom contains an additional proton to balance the additional electron electrically. This is the same situation as prevails in conventional conductors. The conductor as a whole is electrically neutral regardless of how many free electrons exist.

In semiconductor work the addition of controlled impurities to a pure crystal is called **doping.** In this case the doping atoms are arsenic. Atoms such as arsenic which contribute free electrons to the crystal are known as **donor atoms.** Since electrons have a negative charge, doping with a valence-five atom is referred to as *n* doping. The donor atoms themselves are restrained within the crystal structure and do not contribute to current flow when a battery is connected.

1.13   *n*-doped germanium.

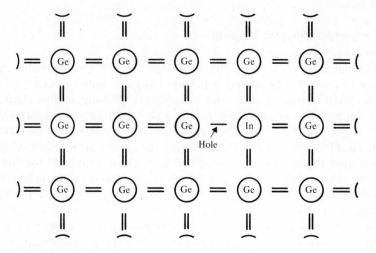

1.14 *p*-doped germanium.

Just as there are valence-five atoms, there are also valence-three atoms. Boron (B), indium (In), and gallium (Ga) are examples of atoms with only three valence electrons. Consider what happens when a valence-three atom replaces one of the original valence-four semiconductor atoms. To complete the bonding four electrons are needed. Since only three electrons are available, all the bonds cannot be completed. The three electrons are shared in the bonding, as shown in Fig. 1.14, but this is insufficient. The crystal structure lacks an electron. Or in semiconductor terminology, the crystal has an excess **hole.**

Since the atom was neutral before the hole was used to replace an electron, the hole has a positive charge. Since holes have positive charge, doping with valence-three atoms is referred to as *p* type doping. Again the entire crystal is still electrically neutral since the doping atom has one less proton. Valence-three atoms are known as **acceptor atoms** since they lack an electron and will therefore accept electrons. As in the case of *n* doping, *p* doping does not upset the charge neutrality of the semiconductor crystal. This is because for every hole there is a corresponding acceptor atom.

What has been said about *n* doping and *p* doping is essentially correct. It should be remembered, however, that the situation is not a static one. Free electrons and holes are moving about in the semiconductor crystal. If an electromotive force such as a battery is connected, electron and hole currents will flow. These currents will be in opposite directions since electrons and holes have opposite polarity.

Prior to doping there were some free electrons in the semiconductor crystal due to thermal energy. Each of the thermally generated free electrons leaves behind a hole, since the vacated site will accept an electron. Therefore, there will be some holes even in a material which is *n* doped. There will, of course, be many more free electrons than holes as a result of doping. It is customary to speak of free electrons as the **majority carrier** and holes as the **minority carrier** in *n*-type material. In *p*-type material, holes are the majority carrier and free electrons are the minority carrier. A pure undoped semiconductor has the same number of free electrons and holes.

It was sufficient to consider free electrons alone in discussing conventional electronic materials. In the case of semiconductors this is not possible. Either the number of free electrons or the number of holes may be increased by doping a semiconductor. Notice that both *n* doping and *p* doping will make the semiconductor a better conductor. In either case the number of current carriers is increased. Conduction in semiconductors is therefore a more complex process since electrons and holes must be accounted for simultaneously.

In conductors, almost every atom contributes a free electron for conduction. In the case of semiconductors this is far from true. A cubic centimeter of germanium which has been purified contains 4.4×10^{22} germanium atoms. There are, however, only 2.4×10^{13} free electrons in 1 cm^3 of germanium. This means that only about one atom out of each thousand million atoms contributes to the conduction process. Doping will add either additional holes or additional free electrons. In either case the semiconductor will become a better conductor as a result of doping. It is customary to speak of light, moderate, and heavy doping. Although the classification is somewhat arbitrary, Table 1.4 gives a realistic breakdown. In terms of an increase in

Table 1.4   Doping Levels in Germanium

Doping	Holes or electrons/cm^3
Light	10^{14}–10^{15}
Moderate	10^{16}–10^{17}
Heavy	10^{18}–10^{19}

free-electron density, even light doping represents a considerable increase over pure germanium. However, in terms of the percentage of atoms contributing electrons to the conduction process the situation is not quite the same. This is illustrated in the following example.

Example 1.4.

Find the percentage of atoms contributing free electrons (or holes) in pure, lightly, moderately, and heavily doped germanium.

Solution Step 1. In pure germanium 2.4×10^{13} out of every 4.4×10^{22} atoms contribute to conduction.

$$\% \text{ conducting} = \frac{\text{atoms conducting}}{\text{total atoms}} \times 100\%$$

For pure germanium this amounts to

$$\frac{2.4 \times 10^{13}}{4.4 \times 10^{22}} \times 100 = 5.45 \times 10^{-8} = 0.0000000545\%$$

Step 2. To be consistent let us select the lower figure in each category of Table 1.4.

$$\text{lightly doped} \% = \frac{10^{14}}{4.4 \times 10^{22}} \times 100 = 2.3 \times 10^{-7} = 0.00000023\%$$

$$\text{moderately doped} \% = \frac{10^{16}}{4.4 \times 10^{22}} \times 100 = 2.3 \times 10^{-5} = 0.000023\%$$

$$\text{heavily doped} \% = \frac{10^{18}}{4.4 \times 10^{22}} \times 100 = 2.3 \times 10^{-3} = 0.0023\%$$

Regardless of the doping level we can see that very small percentages of atoms are involved in the conduction process in a germanium semiconductor. The levels are about the same for silicon. But 1 cm^3 of pure silicon has 5×10^{22} atoms, of which 1.5×10^{10} contribute to the conduction process.

Not only are extremely small percentages involved in conduction, but the resistance of a semiconductor is extremely sensitive to small changes in these small percentages. For example, if the doping level were to change from 1×10^{17} to 1.5×10^{17} the percentage change in doping would be negligible. However, this would change the resistivity by about 50%. It is in the nature of a technological miracle that pure semiconductors can be prepared and that doping levels can be controlled to such fine tolerances.

As in the case of conventional electronic materials, semiconductors are also sensitive to changes in temperature. We saw that conductors experienced an increase in resistance with increasing temperature due to the energy increase of the free electrons. Insulators, on the other hand, experienced a decrease in resistance with increase in temperature due to the increased number of free electrons. In either case the determining factor was the number of electrons. Conductors have many free electrons and insulators have very few. Semiconductors have exactly half the number of valence electrons required to complete a shell (four out of eight). The temperature behavior of semiconductors is even more unusual than in conventional materials.

Up to a point the resistance of a semiconductor increases as temperature increases. That is, the semiconductor is acting the same way a conventional resistor acts. Beyond a certain temperature the resistance of the semiconductor decreases. This is the same performance as was noted for conventional insulators. Figure 1.15 illustrates this. The temperature where the change occurs varies with doping level and with material. For germanium this temperature ranges between room temperature and 150°F. For silicon the temperature at which the resistance characteristic reverses direction is

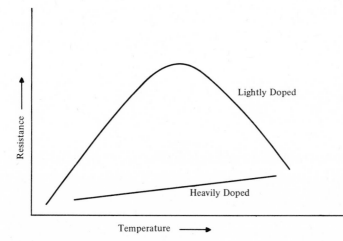

1.15   Semiconductor temperature behavior.

always above 200°F. Figure 1.15 also shows that for a heavily doped semi-conductor the temperature behavior is like that of a conventional conductor. This is because a heavily doped semiconductor has almost as many free electrons (or holes) as a conventional conductor.

The procedure of growing a pure single semiconductor crystal and then doping it either with excess holes or excess electrons is difficult and expensive. If all we are after is a way to manufacture different values of resistance, carbon composition is easier and less expensive. The reason for discussing semiconductors is that they are the materials out of which transistors, integrated circuits, and so on are manufactured. Especially important is the ability to dope semiconductors either with holes or with electrons.

1.7   Vacuum Conduction

Current in both conventional materials and semiconductors is due to attraction and repulsion of charged particles in the material. A source which is external to the material, such as a battery, provides the means of doing the attracting and repelling. From this standpoint conduction in vacuum is impossible. Since a vacuum is the complete absence of matter, there can be neither holes nor electrons in a vacuum. Thus an ideal vacuum is an ideal insulator. Conduction in a vacuum actually refers to the injection into and control of free electrons in an already existing vacuum.

A good (but not perfect) vacuum is first obtained by pumping as much air as is practical out of a glass bottle. The material which will act as the source of free electrons is part of this structure, as shown in Fig. 1.16. The first problem is to inject free electrons from the source into the vacuum. All

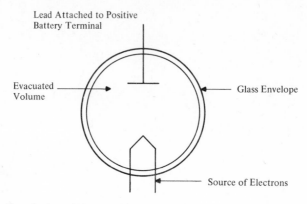

1.16   Injecting electrons into a vacuum.

conductors contain free electrons, and thermal energy is sufficient to permit free electrons to wander within the material. Increasing thermal energy by artificially increasing temperature will generate additional free electrons and also increase the energy of the existing free electrons. If the temperature is made high enough some free electrons will acquire sufficient energy to be "boiled off" the electron source. In this way free electrons are injected into a vacuum. The standard way of heating the material is to use an electromotive force such as a battery.

The temperatures required to impart sufficient energy so that electrons may actually leave the material are rather high. These temperatures range from about 1300°F to 4500°F. Ordinary conductors therefore cannot serve as electron sources for vacuum conduction. They would melt at these temperatures. The material which can withstand such temperatures without melting and still serve as a good source of free electrons is tungsten. To enhance the properties of tungsten, other elements such as barium, strontium, and thorium are frequently used together with tungsten.

Heat is not the only form of energy which can be used to inject electrons into a vacuum. Light may also be used. The phototube is a practical example of the use of light energy to boil electrons off a material into the vacuum.

It is not possible to increase the number of electrons injected into a vacuum indefinitely. The total number of electrons is limited by the fundamental attraction and repulsion properties of charged particles. For every electron which is injected into the vacuum, there is a positively charged atom in the material which is doing the emitting. That is, the tungsten builds up a positive charge as more and more electrons leave the material. The net charge of the emitted electrons is balanced by the equal and opposite positive charge of the tungsten. At some level the tungsten becomes so positively charged that it actually begins to attract electrons from the vacuum back to itself. This is an equilibrium condition. Additional electrons may be injected

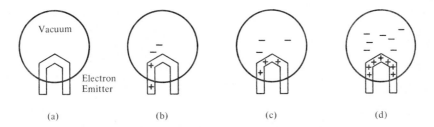

1.17 Electron injection into vacuum. (**a**) No electrons injected if no energy added to emitter. (**b**) Small amount of energy added to emitter. (**c**) Increased energy added to emitter. (**d**) Equilibrium; maximum number of electrons in vacuum.

into the vacuum but an equal number will be simultaneously reabsorbed by the tungsten. This situation is illustrated in Fig. 1.17.

There are some very insignificant differences between conduction in vacuum and conduction in solid materials:

1. A vacuum is a perfect insulator while a solid material contains free electrons or holes. In fact, an electromotive source is required to inject electrons into a vacuum.

2. In vacuum conduction only electrons are involved since only electrons are injected. Solid materials may contain either electrons or holes, or a combination of electrons and holes.

3. A single source of electromotive force is all that is needed for current flow in solids since the free charges are already available. In vacuum two electromotive sources are required: One source injects the electrons into the vacuum; the second source serves the same function as in conduction in a solid. It directs the injected electrons based on attraction and repulsion of charge.

4. In vacuum conduction the same electrons which leave the tungsten must complete the trip through the vacuum to the more positive terminal since these are the only electrons involved. In solid materials very few of the original electrons or holes which are initially directed by the battery make a complete trip through the solid. This is because in drifting toward the positive battery terminal, the electrons undergo collisions with atoms which are in their path. Free electrons may be absorbed during such collisions and other electrons will be ejected from the valence band as replacements. Although the same electrons which start are unlikely to complete the trip, the total number of electrons flowing at any time will remain constant. This is illustrated in Fig. 1.18.

5. In solids relatively small changes in temperature have significant effects on conduction. In a vacuum the tungsten must be at least 1300°F and small changes around room temperature will not be significant. Actually vacuum conduction is not used as such. Vacuum conduction is the basis of vacuum-tube operation.

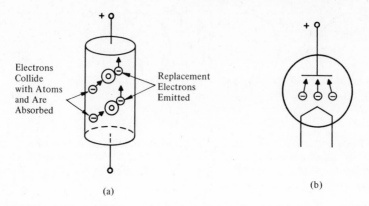

(a)

(b)

1.18 Electron current. (**a**) Solid; electrons collide and are replaced. (**b**) Vacuum; injected electrons make complete trip.

Summary

1. Electronics is the science which deals with controlled movement of electric charge.
2. The outermost electron shell of atoms is the source of electrons for conduction. The coulomb is the unit of charge.
3. Materials are classified as conductors, resistors, or insulators according to their free-electron density.
4. A flow of charges moving in the same direction constitutes a current. The ampere is the unit of current.
5. A device which directs charge based on attraction and repulsion is needed to control current. The strength of such a device is measured in volts.
6. Semiconductors can have either electrons or holes as the principal source of charge.
7. To have conduction in vacuum, electrons must first be injected into the vacuum. In other materials the charges are already available.

Questions

1. What is meant by electronics?
2. What is a free electron?
3. From a charge standpoint, what is the difference between a helium atom and a hydrogen molecule?
4. What is the difference between a positive coulomb and a negative coulomb?
5. How do coulombs and amperes compare with gallons and gallons per minute?
6. To what mechanical unit relating to water flow are volts similar?
7. What is the difference between resistivity and resistance?
8. Archimedes was able to test the purity of a gold crown by using displacement of water. Describe an electronic test to accomplish the same result.
9. Explain why charge neutrality is preserved even after a semiconductor is doped.
10. The first two digits of resistors are the same in every decade. Based on the standard resistor values, what are the first two color stripes of the resistors in any decade?

11. Explain in terms of free-electron density why pure silicon has a higher resistivity than pure germanium

12. What is the principal difference between conduction in solids and conduction in vacuum?

13. Why must air be removed before electrons are injected into a vacuum?

14. What factors limit the number of electrons which can be injected into a vacuum?

Problems

1. Two positive charges are separated by 1 cm. If the separation is changed to 0.5 cm. what is the relationship between the new and old force ?

2. (a) One millionth of an ampere flows in a conductor. How many electrons per second flow past a given point?
   (b) Repeat for 0.001 amp.

3. One ampere flows in a conductor.
   (a) How long does it take for 1000 electrons to flow past a point?
   (b) For 1,000,000 electrons to flow past a point?

4. A piece of copper is 20 cm long and 1 cm in diameter.
   What is the resistance of this piece of copper?

5. A copper wire is 1 cm in diameter. How long will it be if it has a resistance of 1 ohm?

6. A copper rod is 10 cm long and has a cross-sectional area of 1 cm^2. A carbon rod is 9.84 cm long and has a cross-sectional area of 2 cm^2. Which rod has the higher resistance?

7. (a) A resistor is striped brown, red, brown, and silver. Find $R_{nominal}$, R_{max}, and R_{min}.
   (b) What is $R_{nominal}$ if the third stripe is black instead of brown?

8. (a) A certain design requires 25-, 50-, and 75-ohm resistors. Select appropriate resistors from the 10% series.
   (b) Repeat for 250-, 50,000-, and 750,000-ohm values.

9. Find the percentage of atoms contributing electrons for conduction in pure silicon.

10. Repeat for light, moderate, and heavily doped silicon.

Chapter 2 Basic Circuits

2.1   Introduction

The previous chapter introduced the concepts of current, voltage, and resistance. In this chapter important relationships between these quantities are developed. The rest of this book and, in fact, the entire fields of electricity and electronics hinges on the basic relationships between current, voltage, and resistance which are developed in this chapter.

2.2   Circuits

A circuit is a path which permits current to flow. This means that the path must be closed. Free electrons which exist throughout the material constitute the current carriers and these must have a complete path.

Figure 2.1 (a) shows a very simple circuit. There is a battery, a switch, a resistor, some connecting wires, and two meters. One meter is an **ammeter**, which measures current. The other meter is a **voltmeter**, which measures voltage. The circuit of Fig. 2.1 (a) cannot have a current as it is shown, because the switch is open. Therefore there is no complete path for current flow. **No current flows when there is an open circuit.**

If the switch is closed there is a complete path for current flow. **Current flows through a closed circuit.**

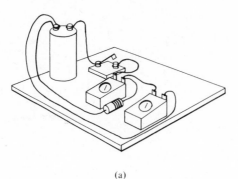
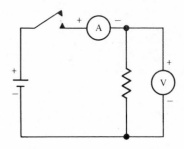

(a)   (b)

2.1   Simple circuit. (**a**) Physical layout. (**b**) Schematic.

The circuit which we are describing is a simple one, and yet it is not easy to make a picture representing this circuit. To overcome this difficulty **schematics** are used in electronics. A schematic is a representation of a circuit using symbols which have been agreed upon. Figure 2.1 (b) shows the schematic for Fig. 2.1 (a). A battery is represented by two parallel lines, one of which is longer. The longer line represents the positive terminal and the shorter line represents the negative terminal. The connecting wires are conductors and are represented by straight lines. The resistor is represented by a zigzag line since it offers greater opposition to current than a conductor. Ammeters and voltmeters are represented by circles which contain an A or a V, respectively. The switch is shown either open or closed as conditions require.

Usually a schematic does not represent the actual physical layout of a circuit or the size of the components. A schematic represents a simple picture of how the various components are interconnected. A **wiring diagram** is used to show the actual physical relationship between components in a circuit. Wiring diagrams are used to assemble circuits; schematics are used to analyze and troubleshoot a circuit.

An ammeter measures the current which flows past any given point in a circuit, so the ammeter must therefore be placed in the circuit.

A voltmeter measures the difference in electronic force which directs charge, based on attraction and repulsion. The voltmeter must therefore be placed between the points whose voltage difference is to be measured. These situations are represented in Fig. 2.1 (b).

Ammeters and voltmeters have positive and negative terminals. The proper polarities must be maintained if the meters are to function. The positive side of the ammeter must be connected to the more positive side of the circuit. More positive means electrically (although not necessarily physically) closer to the positive terminal of the battery.

For example, if we wish to move the ammeter to the negative terminal of the battery, the positive ammeter terminal will have to be placed away from the negative battery terminal. This is illustrated in Fig. 2.2. The positive ammeter terminal is connected to the more positive side of the circuit. In the case of the ammeter in the lower leg of the circuit, this means that the

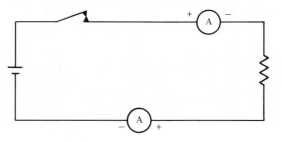

2.2   Proper ammeter polarity.

negative ammeter terminal will be connected directly to the negative battery terminal.

Proper voltmeter polarity must also be observed. The positive terminal of the voltmeter must be connected to the more positive side of the device whose voltage we wish to measure. Similarly, the negative voltmeter terminal must be connected to the more negative terminal of the same device.

The act of making either a voltage or a current measurement requires that we be able to determine on a relative basis which parts of a circuit are more positive than others. Connecting meters incorrectly can cause permanent damage. For example, if an ammeter is connected across a component (the way a voltmeter should be) the ammeter will be destroyed. In less serious cases the meters will attempt to deflect in the reverse direction. Thus we see that to make a simple measurement in a circuit requires some knowledge of how a circuit operates.

Schematics do not usually show meter polarity. The assumption is that if we have enough training to be able to read a schematic then we have enough knowledge to connect meters properly. By the same reasoning, battery polarity is often omitted from schematics.

The direction of current flow is an important consideration in electronic circuits. Based on our present knowledge of the structure of matter, the free electron is the principal charge carrier. This means that in the portion of a circuit which is external to the battery, current flow should be away from the negative terminal of the battery and towards the positive terminal.

Unfortunately, early workers in electricity did not have the mass of information which we have today about the structure of the atom. Early experiments lead to the conclusion that current flowed in the reverse direction. That is, originally it was believed that current flowed from the positive battery terminal through the circuit to the negative battery terminal.

Although we now know that this original assumption was incorrect, most books (including this one) still use the older convention for the direction of current. It is admittedly incorrect but there is no problem as long as we are consistent. It may bother some of us that we are using the incorrect direction

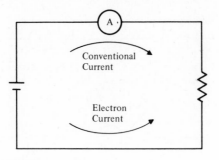

2.3   Direction of current flow.

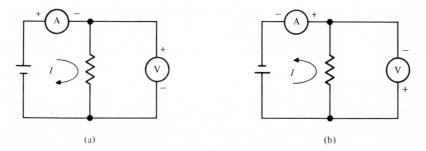

(a)   (b)

2.4 Battery polarity determines current direction. **(a)** Positive current. **(b)** Negative current.

for electron current flow. If this is the case, it may be comforting to realize that the convention which we will be using is correct for hole current, since holes have positive polarity. Figure 2.3 shows the direction of electron and conventional current flow.

If the battery connections in a circuit are reversed, the direction of current flow will also be reversed. This is as it should be since a battery directs charges according to the laws of attraction and repulsion. Reversal of battery polarity is illustrated in Fig. 2.4. In either case the magnitude of the current will be the same. The direction however, will be opposite. It is customary to regard the current in Fig. 2.4 (a) as positive current and the current in Fig. 2.4 (b) as negative current; that is, the currents are in opposite directions. Notice also that meter polarities must be reversed when battery polarity is reversed.

We should always keep in mind that the battery is not the source of free electrons. The connecting wires and the resistor contain free electrons at all times. **The battery furnishes the force which is required to move the free electrons in the same direction.** A flashlight, shown in Fig. 2.5, is one of the simplest examples of a complete circuit. When the switch is open, the electrons in the filament of the bulb and in the adjacent conductors are in random

2.5 A flashlight as a simple circuit. *(Courtesy Union Carbide Corporation.)*

motion, so no current flows. When the switch is closed the battery directs the electrons in the same direction. This current flowing through the filament causes it to glow and there is light.

2.3   Ohm's Law

Although all electrical units contain the dimension of coulombs, we do not usually deal with charge as such. Generally we deal with the derived quantities of current, voltage, and resistance. In 1827, Georg Simon Ohm formulated the law which relates these three quantities. Working with a circuit which was quite similar to that shown in Fig. 2.1, Ohm noted that when the voltage was doubled the current also doubled. Similarly, if the voltage was decreased to half of the original value the current also decreased to half of the original value. This means that current is directly proportional to voltage:

$$I = kV \qquad (2.1)$$

where k is a constant factor. Further investigation by Ohm showed that the constant (k) was equal to the reciprocal of the resistance in the circuit:

$$I = \frac{V}{R} \qquad (2.2)$$

Equation 2.2 is known as **Ohm's law.** It is as important to electronics as $F = ma$ is to mechanics.

All three units in Ohm's law are named in honor of early workers in electricity. Resistance is expressed in ohms. Current is expressed in amperes in honor of Andre Marie Ampère. Voltage is expressed in volts in honor of Alessandro Volta. All three of these pioneers did their work in the early 1800's. Although these men are honored today, it is not always true that significant advances are appreciated as soon as they are discovered. For example, as a result of announcing his discovery Ohm was fired from his teaching position and nearly starved for the next six years.

Ohm's law mathematically relates current, voltage, and resistance. One important result of Ohm's law is that any two of these three quantities determine the value of the third. That is if we specify

1. current and voltage, this determines the value of resistance;
2. current and resistance, this determines the value of voltage;
3. voltage and resistance, this determines the value of current.

These three conditions are demonstrated in Example 2.1:

Example 2.1.

(a) In the circuit of Fig. 2.6 (a) the current is 0.15 Amp. and the battery voltage is 1.5-volts. Find the resistance.

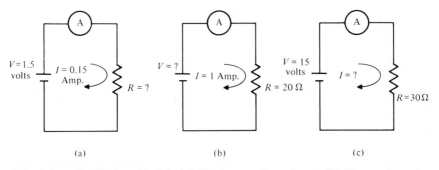

2.6   Schematics for Example 2.1. **(a)** V, I known; determine R. **(b)** known; determine V. **(c)** V, R known; determine I.

(b) In the circuit of Fig. 2.6 (b) the current is 1 Amp. and the resistance is 20 ohms. Find the battery voltage.

(c) In the circuit of Fig. 2.6 (c) the battery voltage is 15-volts and the resistance is 30 ohms. Find the current which flows through the circuit.

Solution for Fig. 2. 6(a) Step 1.   Use Ohm's law to solve for resistance:

$$I = \frac{V}{R}$$

$$R = \frac{V}{I}$$

Step 2.   Insert the known values:

$$R = \frac{1.5 \text{ V}}{0.15 \text{ Amp.}} = 10 \text{ ohms}$$

Solution for Fig. 2.6(b) Step 1.   Solve Ohm's law for voltage:

$$I = \frac{V}{R}$$

$$V = IR$$

Step 2.   Insert the known values:

$$V = 1.0 \text{ Amp.} \times 20 \text{ ohms} = 20 \text{ volts}$$

Solution for Fig. 2.6(c).   Insert known values using Ohm's law:

$$I = \frac{V}{R} = \frac{15 \text{ volts}}{30 \text{ ohms}} = 0.5 \text{ Amp.}$$

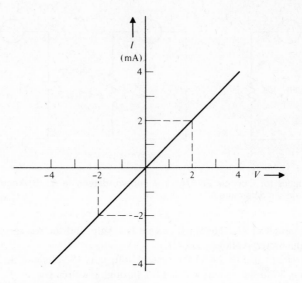

2.7 The *I–V* characteristic of a linear resistor.

It is customary to use the capital Greek letter Ω (omega) as an abbreviation for ohms. For example, schematics will generally indicate a 3300-ohm resistor as 3.3 kΩ, where k = kilo = 10^3. Similarly, M = mega = 10^6. For example, a 3.3-megohm resistor appears as 3.3 MΩ.

Figure 2.7 is a graph of the current-voltage (*I–V*) characteristic of a resistor. It shows the Ohm's law relationship between current and voltage. An increase in voltage results in a corresponding increase in current. Such a relationship is called **linear**; that is, the current is directly proportional to the voltage.

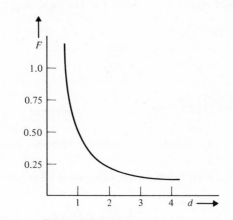

2.8 Coulomb's law; a nonlinear relationship.

Coulomb's law (Eq. 1.1) is an example of an electronic relationship which is **nonlinear**. The electronic force is proportional not to distance but inversely to distance squared and is plotted in Fig. 2.8. Any relationship which does not plot as a straight line is a nonlinear relationship.

Notice in Fig. 2.7 that there is region which has a negative current and a corresponding negative voltage. This is consistent with Ohm's law and is a result of reversing the battery terminals. The corresponding negative voltage causes a current which is equal in magnitude but opposite in sign to flow. For example, referring to Fig. 2.7 we see that if the voltage is 2 volts the resultant current is 2 mA. If we look instead at -2 volts, the resulting current is -2 mA.

In a linear relationship the ratio between the two quantities will be the same at any point. When the two quantities are voltage and current the ratio is resistance. Therefore, by using any point on an $I-V$ characteristic we can determine the value of resistance. For example, from Fig. 2.7 we have

$$R = \frac{E}{I} = \frac{2}{2 \times 10^{-3}} = \frac{-2}{-2 \times 10^{-3}} = \frac{3}{3 \times 10^{-3}} = \cdots = 10^3 \ \Omega = 1 \ \text{k}\Omega$$

so that Fig. 2.7 is a plot of the current through versus the voltage across a $1 \ \text{k}\Omega$ resistor.

Although we have been using Ohm's law to perform calculations, it is important to remember that Ohm's law has a physical meaning and may be stated in words: **In a linear circuit the ratio between voltage and current is a constant and that constant is the resistance.**

Not all resistors obey Ohm's law. Resistors which do not have a linear $I-V$ characteristic are nonlinear resistors. Electronics makes use of both linear and nonlinear devices. Even for linear resistors Ohm's law represents the ideal case. That is, the effects of temperature, pressure, and other factors which will be discussed later are not accounted for. Nevertheless, Ohm's law when properly used is one of the most powerful and frequently used relationships in the entire field of electronics. Also, many other important relationships in electronics are a consequence of Ohm's law.

Ohm's law indicates that an increase in applied voltage results in an increase in current. The increase in current is an increase in the speed of the free electrons. An increase in speed of the free electrons means that there will be an increase in the number of collisions which the free electrons will experience in the same time. Therefore the resistor will become warmer as voltage is increased due to the heat generated as a result of an increased number of electron collisions. That is, more energy will be given off as heat when voltage is increased. **Power is the rate at which energy is used:**

$$P = \frac{\mathscr{E}}{t} \tag{2.3}$$

where

$$P = \text{power}$$

$$\mathscr{E} = \text{energy}$$

$$t = \text{time}$$

In a mechanical system energy may be expressed in foot-pounds, and time in seconds. For example, one horsepower represents 550 foot-pounds per second. The electrical equivalent of power must also be considered. We have just seen that in a mechanical system energy could be expressed in foot-pounds. Energy is the product of distance (foot) and mechanical force (pound). In an electrical system charge (Q) is moved as a result of electrical force (V). Therefore

$$\mathscr{E} = QV \tag{2.4}$$

Since power is the rate at which energy is used we have for electrical power:

$$P = \frac{QV}{t} \tag{2.5}$$

In Chapter 1 we saw that Q/t was the definition of current (Eq. 1.2). Therefore

$$P = IV \tag{2.6}$$

It is informative to determine the dimensions of power using Eq. 2.6. From Chapter 1 (Eq. 1.3) a volt is a joule per coulomb. If we insert the dimensions for current and voltage into Eq. 2.6 the result is

$$P = IV = \frac{\text{coulomb}}{\text{sec}} \times \frac{\text{joule}}{\text{coulomb}} = \frac{\text{joule}}{\text{sec}}$$

A joule/sec is called a **watt.** The watt is also a unit of power, as is the horse-power. It is possible to convert watts to horsepower:

$$1 \text{ hp} = 746 \text{ watts} \tag{2.7}$$

Notice that although it is possible to express power as the product of voltage and current, power is basically not an electrical quantity. This is because power does not contain the dimension coulomb. Of course, this does not mean that power is not important in electronics. It indicates rather that mechanical quantities are vital to electronics. The relationship between horsepower and watts is illustrated in Example 2.2.

Example 2.2.

A certain sports car has a 200-hp engine. Find the equivalent power in watts.

Solution Step 1. Problems in changing units are easily solved by using proportions. In this case we can use Eq. 2.7 along with the proportion

$$\frac{\text{unknown watts}}{\text{watts}} = \frac{\text{known hp}}{\text{hp}}$$

Step 2. Insert the proper values and solve:

$$\frac{\text{unknown watts}}{746} = \frac{200}{1}$$

Unknown watts $= 200 \times 746 = 149{,}200$ watts

By using Eq. 2.6 it is possible to calculate the current if the power and voltage are known. This is illustrated in Example 2.3.

Example 2.3.

Find the current that flows through a 200-watt lamp.

Solution Step 1. Nominal voltage in the United States is approximately 115 volts. This means that the only unknown in Eq. 2.6 is current. Therefore solve Eq. 2.6 for I:

$$P = IV$$

$$I = \frac{P}{V}$$

Step 2. Insert the proper values:

$$I = \frac{200}{115} = 1.74 \text{ Amp.}$$

Increasing voltage across a resistor increases the power which the resistor must dissipate. This means that the resistor will get warmer as voltage is increased. If too much power must be dissipated the resistor will burn out. Electronic circuits require a large variety of power levels. Accordingly, resistors are manufactured in various power ratings. For example there are $\frac{1}{8}, \frac{1}{4}, \frac{1}{2}, 1, 2, 5$, and so on watt resistors. Higher-power resistors are physically larger to permit more heat to be dissipated in the same amount of time. Figure 2.9 shows several resistors of the same value. The smallest one has a $\frac{1}{8}$-watt rating and the largest one has a 2-watt rating.

The power ratings of resistors are based on permissible temperature rise under ideal conditions. That is, a resistor with a specified power rating will have a specified temperature rise when operated at maximum conditions in

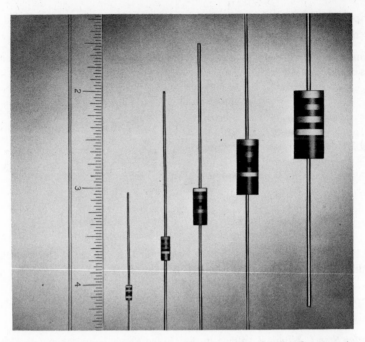

2.9 Power rating determines resistor size. *(Courtesy Allen-Bradley Company.)*

free air. However, resistors are generally operated not in free air but in enclosed chassis. Therefore it is good practice to assign a derating or **safety factor (SF)** when selecting a resistor power rating:

$$P_{\text{rating}} = P_{\text{actual}} \times SF \qquad\qquad (2.8)$$

The safety factor allows for the greater difficulty in dissipating heat in an enclosed area. A typical value for the safety factor is 2 or greater. Example 2.4 illustrates a calculation involving the use of the safety factor.

Example 2.4.

   When the voltage across a resistor in a certain circuit is 100 volts the current is 100 mA. Specify a suitable power rating for this resistor.

   Solution Step 1. Determine the actual power:

$$P_{\text{actual}} = IV = 100 \times 100 \times 10^{-3} = 10 \text{ watts}$$

   Step 2. Use a safety factor of 2:

$$P_{\text{rating}} = P_{\text{actual}} \times SF$$
$$= 10 \times 2 = 20 \text{ watts}$$

A 20-watt resistor should be selected.

It is possible to combine the basic power equation (Eq. 2.6) with Ohm's law to obtain several versions of the power equation which may be used to eliminate some of the calculations, depending on which quantities are known and which remain to be calculated:

$$P = IV$$

And from Ohm's law,

$$I = \frac{V}{R}$$

Substituting this value of I into the power equation yields

$$P = \frac{V}{R} V$$

$$= \frac{V^2}{R} \tag{2.9}$$

Similarly, if $V = IR$ is substituted into the power equation we obtain

$$P = IR \times R$$

or   (2.10)

$$P = I^2 R$$

Equations 2.9 and 2.10 will give the same answer to any power calculation as will Eq. 2.6. However, the additional equations are often useful in eliminating some steps in a calculation, as illustrated in Example 2.5.

Example 2.5.

A toaster which is operated at 120 volts is rated at 1200 watts. Find the resistance of the toaster.

Solution 1 Step 1. Find the current:

$$P = IV$$

$$I = \frac{P}{V} = \frac{1200}{120} = 10 \text{ Amp.}$$

Step 2. Since current and voltage are known, Ohm's law can be used to find the toaster resistance:

$$I = \frac{V}{R}$$

$$R = \frac{V}{I}$$

$$= \frac{120}{10} = 12\,\Omega$$

Solution 2. Equation 2.9 can be used directly to determine resistance when both power and voltage are known:

$$P = \frac{V^2}{R}$$

$$R = \frac{V^2}{P}$$

$$= \frac{(120)^2}{1200} = 12\,\Omega$$

It is possible to use Eqs. 2.9 and 2.10 directly to determine maximum permissible voltage and current levels for resistors of various wattage ratings. This is illustrated in Example 2.6.

Example 2.6.

Determine the maximum voltage and current ratings for a 1-kΩ resistor which has a 1-watt rating.

Solution Step 1. To determine the permissible voltage rating solve Eq. 2.9 for V:

$$P = \frac{V^2}{R}$$

$$V^2 = PR \qquad V = \sqrt{PR}$$

Step 2. Insert the known values:

$$V = \sqrt{1 \times 1000} = 31.6\,\text{volts}$$

Step 3. To determine the permissible current rating solve Eq. 2.10 for I:

$$P = I^2 R$$

$$I^2 = \frac{P}{R} \qquad I = \sqrt{P/R}$$

Step 4. Insert the known values:

$$I = \sqrt{\tfrac{1}{1000}} = 31.6\,\text{mA}$$

Step 5. As a check use the fundamental equation for power (Eq. 2.6) with the calculated values:

$$P = IV$$

$$= 31.6 \times 10^{-3} \times 31.6 = 1000 \times 10^{-3}$$

$$= 1\,\text{watt}\ \checkmark$$

The calculations in Example 2.6 were made without considering a safety factor. A more realistic solution would have been to derate the resistor by a factor of 2; that is, the calculation should have been made based on a $\frac{1}{2}$-watt resistor rather than the 1-watt rated value. This type of consideration is covered in the problems at the end of this chapter. Equation 2.9 indicates that **power and voltage are not related linearly.** Similarly, Eq. 2.10 indicates that **power and current are not related linearly.** However, the fundamental equation for power (Eq. 2.6) seems to indicate that both current and voltage are related linearly. Actually, the nonlinearity statements are correct. The fundamental power equation does not take into account the interdependence of voltage and current which Ohm's law imposes. For example, if the voltage across a resistor is tripled, the current through the resistor will also triple. Thus, tripling the voltage across a resistor results in a nine-fold increase in power. This serves to demonstrate the nonlinear nature of power, and also to indicate that rash judgements should not be made concerning relationships between quantities.

All three forms of the power equation show that, regardless of the polarity of the applied voltage, **power will be a positive quantity.** Ohm's law indicates that both voltage and current must have the same sign if resistance is to be a positive value. Therefore a negative voltage will result in a negative current. Since the product of two negative numbers is positive, a negative voltage still results in positive power. Similarly, if the other forms of the power equation are considered we see that they depend on either voltage squared or current squared. Since a negative number squared is a positive number, we again observe that a negative voltage must result in power being a positive quantity. The meaning of the positive sign for power is that power is being dissipated. A negative power would indicate that power is being absorbed.

2.4 Series Circuits

In Chapter 1 the value of a resistor was determined by considering the material used as well as the geometry (Eq. 1.4). In Fig. 2.10 (a) there is a

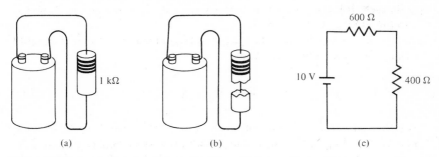

2.10 Splitting a resistor. (a) Before. (b) After. (c) Schematic for after.

1-kΩ resistor connected to a 10 volt battery. By using Ohm's law we can determine the current to be

$$I = \frac{V}{R} = \frac{10}{10^3} = 10^{-2}\,\text{Amp} = 10\,\text{mA}$$

Suppose that we now cut the resistor into two pieces as shown in Fig. 2.10 (b) and make one piece 60% of the original length. This means that the shorter piece will be 40% of the original length. If these two pieces of the original resistor are reconnected, has there been any change in the circuit? Not according to

$$R = \rho\frac{L}{A} \tag{1.4}$$

We changed neither the geometry of the resistor nor the material out of which the resistor is made when the resistor was split. All that has been done is to separate the overall length of the resistor into two pieces. The total resistance is still equal to the original 1 kΩ. Therefore the current is still the same as before the resistor was split. Since the longer piece is 60% of the original resistor it will be 60% of the original resistance; that is, the longer resistor will be 600 Ω and the shorter resistor will be 400 Ω. Since we have changed the overall circuit we can determine the voltage drop across each of the resistors by using Ohm's law:

$$V_{600} = IR = 10^{-2} \times 6 \times 10^2 = 6\,\text{volts}$$
$$V_{400} = IR = 10^{-2} \times 4 \times 10^2 = 4\,\text{volts}$$

If we add the voltage drops across the two resistors (6 volts + 4 volts) we get a total of 10 volts. This is the same as the battery voltage.

The simple experiment which has just been described illustrates the important properties of a series circuit. **A series circuit is one in which all the components are connected in tandem and there is only one path for current to flow through.** If there is only one path for current flow, the current is everywhere the same in a series circuit.

We can also see that the total resistance (R_T) in a series circuit is equal to the sum of the individual resistances:

$$R_T = R_1 + R_2 + R_3 + \cdots \tag{2.11}$$

Another important conclusion from the resistor splitting experiment concerns the voltage drops: **In a series circuit the battery voltage is equal to the sum of the voltage drops across all of the resistors.** A voltage drop is the voltage across a resistor when a current exists.

$$V_{\text{battery}} = V_{R_1} + V_{R_2} + V_{R_3} + \cdots \tag{2.12}$$

A large variety of problems can be solved by combining Ohm's law with the properties of series circuits. Example 2.7 shows a method of determining the value of an unknown resistor which is inaccessible.

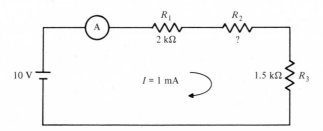

2.11   Series circuit with an unknown resistor.

Example 2.7.

In the circuit of Fig. 2.11, R_2 is a resistor which cannot be reached. Determine the value of R_2.

Solution Step 1. This is a series circuit. Therefore

$$V_{\text{battery}} = V_{R_1} + V_{R_2} + V_{R_3}$$

In the series circuit the current is the same everywhere. Thus

$$V_{\text{battery}} = I(R_1 + R_2 + R_3) = IR_T$$

Step 2. Use Ohm's law to find R_T:

$$R_T = \frac{V_{\text{battery}}}{I}$$

$$= \frac{10 \text{ V}}{10^{-3}\text{Amp}}$$

$$R_T = 10\,\text{k}\Omega$$

Step 3. Solve for R_2:

$$R_T = R_1 + R_2 + R_3$$
$$10\,\text{k}\Omega = 2\,\text{k}\Omega + R_2 + 1.5\,\text{k}\Omega$$
$$R_2 = 6.5\,\text{k}\Omega$$

Series circuits may also be used to find other things besides electronic values, as shown in Example 2.8.

Example 2.8.

A short circuit has occurred between two copper wires which are in an underground cable. The wires in the cable are 0.1 cm in diameter. When a 1.5 volt battery is connected between the shorted wires the current is 10 mA. How far from the point of measurement should a hole be dug in order to repair the cable?

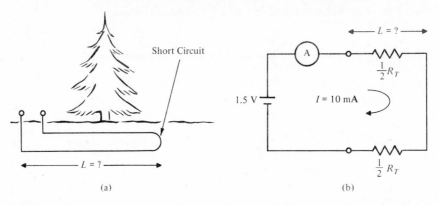

2.12   Locating a short circuit. **(a)** Short circuit occurs. **(b)** Equivalent circuit.

Solution Step 1. Draw an equivalent circuit as shown in Fig. 2.12. Since the wires are both copper and the same diameter, one half of the total resistance will be in each wire.

Step 2. Find the total resistance in the short circuit using Ohm's law:

$$R_T = \frac{V}{I} = \frac{1.5}{10 \times 10^{-3}} = 150\,\Omega$$

Step 3. The series circuit consists of two equal resistors with a total resistance of $150\,\Omega$. Therefore each resistor will be one half of the total:

$$\tfrac{1}{2}R_T = 75$$

Step 4. Using Eq. 1.4, $R = \rho L/A$ we can solve for L since this is the only unknown:

$$L = \frac{RA}{\rho}$$

Step 5. To find the length we must first determine the area of the wires.

$$A = \pi\frac{D^2}{4} = \frac{\pi(10^{-1})^2}{4} = 7.85 \times 10^{-3}\,\text{cm}^2$$

Step 6. From Table 1.2, $\rho_{\text{copper}} = 1.72 \times 10^{-6}$ ohm-cm. Insert the known values to determine L:

$$L = \frac{RA}{\rho} = \frac{7.5 \times 10^1 \times 7.85 \times 10^{-3}}{1.72 \times 10^{-6}}$$

$$= 3.42 \times 10^5 \text{ cm} = 3.42 \times 10^3 \text{ meters}$$

Since 1 meter $= 3.27$ ft,

$$L = 3.42 \times 10^3 \text{ m} \times 3.27 \text{ ft/m} = 1.12 \times 10^4 \text{ ft}$$

That is, the hole to repair the short circuit should be dug 11,200 ft from where the measurement is made.

A more common application of series circuits is the **voltage divider** circuit shown in Fig. 2.13. Since this is a series circuit, the current will be equal to the voltage divided by the total resistance:

$$I = \frac{V_{\text{in}}}{R_T} = \frac{V_{\text{in}}}{R_1 + R_2} \qquad \text{(2.13)}$$

The output voltage is the voltage which appears across R_2, this can be determined by using Ohm's law:

$$V_{\text{out}} = V_{R_2} = IR_2$$

If we substitute the value of current obtained in Eq. 2.13 into the equation for output voltage,

$$V_{\text{out}} = IR_2 = \frac{V_{\text{in}}}{R_1 + R_2} \times R_2$$

or   **(2.14)**

$$\frac{V_{\text{out}}}{V_{\text{in}}} = \frac{R_2}{R_1 + R_2} = \frac{R_2}{R_T}$$

2.13   Voltage divider.

Equation 2.14 shows us how to select a specific fraction of an input voltage by using two resistors in series. An example illustrating voltage divider action is the following.

Example 2.9

Determine the ratio of resistances in a voltage divider which will give one quarter of the voltage which is available from a 1.5 volt battery.

Solution Step 1. We are not really concerned with the actual voltage but only in the fact that the output is to be one quarter of the input:

$$V_{out} = \tfrac{1}{4} V_{in}$$

or

$$\frac{V_{out}}{V_{in}} = \frac{1}{4}$$

Step 2. The voltage divider equation (Eq. 2.14) can now be used directly:

$$\frac{V_{out}}{V_{in}} = \frac{R_2}{R_1 + R_2} = \frac{1}{4}$$

Step 3. Solve for the ratio of the resistors:

$$4R_2 = R_1 + R_2$$

or

$$3R_2 = R_1$$

For example, if $R_1 = 1\,k\Omega$, $R_2 = 3\,k\Omega$; if $R_1 = 10\,k\Omega$, $R_2 = 30\,k\Omega$, and so on.

Any value which satisfies the ratio $3R_2 = R_1$ will give us one quarter of the input voltage. The precise values to be used will be determined by how much current we wish to flow in the circuit.

This type of voltage divider permits only a fixed ratio of the input voltage to appear at the output terminals. Many applications in electronics require a voltage divider which permits a variable percentage of the input voltage to appear as an output. The volume control on a radio and the brightness control on a television are two such examples. Figure 2.14 shows a variable voltage divider. It is called a **potentiometer**. It is made by having a "**wiper**" slide across a resistor. The input voltage is placed across the end terminals of the potentiometer. The output voltage is taken between one end and the wiper terminal. Potentiometers are available in both carbon composition and wirebound types. These are the same materials from which the fixed

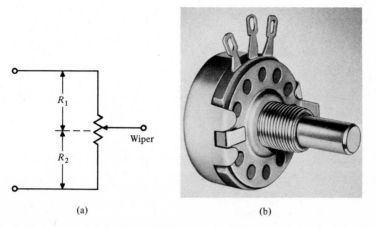

(a) (b)

2.14 Potentiometer. (**a**) Symbol. (**b**) Photograph. *(Photograph courtesy Allen-Bradley Company.)*

resistors discussed in Chapter 1 were constructed. Very accurate potentiometers are available with counter dials as shown in Fig. 2.15. The dial reading in such a case gives a direct reading of output/input ratio.

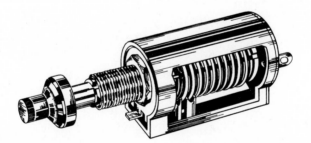

2.15 Precision potentiometer. *(Courtesy Clarostat Mfg. Co., Inc.)*

It is also possible to use voltage divider calculations when there are more than two resistors. Figure 2.16 shows a series circuit which can be considered as a voltage divider which contains three resistors. If we are only interested in the voltage across each of the resistors we can consider each resistor as the output resistor of a voltage divider. In this way we can solve for each voltage without first determining the current. This is shown in Example 2.10.

Example 2.10

Determine the voltage across each of the resistors in Fig. 2.16; use the voltage divider principle.

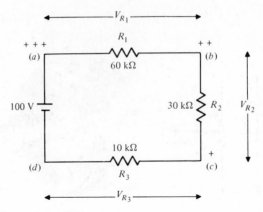

2.16   Three-resistor voltage divider.

Solution Step 1. Determine the total resistance:

$$R_T = R_1 + R_2 + R_3$$
$$= 60\,\text{k}\Omega + 30\,\text{k}\Omega + 10\,\text{k}\Omega = 100\,\text{k}\Omega$$
$$= 100 \times 10^3\,\Omega$$

Step 2. Consider each resistor as the output of a voltage divider and determine each voltage:

$$V_{R_1} = \frac{V_{in}R_1}{R_T} = \frac{100 \times 60 \times 10^3}{100 \times 10^3} = 60\,\text{V}$$

$$V_{R_2} = \frac{V_{in}R_2}{R_T} = \frac{100 \times 30 \times 10^3}{100 \times 10^3} = 30\,\text{V}$$

$$V_{R_3} = \frac{V_{in}R_3}{R_T} = \frac{100 \times 10 \times 10^3}{100 \times 10^3} = 10\,\text{V}$$

Notice that the sum of the voltage drops across the resistors (60 V + 30 V + 10 V) is equal to the battery voltage. This will always be a characteristic of series circuits.

In Fig. 2.16 point *a* is the most positive potential in the circuit and point *d* is the least positive (or most negative) potential in the circuit. The voltage across R_1 (also called V_{R_1}) is V_{ab}, which has been determined to be 60 volts. Any voltage is always a difference in potential between two points, and the points must be specified. For example, although the voltage across R_1 is 60 volts, the voltage between the lower potential side of R_1 (point *b*) and the most negative point in the circuit (point *d*) is 40 volts.

It is also important to remember that V_{ab} is not equal to V_{ba}. V_{ab} is +60 V while V_{ba} is −60 V. This situation can be readily verified by measuring the voltage across a resistor and then reversing the meter leads. The voltmeter

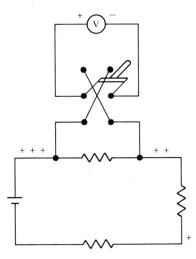

2.17   Illustrating voltage polarity.

will deflect in the opposite direction. This condition is demonstrated in Fig. 2.17. The polarity reversing switch will connect the voltmeter properly (the positive side of the voltmeter to the more positive side of the resistor) when it is in the down position. If the reversing switch is in the up position its leads are incorrectly connected and the meter will attempt to read in the wrong direction. This may permanently damage the meter.

Voltage readings have meaning only when the reference point is given. For example, if you place your hands across a 1.5 volt battery, the voltage across your body will be 1.5 volts. Similarly, if you place one hand at 1000.5 volts as a reference voltage and the other hand at 999.0 volts above the same reference point, the voltage across your body will still be only 1.5 volts. This is illustrated in Fig. 2.18.

Just as it is possible to place resistors in series, it is also possible to place batteries in series. In fact this is the condition illustrated in Fig. 2.18. If 670 batteries, each with 1.5 volt ratings, are placed in series the total voltage with respect to the bottom battery will be 1000.5 volts ($670 \times 1.5 = 1000.5$ V). In order to obtain higher voltages by placing batteries in series, it is necessary to observe the proper battery polarity. **The positive terminal of one battery must be connected to the negative terminal of the next battery.** This is the same way as resistors are connected in a series circuit. Referring again to Fig. 2.16, we see that the more positive side of R_2 is connected to the more negative side of R_1.

Figure 2.19 shows three different ways to connect two 1.5-volts batteries in series with three different results. In Fig. 2.19 (a) the batteries are connected plus to minus and the voltages add. In Fig. 2.19 (b) the batteries are connected minus to minus and therefore the voltages oppose or "buck" each other.

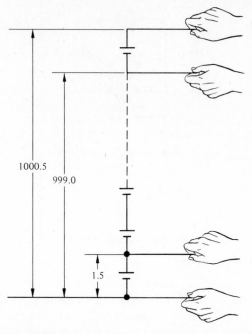

1000.5

999.0

1.5

2.18   Two ways to get 1.5 V.

The result is the difference in voltage, in this case zero volts. There would also be no voltage across the output terminals if plus were connected to plus since this is also a "bucking" situation. In Fig. 2.19 (c) the batteries are connected in series aiding, but the common point has been made the reference voltage instead of the most negative terminal. This gives us the capability of getting both a positive and a negative voltage at the same time. Although the common point is shown as being connected to "ground" this is rarely the case in practice. More commonly some point such as the chassis itself is selected as the reference point and all other voltages in the circuit are either positive or negative with respect to it.

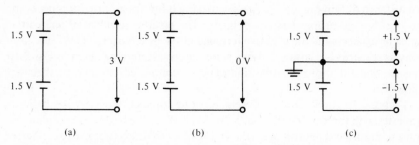

2.19   Connecting 1.5-v batteries in series. **(a)** Aiding. **(b)** Opposing. **(c)** Two-polarity.

2.5   Parallel Circuits

In a series circuit there is only one path for current to flow along. There-fore if a switch is placed anywhere in a series circuit it will stop the entire current flow when it is opened, as shown in Fig. 2.20 (a). In many applications it is desirable to control portions of a circuit independently of other parts

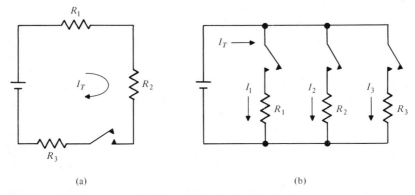

2.20   Interrupting current. **(a)** Series circuit. **(b)** Parallel circuit.

of the same circuit. Home lighting is such a situation. Independent control is accomplished by connecting components in **parallel** instead of in series, as shown in Fig. 2.20 (b). The three resistors and the battery are all connected together at both ends; that is, all the elements are connected in parallel. In this way any or all of the resistors may be operated independently of each other by means of individual switches.

It is easy to see that a parallel circuit will have different characteristics than a series circuit. For one thing the total current which a battery must direct in a parallel circuit will depend on exactly how many switches are closed, while in a series circuit the total current is constant since there is only one circuit. There are other differences between series and parallel circuits. There is one crucial factor which series and parallel circuits have in common: All circuits are governed by Ohm's law. This fact will allow us to analyze the performance of any circuit.

For example, in Fig. 2.20 (b) all the resistors are connected together at both ends. Also all the resistors are connected directly across the battery. This means that **in a parallel circuit the voltage across every element is the same.** This fact, when combined with Ohm's law, permits us to determine all the characteristics of a parallel circuit. The current through each resistor is

$$I_1 = \frac{V}{R_1} \qquad I_2 = \frac{V}{R_2} \qquad I_3 = \frac{V}{R_3} \qquad \text{etc.} \qquad \textbf{(2.15)}$$

The same voltage has been used to determine the individual currents since this is a characteristic of a parallel circuit.

The sum of the currents through the individual resistors must be equal to the total current which the battery is providing; that is, **the total current which leaves the positive battery terminal must be equal to the current which enters the negative terminal of the battery.** This is because there is no place to "store" current. It is possible to describe this situation more compactly as follows: The current that enters a junction is equal to the current that leaves the junction. Therefore, in Fig. 2.20 (b) the total current is equal to the sum of the currents which flow through the individual resistors:

$$I_T = I_1 + I_2 + I_3 \tag{2.16}$$

We have already used Ohm's law to determine the individual currents (Eq. 2.15) which flow through the resistors. Therefore Eq. 2.16 can be rewritten as

$$I_T = \frac{V}{R_1} + \frac{V}{R_2} + \frac{V}{R_3} \tag{2.17}$$

Since current is equal to voltage divided by resistance, the total current must be equal to voltage divided by the total resistance in the circuit:

$$I_T = \frac{V}{R_T} \tag{2.18}$$

If this expression is substituted into Eq. 2.17 we get

$$\frac{\cancel{V}}{R_T} = \frac{\cancel{V}}{R_1} + \frac{\cancel{V}}{R_2} + \frac{\cancel{V}}{R_3}$$

or   (2.19)

$$\frac{1}{R_T} = \frac{1}{R_1} + \frac{1}{R_2} + \frac{1}{R_3}$$

Equation 2.19 says that **in a parallel circuit the reciprocal of the total resistance is equal to the sum of the reciprocals of the individual resistances.** For example, if a 10-Ω, a 20-Ω, and a 50-Ω resistor are connected in parallel the total resistance can be found using Eq. 2.19:

$$\frac{1}{R_T} = \frac{1}{10} + \frac{1}{20} + \frac{1}{50}$$

$$\frac{1}{R_T} = 0.1 + 0.05 + 0.02 = 0.17$$

and

$$R_T = \frac{1}{0.17} = 5.88 \ \Omega$$

The total resistance of a parallel circuit is less than the smallest resistor in the circuit. In a series circuit adding resistors increases the total resistance but in a parallel circuit adding resistors decreases the total resistance.

At first thought it may seem odd that adding resistors can decrease the total resistance in any type of circuit at all. We cannot dispute the derivation of Eq. 2.19 since it is based on Ohm's law and the fact that in a parallel circuit the voltage is the same across all the components. However, it is useful to try and explain physically how it is possible that adding resistors can decrease the resistance in a parallel circuit while increasing the resistance of a series circuit.

In this connection it may be useful to recall the automobile-and-road analogy that was used in Chapter 1 to discuss the effect which length and area have on resistance (Eq. 1.4).

In a series circuit, if we add resistors the electrical path is made longer and it is more difficult for electrons to make a complete trip through the circuit. This is similar to making a road longer. It is harder for the car to make an entire journey and return. However, if more lanes are added to the road, more cars can complete the journey in the same time. Similarly, if more resistors are placed in parallel there are more paths for current to flow through and more electrons can complete the trip in the same time. Therefore, in a series circuit adding resistors increases resistance but in a parallel circuit adding resistors decreases resistance.

Example 2.11 illustrates a parallel circuit problem.

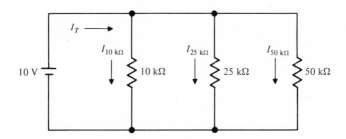

2.21   Three-resistor parallel circuit.

Example 2.11

For the circuit of Fig. 2.21 find the total current and also a single resistor which is equivalent to the parallel combination of the resistors.

Solution Step 1. The total current is equal to the sum of the individual currents:

$$I_T = I_{10\,k\Omega} + I_{25\,k\Omega} + I_{50\,k\Omega}$$

Step 2. Since the resistors are in parallel the voltage across each is the battery voltage and the individual currents can be determined by using Ohm's law:

$$I_{10\,k\Omega} = \frac{10}{10 \times 10^3} = 1\,\text{mA}$$

$$I_{25\,k\Omega} = \frac{10}{25 \times 10^3} = 0.4\,\text{mA}$$

$$I_{50\,k\Omega} = \frac{10}{50 \times 10^3} = 0.2\,\text{mA}$$

Step 3. The total current is the total of the individual currents:

$$I_T = I_{10\,k\Omega} + I_{25\,k\Omega} + I_{50\,k\Omega}$$
$$= 1\,\text{mA} + 0.4\,\text{mA} + 0.2\,\text{mA} = 1.6\,\text{mA}$$

Step 4. The total resistance is the voltage divided by the total current:

$$R_T = \frac{V}{I_T} = \frac{10}{1.6 \times 10^{-3}} = 6.25 \times 10^3\,\Omega$$

Solution 2 Step 1. Find R_T, which is the same as the single resistor which will replace the combination using the law for combining resistors in parallel.

$$\frac{1}{R_T} = \frac{1}{R_1} + \frac{1}{R_2} + \frac{1}{R_3}$$

$$= \frac{1}{10 \times 10^3} + \frac{1}{25 \times 10^3} + \frac{1}{50 \times 10^3}$$

$$= 0.1 \times 10^{-3} + 0.04 \times 10^{-3} + 0.02 \times 10^{-3} = 0.16 \times 10^{-3}$$

$$R_T = \frac{1}{0.16 \times 10^{-3}} = 6.25 \times 10^3\,\Omega$$

Step 2. Since

$$I_T = \frac{V}{R_T}$$

we get

$$I_T = \frac{10}{6.25 \times 10^3} = 1.6 \times 10^{-3}\,\text{Amp} = 1.6\,\text{mA}$$

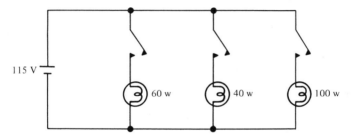

2.22   Three light bulbs in parallel.

Notice that both solutions yield the same answers for resistance and current.
Another type of parallel circuit problem involves light bulbs which are connected in parallel. This situation is illustrated in Example 2.12.

Example 2.12

Figure 2.22 shows three light bulbs which are connected in parallel. Find the total current and the total resistance when all three switches are closed.

Step 1. By using the basic equation for power (Eq. 2.6) we can determine the current which flows through each bulb:

$$P = IV$$

$$I = \frac{P}{V}$$

$$I_{60\,\text{watt}} = \frac{60}{115} = 0.521 \text{ Amp.}$$

$$I_{40\,\text{watt}} = \frac{40}{115} = 0.348 \text{ Amp.}$$

$$I_{100\,\text{watt}} = \frac{100}{115} = 0.87 \text{ Amp.}$$

Step 2. Since the bulbs are in parallel, the total current will be the sum of the individual lamp currents:

$$I_T = I_{60\,\text{watt}} + I_{40\,\text{watt}} + I_{100\,\text{watt}}$$

$$= 0.521 \text{ Amp} + 0.348 \text{ Amp} + 0.87 \text{ Amp} = 1.739 \text{ Amp}$$

Step 3. In a parallel circuit the total resistance is equal to the voltage divided by the total current:

$$R_T = \frac{V}{I_T} = \frac{115}{1.739} = 66.2 \,\Omega$$

As in the case of the previous example there are alternative solutions. All the other methods will also yield the same answers.

Table 2.1 Series Parallel Comparison

	I	*V*	*R*
Series	everywhere the same	$V_{\text{battery}} = $ sum of drops across resistors	$R_T = R_1 + R_2 + R_3 + \cdots$
Parallel	$I_T = I_1 + I_2 + I_3 + \cdots$	$V_{\text{battery}} = V_{R_1} = V_{R_2} = V_{R_3}$	$\dfrac{1}{R_T} = \dfrac{1}{R_1} + \dfrac{1}{R_2} + \dfrac{1}{R_3} + \cdots$

In many cases we shall be interested in the parallel combination of only two resistors. It will therefore be convenient to develop a special form of the general equation for resistors in parallel which does not involve taking a reciprocal. For two resistors in parallel the general form is

$$\frac{1}{R_T} = \frac{1}{R_1} + \frac{1}{R_2}$$

Putting this into the lowest common denominator gives

$$\frac{1}{R_T} = \frac{R_1 + R_2}{R_1 R_2}$$

or   (2.20)

$$R_T = \frac{R_1 R_2}{R_1 + R_2}$$

That is, if we have two resistors in parallel, their total resistance is equal to the product of the two resistors divided by the sum of the two resistors. For example, if a 10-kΩ and a 15-kΩ resistor are connected in parallel the total resistance of this combination will be

$$R_T = \frac{10 \times 10^3 \times 15 \times 10^3}{10 \times 10^3 + 15 \times 10^3} = \frac{150 \times 10^6}{25 \times 10^3} = 6 \times 10^3 \ \Omega$$

If two equal resistors are connected in parallel, the total resistance will be equal to half of the resistance of each resistor. For example, if two resistors which are both 100 Ω are connected in parallel, the total resistance will be 50 Ω.

Table 2.1 compares current, voltage, and resistance in series and parallel circuits. It must always be remembered that regardless of the way components are connected the circuit performance is governed by Ohm's law.

Summary

1. A complete (closed) circuit is required for current to flow.
2. A schematic is a picture used to describe electronic circuits.
3. Ohm's law describes the relationship between current, voltage, and resistance in any circuit.
4. In a series circuit, the current is the same throughout.
5. In a parallel circuit, the total current is the sum of the individual currents.

Questions

1. Explain what is meant by
   (a) An open circuit
   (b) A closed circuit
2. What is the purpose of a schematic?
3. What is the difference between electron current and conventional current?
4. Describe Ohm's law in words.
5. Determine which is correct and give reasons:
   (a) Voltage through a resistor
       Voltage across a resistor
   (b) Current through a resistor
       Current across a resistor
6. Distinguish between linear and nonlinear relationships.
7. Using the same components, describe how a negative current can be made to flow instead of a positive current.
8. What is the difference between energy and power?
9. What is the purpose of specifying a safety factor for a resistor?
10. Describe the significance of a positive sign for power dissipation.
11. Describe why power dissipation will be a positive quantity even when the applied voltage is negative.
12. What is meant by a series circuit?
13. Describe why the current is the same throughout a series circuit.
14. Describe what is meant by a parallel circuit.
15. What quantity is the same for each element in a parallel circuit?
16. Compare series and parallel circuits as to:
    (a) Their current relationships
    (b) Their voltage relationships
    (c) The effect of adding additional resistors
17. What do series and parallel circuits have in common?

Problems

1. What voltage is required to produce
   (a) 1 mA current through a 1.5 kΩ resistor
   (b) 10 mA current through a 1.5 kΩ resistor
   (c) 100 mA current through a 1.5 kΩ resistor
2. Using a 10-volt battery, what value of resistance is required to produce
   (a) 1 μA current
   (b) 10 μA current
   (c) 50 μA current
3. A 25-V battery is connected to a 10 kΩ resistor.
   (a) What is the resultant current?
   (b) What should the resistance be to produce twice the original current?
   (c) What should the resistance be to produce half the original current?

4. What horsepower generator is required to operate a 150-watt lamp?

5. How many watts are available from a 50-horsepower motor?

6. A 1000-watt clothes iron is operated from a 115-volt source. Find:
   (a) Resulting current
   (b) Resistance of the iron
   (c) Equivalent horsepower

7. Find the actual power dissipation for Problem 1 and using a safety factor of 2 specify power ratings for the resistors.

8. Determine the resistance of a 200-watt lamp assuming that it is operated from a 115-volt source

9. A resistor with red, red, brown, silver stripes is connected to a 25-volt battery. Determine the actual power dissipation assuming
   (a) Resistor has minimum value
   (b) Resistor has nominal value
   (c) Resistor has maximum value

10. (a) Determine the maximum voltage which should be applied across a $\frac{1}{2}$-watt resistor with yellow, violet, red, gold stripes.
   (b) Repeat using a safety factor of 2.

11. Repeat both parts of Problem 10 for a brown, black, orange, gold resistor.

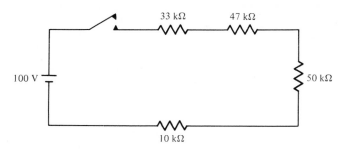

2.23   Circuit for Problem 12.

12. For the circuit shown in Fig. 2.23 determine
   (a) The current which flows when the switch is closed
   (b) The voltage drop across each resistor
   (c) The power dissipated by each resistor
   (d) Specify a safe power rating for each resistor.

13. A short occurs between two copper wires in an underground cable. The wires are 0.2 cm. in diameter. When a 1.5-V battery is connected between the shorted wires the current is 50 mA. How far from the measuring point should a hole be dug to repair the cable?

14. A 6-volt car radio draws 1.9 Amp. It is desired to operate this radio in a 12-volt car.
   (a) What value of resistance should be placed in series with the radio?
   (b) What should be the power rating of the resistor?

15. For the circuit shown in Fig. 2.24 assume that the resistors have the nominal value. Find
   (a) The current

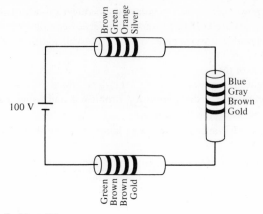

2.24   Circuit for Problem 15.

(b) Power dissipation in each resistor
(c) Suitable power ratings for each resistor

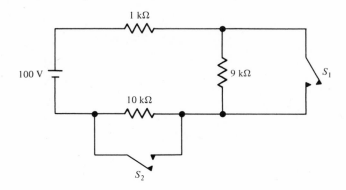

2.25   Circuit for Problem 16.

16. For the circuit shown in Fig. 2.25 find the voltage across each resistor when
    (a) S_1 and S_2 are both closed
    (b) S_1 is open and S_2 is closed
    (c) S_1 is closed and S_2 is open
    (d) S_1 and S_2 are both open
17. Determine the battery value and the unknown resistor in Fig. 2.26.
18. For the circuit shown in Fig. 2.27 find the total current when
    (a) Only S_1 is closed
    (b) S_1 and S_2 are closed
    (c) All three switches are closed.
19. A 1 kΩ resistor is connected across a 100-volt battery.
    (a) Specify a safe power rating for the resistor.

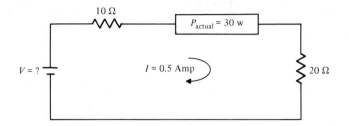

2.26 Circuit for Problem 17.

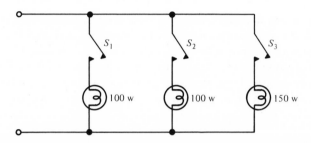

2.27 Circuit for Problem 18.

   (b) Replace the resistor with two equal series resistors with a total resistance of 1 kΩ and specify safe power ratings.

   (c) Replace with two equal resistors in parallel so that the total resistance is 1 kΩ and specify safe power ratings.

20. Determine R_x in Fig. 2.28.

21. Prove that if two equal resistors are connected in parallel the total resistance will be half the individual resistance. (*Hint*: $R_1 = R_2$ for two resistors in parallel.)

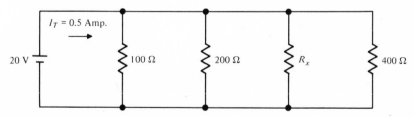

2.28 Circuit for Problem 20.

Chapter 3 Advanced Circuits

3.1   Introduction

Circuits which are more complex than either series or parallel circuits must be discussed. Many useful circuits are more involved than series or parallel circuits. Understanding of transistor and vacuum-tube amplifiers requires analyzing circuits which are almost the same as those described in this chapter. None of the methods presented use anything except Ohm's law. Keeping this in mind will help in understanding the various methods.

3.2   Circuits without Current

Many applications in electronics are based on obtaining circuits which have no current. The most obvious example of a circuit with no current is an open circuit. Figure 3.1 shows several different open circuits. Figures 3.1 (a) and 3.1 (b) are common conditions for zero current; Fig. 3.1 (c) is also an open circuit since there is no path for current to flow. Since there is no current flow in Fig. 3.1 (c), there is no voltage drop across the resistor which is in series with the battery. This is a direct consequence of Ohm's law.

$$V_R = IR$$

if

$$I = 0$$

$$V = 0R$$

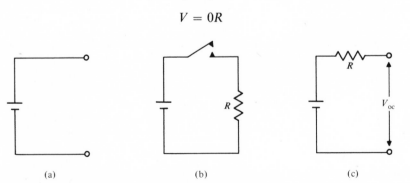

(a)	(b)	(c)

3.1   Types of open circuits. **(a)** Idle battery. **(b)** Open switch. **(c)** Open circuit.

therefore

$$V = 0$$

If there is no voltage drop across the resistor in Fig. 3.1 (c) then the open-circuit voltage is equal to the battery voltage. This is a direct consequence of series-circuit action:

$$V_{\text{battery}} = V_R + V_{\text{oc}}$$

but $V_R = 0$ since there is no current, so

$$V_{\text{battery}} = V_{\text{oc}}$$

The important point about such a circuit is that the open-circuit voltage will be the same as the battery voltage regardless of what value resistor is used. The resistor in series with the battery may be only $1\,\Omega$ or it may be $10,000,000\,\Omega$. The open-circuit voltage will still be equal to the battery voltage since no current flows through the resistor.

The circuits of Fig. 3.1 had no current because all were open circuits. Figure 3.2 shows closed circuits in which there is no current. In Fig. 3.2 (a) there is no current because there is no voltage source; in Fig. 3.2 (b) there is no current because the batteries have the same value and are "bucking." The same polarity terminals are connected together, so the net voltage is zero and there can be no current flow. Since the net voltage in Fig. 3.2 (b) is zero the value of the resistor R is unimportant. No current will flow regardless of whether the resistor is large or small. This is also a direct consequence of series-circuit action:

$$V_1 - V_2 = V_R$$

but

$$V_1 = V_2$$

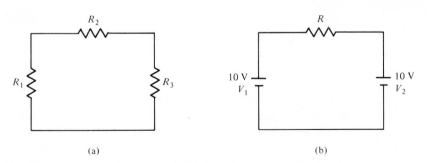

(a)   (b)

3.2   Closed circuits with no current. **(a)** No voltage source. **(b)** Equal voltage sources opposing.

therefore

$$0 = V_R$$

and it does not matter what value R has.

Circuits with zero current have many applications and will occur repeatedly throughout this book.

3.3   Series-Parallel Circuits

Figure 3.3 (a) shows a circuit which is neither a series nor a parallel circuit. However, the circuit has some of the characteristics of both series and parallel circuits.

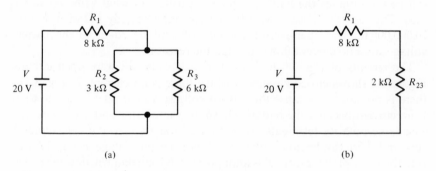

(a)   (b)

3.3   Series-parallel circuit. (a) Actual circuit. (b) Equivalent series circuit.

Resistors R_2 and R_3 are in parallel since they are connected together at both ends. This parallel combination is in series with R_1. A circuit which has some components in parallel and some components in series is called a **series-parallel circuit.**

It is important to become familiar with the precise terminology in describing circuits. For Fig. 3.3 (a) we can say either of the following:

1. R_1 is in series with the parallel combination of R_2 and R_3.
2. the parallel combination of R_2 and R_3 is in series with R_1.

Other statements will not accurately describe the configuration shown in Fig. 3.3 (a).

Series-parallel circuits are analyzed by reducing the circuit to a simple series circuit. This is accomplished by finding the total resistance of the parallel combination. After the equivalent series circuit has been analyzed the original circuit is then evaluated. This method is demonstrated in Example 3.1.

Example 3.1

In the circuit shown in Fig. 3.3(a), $R_1 = 8$ kΩ, $R_2 = 3$ kΩ, $R_3 = 6$ kΩ, and $V = 20$ volts. Find the current through and the voltage across each resistor.

Solution Step 1. Find the total resistance of the parallel combination using Eq. 2.20:

$$R_{23} = \frac{R_2 R_3}{R_2 + R_3} = \frac{3 \times 10^3 \times 6 \times 10^3}{9 \times 10^3} = 2 \times 10^3 \, \Omega$$

Step 2. Redraw the circuit as in Fig. 3.3(b), and find the total resistance of the equivalent series circuit:

$$R_T = R_1 + R_{23} = 8 \times 10^3 = 2 \times 10^3 = 10 \times 10^3 \, \Omega$$

Step 3. Find the current through the equivalent series circuit using Ohm's law:

$$I = \frac{V}{R_T} = \frac{20}{10 \times 10^3} = 2 \times 10^{-3} \, \text{Amp}$$

Step 4. The current through the equivalent series circuit actually flows through R_1, so the voltage across R_1 is

$$V_R = IR_1 = 2 \times 10^{-3} \times 8 \times 10^3 = 16 \, \text{volts}$$

Step 5. In a series circuit the battery voltage is equal to the voltage drops across the resistors (Eq. 2.12). Therefore

$$V_{\text{battery}} = V_{R_1} + V_{R_{23}}$$
$$20 = 16 + V_{R_{23}}$$
$$V_{R_{23}} = 4 \, \text{volts}$$

Step 6. The voltage across the equivalent resistor R_{23} is the same as the voltage across the original parallel combination. Therefore

$$V_{\text{parallel}} = V_{R_{23}} = 4 \, \text{volts}$$

Step 7. In a parallel circuit the voltage across all components is the same. Therefore

$$V_{R_2} = V_{R_3} = V_{R_{23}} = 4 \, \text{volts}$$

Step 8. The currents through R_2 and R_3 are found using Ohm's law:

$$I_2 = \frac{V_{R_2}}{R_2} = \frac{4}{3 \times 10^3} \qquad I_3 = \frac{V_{R_3}}{R_3} = \frac{4}{6 \times 10^3}$$
$$= 1.333 \, \text{mA} \qquad\qquad = 0.667 \, \text{mA}$$

Step 9. To check these calculations, determine if the current entering the junction of these three resistors equals the current leaving this junction (Eq. 2.16):

$$I_{R_1} \overset{?}{=} I_{R_2} + I_{R_3}$$
$$2 \times 10^{-3} \overset{?}{=} 1.333 \times 10^{-3} + 0.667 \times 10^{-3}$$
$$2 \times 10^{-3} = 2 \times 10^{-3} \quad \checkmark$$

Therefore the calculations are correct.

The method which has been used to solve this series-parallel circuit can be extended to more complicated series-parallel circuits. Figure 3.4 shows several more involved series-parallel circuits. Such circuits will require more computations than were used in Example 3.1, but no additional techniques are required. The same general method of first reducing to an equivalent

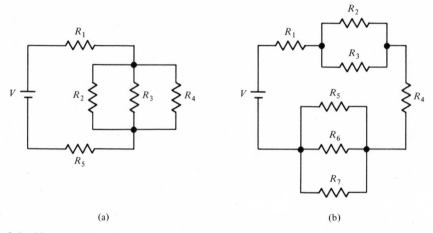

(a)   (b)

3.4   More complicated series-parallel circuits.

series circuit and then working back to the parallel portions is all that is needed.

Series and parallel configurations were introduced in Chapter 2. Both types of circuit are analyzed by applying Ohm's law in the proper manner. The next step in circuit complexity is the series-parallel circuit. As we have just seen, a series-parallel circuit is also solved by using Ohm's law. The same method is being extended to more difficult circuits.

In describing the relationship between components in a series-parallel circuit it is not necessary to describe the components in numerical order. For example, a correct and compact manner of describing the configuration of Fig. 3.4 (a) is that the parallel combination of R_2, R_3, and R_4 is in series with R_1 and R_5.

Similarly, the schematic of Fig. 3.4 (b) is correctly described as the parallel combination of R_2 and R_3, and the parallel combination of R_5, R_6, and R_7, both in series with R_1 and R_4.

To determine if these descriptions are correct, we can make a schematic based only on the above statements, without referring to Fig. 3.4. These schematics are shown in Figs. 3.5 (a) and 3.5 (b).

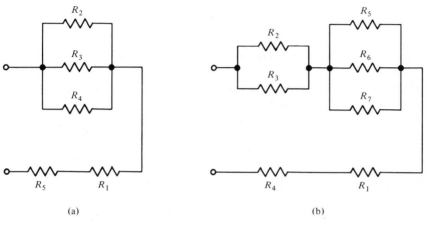

(a)   (b)

3.5   Identical circuits to Fig. 3.4.

At first glance the schematics of Fig. 3.5 appear to be quite different from those of Fig. 3.4. However, the difference is only in drafting and not in electrical performance. Electrically the component relationships in both figures are identical: If the same voltages are applied to the circuits of both figures the voltage drops across corresponding resistors will be the same and the corresponding currents will also be identical. This is what is meant by circuit **equivalence.** Equivalence is not determined by comparing circuits line for line. **Equivalency between circuits means that the same voltages and currents exist if the same voltage source is applied.** Being able to determine circuit equivalence is not a skill which is developed overnight. Rather it is acquired by continued work with a large number of circuits.

3.4   Superposition

The circuit shown in Fig. 3.6 (a) is a series-parallel circuit. To analyze it all we need do is combine the two batteries which are in series into a single equivalent circuit.

However, the circuit shown in Fig. 3.6 (b) is not a series-parallel circuit because the batteries are connected in a different manner. **It is the battery**

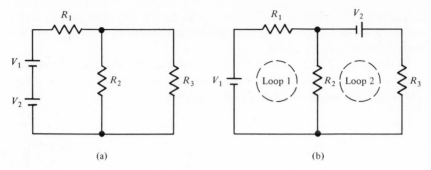

(a)   (b)

3.6   Circuits with two batteries. **(a)** Series-parallel. **(b)** Two-loop.

**placement which determines if a circuit is series, parallel, series-parallel, or
something else.** Figure 3.6 (b) is a "something else." It is referred to as a
two-loop circuit. A loop has a complete path for current flow. Loop 1 consists of
V_1, R_1, and R_2. Loop 2 consists of V_2, R_2, and R_3. It is also possible to
consider Fig. 3.5 (a) as a two-loop circuit. However, loops are generally
thought of when there is a separate battery in each loop.

Both of the batteries in Fig. 3.6 (b) have an effect on total circuit performance. This type of circuit can be solved by using an extension of Ohm's law
which is called **superposition. Superposition involves adding the individual
results of each battery one at a time.** That is, V_2 is first replaced with a short
circuit and the effect on the circuit of V_1 is determined. With V_2 removed the
remaining circuit is a series-parallel circuit.

Next, V_2 is returned to the circuit and V_1 is replaced by a short circuit.
With V_1 removed the remaining circuit is also a series-parallel circuit. The
contributions of each battery are then combined and this completely solves
the circuit. This situation is shown in Fig. 3.7.

Superposition can also be used in circuits which have more than two loops
and/or more than two batteries. We must remember to work with only one
battery at a time and to remove all the other batteries and replace each with a
short circuit. After the contribution of each battery has been determined the
resulting currents are combined.

For example, in Fig. 3.7 (a) we might want to determine the current
through R_2. Using superposition the current through R_2 will be

$$I_{R_2} = I_{R_2(V_1)} \pm I_{R_2(V_2)} \tag{3.1}$$

where $I_{R_2(V_1)}$ means the current through R_2 due to V_1. This is not the same
as $(I_{R_2})(V_1)$, which indicates multiplication. The $\pm$ sign does not mean that
we have a choice. It means that we must determine if the currents which
result from the individual batteries are aiding or bucking.

Notice in Fig. 3.7 (b) and Fig. 3.7 (c) that removing either battery results
in a series-parallel circuit, which we already know how to solve. However,

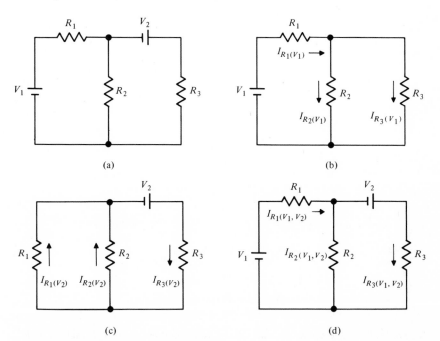

(a)   (b)

(c)   (d)

3.7 Applying superposition. **(a)** Original circuit. **(b)** Circuit with V_2 removed. **(c)** Circuit with V_1 removed. **(d)** Circuit completely solved.

we should also notice that a different series-parallel circuit arises in each case. When V_2 is removed the parallel combination of R_2 and R_3 is in series with R_1. When V_1 is removed the parallel combination of R_1 and R_2 is in series with R_3. Thus, **each battery will have a different series-parallel circuit to be analyzed when superposition is used.** Use of superposition is illustrated in Example 3.2.

Example 3.2

In Fig. 3.7 (a), $V_1 = 50$ volts, $V_2 = 25$ volts, $R_1 = 300\,\Omega$, $R_2 = 300\,\Omega$, and $R_3 = 600\,\Omega$. Find I_{R_2}.

Solution Step 1. Remove V_2 [Fig. 3.7 (b)] to solve for the current through R_2 due to V_1.

Step 2. For this situation find the total resistance:

$$R_T = R_1 + \frac{R_2 R_3}{R_2 + R_3}$$

$$= 300 + \frac{300 \times 600}{900}$$

$$= 500\,\Omega$$

Step 3. The total current due to V_1 is

$$I_{T(V_1)} = \frac{V_1}{R_T}$$

$$= \frac{50}{500}$$

$$= 0.1 \text{ Amp.}$$

Step 4. The voltage drop across R_1 due to V_1 is

$$V_{R_1(V_1)} = I_{R_1(V_1)}R_1 = 0.1 \times 300 = 30 \text{ volts}$$

Step 5. The voltage drop across the parallel combination is found by using Eq. 2.12:

$$V_{\text{battery}} = V_{R_1} + V_{\text{parallel}}$$

$$50 = 30 + V_{\text{parallel}}$$

$$V_{\text{parallel}} = 20 \text{ volts}$$

Step 6. The voltage across the equivalent parallel combination of R_2 and R_3 is the same as the voltage across R_2 and R_3. Therefore

$$I_{R_2(V_1)} = \frac{V_{R_2}}{R_2}$$

$$= \frac{20}{300}$$

$$= 0.06667 \text{ Amp.}$$

Step 7. Remove V_1 and replace V_2 [Fig. 3.7 (c)] to solve for the current through R_2 due to V_2.

Step 8. For this situation the total resistance is

$$R_T = R_3 + \frac{R_1 R_2}{R_1 + R_2}$$

$$= 600 + \frac{300 \times 300}{600}$$

$$= 750 \, \Omega$$

Step 9. The total current due to V_2 is

$$I_{T(V_2)} = \frac{V_2}{R_T} = \frac{25}{750} = 0.0333 \text{ Amp.}$$

Step 10. The voltage drop across R_3 due to V_2 is

$$V_{R_3(V_2)} = I_{T(V_2)}R_3$$
$$= 0.0333 \times 600$$
$$= 20 \text{ volts}$$

Step 11. The voltage drop across the parallel combination of R_1 and R_2 is found using Eq. 2.12:

$$V_{\text{battery}} = V_{R_3} + V_{\text{parallel}}$$
$$25 = 20 + V_{\text{parallel}}$$
$$V_{\text{parallel}} = 5 \text{ volts}$$

Step 12. The current through R_2 due to V_2 is

$$I_{R_2(V_2)} = \frac{V_{R_2}(V_2)}{R_2}$$
$$= \frac{5}{300}$$
$$= 0.01667 \text{ Amp.}$$

Step 13.

$$I_{R_2} = I_{R_2(V_1)} \pm I_{R_2(V_2)}$$

We must determine if these currents are aiding or bucking. In Fig. 3.7 (b) we see that the current through R_2 due to V_1 flows from the top of R_2 to the bottom of R_2. That is, $I_{R_2(V_1)}$ flows down through R_2. In Fig. 3.7 (c) we see that $I_{R_2(V_2)}$ flows up through R_2. Therefore the currents due to V_1 and V_2 are bucking, and

$$I_{R_2} = I_{R_2(V_1)} - I_{R_2(V_2)}$$
$$= 0.0667 - 0.01667$$
$$= 0.05 \text{ Amp.}$$

The use of superposition enables us to determine the current through or the voltage drop across any resistor in a multiloop, multibattery circuit. However, it allows calculations to be made for only one resistor at a time. For example, if we wish to determine the voltage across R_3 of Fig. 3.7 (a), many of the calculations which were made for R_2 are not applicable. This is illustrated in Example 3.3.

Example 3.3

Find the voltage across R_3 using the same value components as were used in Example 3.2.

Solution Step 1. From Fig. 3.7 (b) we see that the total current due to V_1 is the same as in the previous example. Therefore

$$I_{T(V_1)} = 0.1 \text{ Amp.}$$

Step 2. The voltage drop across R_3 due to V_1 is therefore the same as in the previous example:

$$V_{R_3} = 20 \text{ volts}$$

Step 3. The current through R_3 due to V_1 is therefore

$$I_{R_3(V_1)} = \frac{V_3}{R_3}$$

$$= \frac{20}{600}$$

$$= 0.0333 \text{ Amp.}$$

Step 4. The total current due to V_2 is the same as in the previous example. Therefore

$$I_{T(V_2)} = 0.0333 \text{ Amp.}$$

Step 5. $I_{T(V_2)}$ is actually the total current which flows through R_3 due to V_2. Therefore

$$I_{R_3(V_2)} = 0.0333 \text{ Amp.}$$

Step 6. In this case both currents $I_{R_3(V_1)}$ and $I_{R_3(V_2)}$ flow through R_3 in the same direction. These currents therefore add:

$$I_{R_3} = I_{R_3(V_1)} + I_{R_3(V_2)} = 0.0333 + 0.0333$$

$$= 0.0666 \text{ Amp.}$$

Step 7. To find V_{R_3}:

$$V_{R_3} = I_{R_3}R_3$$

$$= 0.0666 \times 600$$

$$= 40 \text{ volts}$$

It would be convenient to be able to check superposition calculations. Unfortunately, the check involved in verifying a superposition calculation is as involved as superposition itself. Therefore, the best check on a superposition calculation is to work carefully. It is true that a great many steps must be performed when superpositon is used. However, if we keep in mind the basic principles involved, superposition is not difficult. Essentially only two types of operation are involved:

1. Solving a series-parallel circuit for as many batteries as exist in the circuit. This is a direct application of Ohm's law.
2. Determining whether the currents due to the individual batteries aid or oppose. This is determined by inspecting the schematic.

Thus, despite the fact that superposition requires many individual steps to arrive at an answer, the principle itself is quite straightforward. The calculations involved in using superposition become increasingly more involved as more batteries and/or more loops are added to a circuit. For example, if a third battery were to be inserted in the R_2 leg of Fig. 3.7 (a), three sets of calculations would be required. We would also have to keep in mind the direction of three currents instead of two currents.

3.5 Loop Equations

There is another method of analyzing multiloop, multibattery circuits which depends only on the number of loops and not at all on the number of batteries. This method of analysis is called the method of **loop equations.** Figure 3.8 is actually the same circuit as shown in Fig. 3.3 (a), except loop currents have been indicated. Loop 1 of Fig. 3.8 consists of V_1, R_1, and R_2. Loop current I_1 is assumed to flow through this loop. Loop 2 consists of R_2 and R_3. Loop current I_2 is assumed to flow through this loop. Loop currents are somewhat unreal. In Fig. 3.8, loop current I_1 does flow through R_1 and loop current I_2 does not flow through R_3. However, it is the difference between these currents $(I_1 - I_2)$ which flows through R_2. In fact, whenever two loops have a common component (R_2 in this case), the difference between the loop currents will flow through the common component. It is the difference in loop currents rather than the sum of the loop currents, because of the direction of the individual loop currents. **Loop currents are all assumed to flow clockwise.** Therefore in a common element the currents will

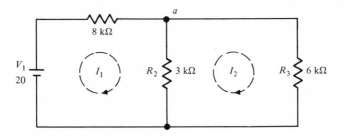

3.8 Two-loop circuit with a single battery.

be flowing in opposite directions. For example, in Fig. 3.8 loop current I_1 flows from top to bottom through R_2. Loop current I_2, on the other hand, flows from bottom to top through R_2. That is, the loop currents are bucking and not aiding.

Before proceeding with loop equations we should first assure ourselves that the principle of loop currents is valid. This can be accomplished by determining if the current which enters a junction is equal to the current which leaves the junction when loop currents are used. In Fig. 3.8 the current which enters the junction at point a is loop current I_1. Two currents leave this junction; loop current I_2 flows to R_3 and the difference between the loop currents $I_1 - I_2$ flows through R_2. Therefore, to determine if entering current equals leaving current,

$$I_{\text{entering}} \overset{?}{=} I_{\text{leaving}}$$
$$I_1 \overset{?}{=} I_2 + (I_1 - I_2)$$
$$= I_2 + I_1 - I_2$$
$$I_1 = I_1 \quad \checkmark$$

This verifies that the concept of loop currents is valid since we have seen that the current which enters a junction is indeed equal to the current which leaves that junction.

This situation at a junction of current balance (Eq. 2.10), entering and leaving, is commonly referred to as **Kirchhoff's current law.** Similarly, the statement that the battery voltage is equal to the sum of the resistor voltage drops in a loop (Eq. 2.12) is known as **Kirchhoff's voltage law.** Kirchhoff was a German physicist who worked during the middle of the last century. In addition to working with electricity, Kirchhoff also made important contributions in the fields of spectroscopy and heat transfer.

Kirchhoff's voltage law (Eq. 2.12), which we have already used without calling it thus, is the basis of loop analysis. There must be a loop equation for each loop of a circuit. It may be helpful to think of loops as window frames. Around each "window frame" the battery voltage must be equal to the IR voltage drops. Thus, For Fig. 3.8 we have.

For loop 1,

$$V_1 = I_1 R_1 + (I_1 - I_2)R_2$$

or, multiplying out,

$$V_1 = I_1 R_1 + I_1 R_2 - I_2 R_2 \qquad \text{(3.2)}$$

and combining terms,

$$V_1 = I_1(R_1 + R_2) - I_2 R_2$$

In loop 2 of Fig. 3.8 there are no batteries. Therefore the sum of the voltage drops across the resistors must be equal to zero:

$$0 = (I_2 - I_1)R_2 + I_2R_3$$

or

$$0 = -I_1R_2 + I_2R_2 + I_2R_3 \qquad (3.3)$$

or

$$0 = -I_1R_2 + I_2(R_2 + R_3)$$

If we write Eqs. 3.2 and 3.3 together,

$$\left\{ \begin{aligned} V_1 &= I_1(R_1 + R_2) - I_2R_2 \\ 0 &= -I_1R_2 + I_2(R_2 + R_3) \end{aligned} \right\} \qquad \begin{aligned} &(3.4a) \\ &(3.4b) \end{aligned}$$

we have a pair of equations with two unknowns. This is similar to solving two equations which contain the two unknowns x and y. The same methods apply to Eqs. 3.4a and 3.4b except that the unknowns are the loop currents I_1 and I_2.

There is an interesting and useful pattern in Eqs. 3.4a and 3.4b. Equation 3.4a is written for **loop 1** of Fig. 3.8. **The I_1 term which is positive contains all of the resistors in loop 1. The I_2 term which is negative contains the resistor which is common to both loops.**

Equation 3.4b, which is written for **loop 2,** has a similar pattern. **The positive I_2 term contains all the resistors in loop 2. The I_1 term is negative and contains the resistor which is common to both loops.**

The reason that resistor R_2, which is common to both loops, is accompanied by a minus sign already has been discussed. The loop currents flow in opposite directions through the common resistor.

Example 3.4 is a numerical example which illustrates the loop equation method.

Example 3.4

Find the current through each resistor in Fig. 3.8 using loop equations.

Solution Step 1. Equations 3.4a and 3.4b are correct for Fig. 3.8:

$$V_1 = I_1(R_1 + R_2) - I_2R_2$$

$$0 = -I_1R_2 + I_2(R_1 + R_2)$$

Step 2. Insert the numerical values according to Fig. 3.8:

$$20 = I_1(8 \times 10^3 + 3 \times 10^3) - I_2(3 \times 10^3)$$

$$0 = -I_1(3 \times 10^3) + I_2(3 \times 10^3 + 6 \times 10^3)$$

Step 3. Combine the terms:

$$20 = I_1 \times 11 \times 10^3 - I_2 \times 3 \times 10^3$$
$$0 = -I_1 \times 3 \times 10^3 + I_2 \times 9 \times 10^3$$

Step 4. Multiply the top equation by 3 and recopy the second equation:

$$60 = I_1 \times 33 \times 10^3 - I_2 \times 9 \times 10^3$$
$$0 = -I_1 \times 3 \times 10^3 + I_2 \times 9 \times 10^3$$

Step 5. Add these two equations and solve for I_1:

$$60 = I_1 \times 30 \times 10^3$$
$$I_1 = \frac{60}{30 \times 10^3} = 2 \times 10^{-3} \text{ Amp.}$$

From Fig. 3.8 we see that loop current I_1 is the current which actually flows through R_1. Therefore,

$$I_{R_1} = 2 \times 10^{-3} \text{ Amp.}$$

Step 6. Use the value just obtained for I_1 in the equation for loop 1 to solve for I_2:

$$20 = I_1 \times 11 \times 10^3 - I_2 \times 3 \times 10^3$$
$$= 2 \times 10^{-3} \times 11 \times 10^3 - I_2 \times 3 \times 10^3$$
$$= 22 - I_2 \times 3 \times 10^3$$
$$-2 = -I_2 \times 3 \times 10^3$$
$$I_2 = \frac{2}{3 \times 10^3} = 0.6667 \times 10^{-3} \text{ Amp.}$$

From Fig. 3.8 we see that loop current I_2 is the current which actually flows through R_3. Therefore,

$$I_{R_3} = 0.6667 \times 10^{-3} \text{ Amp.}$$

Step 7. Since the loop currents flow in opposite directions through the common resistor R_2, I_{R_3} will be the difference between the two loop currents:

$$I_{R_2} = I_1 - I_2$$
$$= 2 \times 10^{-3} - 0.6667 \times 10^{-3}$$
$$= 1.3333 \times 10^{-3} \text{ Amp.}$$

Although the circuit of Fig. 3.8 has just been analyzed as a two loop circuit, it is the same series-parallel circuit as in Fig. 3.3 (Example 3.1).

Both series-parallel analysis and the loop equation method give the same answers for currents through each resistor. This should give us some confidence in using loop equations. In fact, it is probably not too efficient to use loop equations on a series-parallel circuit except to observe that identical results are obtained.

Loop equations do offer a significant advantage when there are batteries in each loop. In each loop the sum of the voltage drops across each resistor must equal the battery voltage in that loop. This is Kirchhoff's voltage law (Eq. 2.12). Kirchhoff's voltage law is, as we have seen, a consequence of Ohm's law, so that what we are doing in applying loop equations is actually an extension of Ohm's law. The use of loop equations in a two-loop, two-battery situation is illustrated in Example 3.5.

Example 3.5

Use loop equations to determine the current through each resistor in Fig. 3.9. (This is the circuit which was partially solved in Examples 3.2 and 3.3 using superposition.)

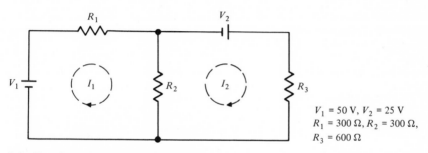

$V_1 = 50$ V, $V_2 = 25$ V
$R_1 = 300\ \Omega,\ R_2 = 300\ \Omega,$
$R_3 = 600\ \Omega$

3.9   Two-loop circuit with two batteries.

Solution Step 1. Write the equations for each loop:

$$V_1 = I_1(R_1 + R_2) - I_2 R_2$$
$$V_2 = -I_1 R_2 + I_2(R_2 + R_3)$$

Step 2. Insert the proper values and combine terms:

$$50 = I_1 \times 600 - I_2 \times 300$$
$$25 = -I_2 \times 300 + I_2 \times 900$$

Step 3. Multiply the top equation by 3 and recopy the bottom equation as is:

$$150 = I_1 \times 1800 - I_2 \times 900$$
$$25 = -I_1 \times 300 + I_2 \times 900$$

Step 4. Add these two equations and solve for I_1:

$$175 = I_1 \times 1500$$

$$I_1 = \frac{175}{1500} = 0.1167 \text{ Amp.}$$

From Fig. 3.9 we see that loop current I_1 is actually the current which flows through R_1. Therefore,

$$I_{R_1} = 0.1167 \text{ Amp.}$$

Step 5. Use the value just obtained for I_1 in the equation for loop 1 to solve for I_2:

$$50 = I_1 \times 600 - I_2 \times 300$$

$$= 0.1167 \times 600 - I_2 \times 300$$

$$= 70 - I_2 \times 300$$

$$-20 = -I_2 \times 300$$

$$I_2 = \frac{20}{300} = 0.0667 \text{ Amp.}$$

From Fig. 3.9 we see that loop current I_2 actually flows through R_3. Therefore,

$$I_{R_3} = 0.667 \text{ Amp.}$$

This is the same answer as was obtained using superposition in Example 3.3.

Step 6. As in the previous example, the difference in loop currents flows through the common resistor:

$$I_{R_2} = I_1 - I_2$$

$$= 0.1167 - 0.0667$$

$$= 0.05 \text{ Amp.}$$

This is the same answer as was obtained using superposition in Example 3.2.

Thus we see that loop equations permit us to get the same answers as superposition. For our applications there are two advantages to using loop equations:

1. Generally less computation is involved in the use of loop equations. This is especially true if more than two batteries are involved. The number of loops and not the number of batteries determines how many equations are required.
2. The equations required for loop equations can be written in "cookbook" fashion by inspecting the circuit. In each loop the loop current

flows through every resistor in the loop. In addition, the negative loop current from the adjacent loop also flows through those resistors which are common to more than one loop.

As in the case of superposition, we must be careful to observe proper polarities. Figure 3.10 is the same as Fig. 3.9 with one important exception: The polarity of V_2 has been reversed. In solving this circuit the battery reversal must be accounted for. Since we are using conventional current, a **battery voltage is taken as positive if the current leaves the positive terminal of the battery**; this is the only type of situation we have considered so far. However, in loop 2 of Fig. 3.10 the current enters the positive battery terminal

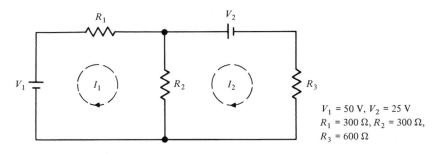

3.10 Reversing battery polarity.

and leaves through the negative battery terminal. This is the reverse of the situation which results with a positive battery voltage. Therefore this must be taken to be a negative voltage. Changing the polarity of a battery in a single-battery circuit changes the direction (i.e., the polarity) of the current but does not change the magnitude.

In a multibattery circuit, changing the polarity of some but not all of the batteries may or may not change the current polarity, but the magnitude of all the currents will certainly be changed. This is illustrated in Example 3.6.

Example 3.6

Find the current through each resistor in Fig. 3.10.

Solution Step 1. By inspection write the equations for both loops:

$$V_1 = I_1(R_1 + R_2) - I_2 R_2$$
$$-V_2 = -I_2 R_2 + I_2(R_2 + R_3)$$

The reason for the negative sign in front of V_2 has already been discussed.

Step 2. Insert the proper values:

$$50 = I_1 \times 600 - I_2 \times 300$$

$$-25 = I_1 \times 300 + I_2 \times 900$$

Step 3. Multiply the top equation by 3 and recopy the bottom equation as is:

$$150 = I_1 \times 1800 - I_2 \times 900$$

$$-25 = -I_1 \times 300 + I_2 \times 900$$

Step 4. Add these two equations and solve for I_1:

$$125 = I_1 \times 1500$$

$$I_1 = \frac{125}{1500} = 0.0834 \text{ Amp.}$$

By inspection of the circuit we see that loop current I_1 actually flows through R_1. Therefore,

$$I_{R_1} = 0.0834 \text{ Amp.}$$

Step 5. Use the value just obtained for I_1 in the equation for loop 1 to solve for I_2:

$$50 = I_1 \times 600 - I_2 \times 300$$

$$= 0.0834 \times 600 - I_2 \times 300$$

$$= 50 - I_2 \times 300$$

$$0 = I_2 \times 300$$

$$I_2 = 0 \text{ Amp.}$$

There is no loop current I_2 and since I_2 is the same as I_{R_3},

$$I_{R_3} = 0$$

The first section of this chapter discussed situations in which a closed circuit could exist with a battery, and yet no current would result. This is such a case.

Step 6. Since R_2 is common to both loops:

$$I_{R_2} = I_1 - I_2$$

$$= 0.0834 - 0$$

$$= 0.0834 \text{ Amp.}$$

Thus we see that reversing battery polarity has a profound effect on circuit performance. The actual values which were obtained with and without battery reversal are shown in Table 3.1. In this particular case no current polarities were reversed, but a current did go to zero. In other circuits the algebraic solution for the currents may yield a negative current. Such a situation indicates that the magnitude is correct but that the polarity is incorrect; that is, a minus sign for a loop current indicates a negative current.

Table 3.1   Comparison of Fig. 3.9 and Fig. 3.10

	I_{R_1} (amp)	I_{R_2} (amp)	I_{R_3} (amp)
Fig. 3.9	0.1167	0.0500	0.0667
Fig. 3.10	0.0834	0.0834	0.0000

A negative sign arises because we are assuming that all currents are clockwise. This is a useful assumption since it simplifies writing the loop equations. It also helps furnish a check that we have written the correct equations. With the assumption that all loop currents are clockwise, the only current term in each equation which is positive is the one for the loop in question. This is illustrated by writing the equation for Fig. 3.11:

Loop 1 $V_1 + V_3 = I_1(R_1 + R_3 + R_4) - I_2 R_3 - I_3 R_4$

Loop 2 $-V_2 = I_1 R_3 \qquad\qquad + I_2(R_2 + R_3 + R_5) - I_3 R_5$

$$(3.5)$$

Loop 3 $-V_3 = -I_1 R_4 \qquad\qquad - I_2 R_5 + I_3(R_4 + R_5$
$$+ R_6 + R_7 + R_8)$$

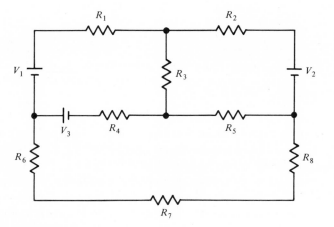

3.11   Three-loop circuit.

In each loop only that loop-current term is positive. All other loop-current terms have a negative sign and corresponding terms contain the same resistor. Corresponding terms are indicated by arrows. It is a great convenience to assume all loop currents to be clockwise, since it greatly simplifies writing the correct equations. The only price we pay for this convenience is the need to interpret properly a negative loop current as flowing in the opposite (counter-clockwise) direction.

The remainder of this book will not require analyzing circuits with more than two loops. Equations 3.5 are shown only to demonstrate the ease with which loop equations may be written.

Superposition and loop equations are by no means the only techniques for solving multiloop, multibattery problems. There are other methods. However, the other methods are also extensions of Ohm's law, as are superposition and loop equations. Moreover, either superposition or loop equations will enable us to analyze all the situations which arise in this book.

3.6   Maximum Power Transfer

Until now batteries have been considered to be ideal voltage sources. **An ideal voltage source is one which can deliver its open-circuit voltage to any value of load resistance.** Values of load resistance can range anywhere from an open circuit (infinite resistance) to a short circuit (zero resistance). An ideal voltage source has no internal resistance, as shown in Fig. 3.12 (a).

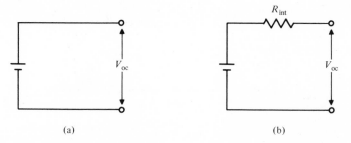

3.12   Voltage sources. **(a)** Ideal. **(b)** Real.

It is impossible to make an ideal voltage source. A real battery is made of real materials, and all real materials have resistance. Thus a real battery must have some resistance. A real voltage source is shown in Fig. 3.12 (b). R_{int} represents the total internal resistance of all the materials which constitute the battery. It is obvious that if we open a battery we shall not see an ideal battery in series with a resistor; thus Fig. 3.12 (b) is only a mathematical model of a real battery. This model shows that the terminals of the ideal

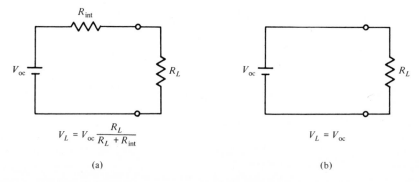

3.13   Battery with load. (a) Real battery. (b) Ideal battery.

battery are not available to us. We cannot connect to a battery without connecting to the internal resistance of the battery.

Since there is an internal resistor in series with the battery, a load which is attached to a battery is in series with that resistor. If the battery were ideal, any load would be directly in parallel with such a battery. This situation is shown in Fig. 3.13.

Thus when a load is attached to a real battery voltage divider action (Eq. 2.14) occurs; that is, the value of internal resistance as well as the load resistance determine what the load voltage will be. This is illustrated in Example. 3.7.

Example 3.7

A 20-volt battery has an internal resistance of $2\,\Omega$. What will be the load voltage for 1-, 10-, and 100-Ω load resistors?

Solution Step 1. The voltage divider equation (Eq. 2.14) is directly applicable for the circuit of Fig. 3.13 (a). Therefore, for $R_L = 1\,\Omega$,

$$V_L = V_{oc}\frac{R_L}{R_L + R_{int}}$$

$$= 20\frac{1}{1 + 2}$$

$$= 6.67 \text{ volts}$$

Step 2. For $R_L = 10\,\Omega$,

$$V_L = V_{oc}\frac{R_L}{R_L + R_{int}}$$

$$= 20\frac{10}{10 + 2}$$

$$= 16.67 \text{ volts}$$

Step 3. For $R_L = 100\,\Omega$,

$$V_L = V_{oc}\frac{R_L}{R_L + R_{int}}$$

$$= 20\frac{100}{100 + 2}$$

$$= 19.6 \text{ volts}$$

Example 3.7 shows how the internal battery resistance affects the load voltage. To obtain a load voltage which is anywhere near the rated battery voltage, the load resistance will have to be much greater than the internal battery resistance. If we could build an ideal battery, the load voltage would be equal to the open-circuit voltage regardless of the value of load resistance.

Since in a real situation the voltage which appears across the load is different with different resistors, the load power will also vary as the load varies. Figure 3.14 shows three different possible loads which can be connected to a real battery. In Fig. 3.14 (a) the load is a short circuit. For

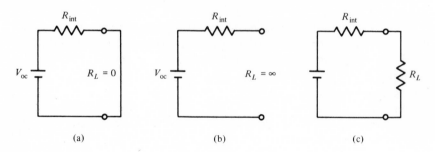

(a)   (b)   (c)

3.14   Real battery loads. (**a**) Short circuit. (**b**) Open circuit. (**c**) Resistor.

this condition no power will be delivered to the load even though current flows, because the load has zero resistance:

$$P = I^2 R$$

if   **(2.10)**

$$R = 0$$

$$P = I^2 \times 0 = 0 \text{ watts}$$

In Fig. 3.14 (b) there is an open circuit. For this condition there will be no current and therefore no power will be delivered to the load:

$$P = I^2 R$$

if

$$I = 0$$

$$P = 0^2 \times R = 0 \text{ watts}$$

In Fig. 3.14 (c) an actual load resistor is connected to the battery. In this case power will be delivered to the load. This is a true series circuit:

$$P_L = I^2 R_L$$

Therefore

$$P_L = \frac{V_{oc}^2}{(R_{int} + R_L)^2} R_L \qquad (3.6)$$

Equation 3.6 permits us to determine the power which can be delivered to a load. Example 3.8 illustrates the use of this power equation.

Example 3.8

A battery with an open-circuit voltage of 10 volts has an internal resistance of $2\,\Omega$. Find the power which can be delivered to $1\text{-}\Omega$, $2\text{-}\Omega$, and $3\text{-}\Omega$ loads. Plot a graph of load power versus load resistance.

Solution Step 1. From the given information we have $V_{oc} = 10$ volts, $R_{int} = 2\,\Omega$, and three different values of R_L. Equation 3.6 can be used directly.

Step 2. For $R_L = 1\,\Omega$,

$$P_L = \frac{V_{oc}^2}{(R_{int} + R_L)^2} R_L$$

$$= \frac{10^2}{(2+1)^2} 1$$

$$= 11.1 \text{ watts.}$$

Step 3. For $R_L = 2\,\Omega$,

$$P_L = \frac{10^2}{(2+2)^2} 2$$

$$= 12.5 \text{ watts}$$

Step 4. For $R_L = 3\,\Omega$,

$$P_L = \frac{10^2}{(2+3)^2} 3$$

$$= 12 \text{ watts}$$

Step 5. In addition we have seen that no power will be delivered to either an open or a short circuit. This gives a total of five values:

$R_L(\Omega)$	P_L(watts)
0	0
1	11.1
2	12.5
3	12
infinite	0

Figure 3.15 is the graph for this example.

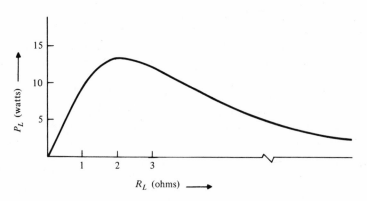

3.15   Load resistance versus load power.

Notice in Fig. 3.15 that there is a maximum power (12.5 watts in this particular case). The maximum load power occurs when the load resistance is equal to the internal resistance of the voltage source. This condition will be true for all voltage sources. Moreover, this is an important factor in electronics and is known as the maximum power transfer theorem: **Maximum power will be delivered to a load when the resistance of the load is equal to the internal resistance of the voltage source.**

One important application of the maximum power transfer theorem is the determination of the internal resistance of a voltage source. This can be made clear by an illustrative example.

Example 3.9

For the battery used in Example 3.8, determine the voltage across the load when load power is a maximum.

Solution Step 1. From Example 3.8, $V_{oc} = 10$ volts and $R_{int} = 2\,\Omega$. Also, from the maximum power transfer theorem P_L will be a maximum when $R_L = R_{int}$.

Step 2. For this particular example maximum power occurs when $R_L = 2\,\Omega.$

Step 3. Figure 3.16 shows this condition using either the voltage divider equation (2.14) or solving the series circuit directly.

Voltage divider	Series circuit
$V_{R_L} = \dfrac{V_{oc}}{R_{int} + R_L} R_L$	$I_{R_L} = \dfrac{V_{oc}}{R_{int} + R_L}$
$= \dfrac{10}{2 + 2} 2$	$= \dfrac{10}{2 + 2}$
$= 5$ volts	$= 2.5$ Amp.
	$V_{R_L} = IR_L$
	$= 2.5 \times 2$
	$= 5$ volts

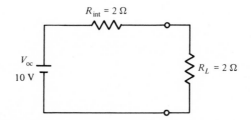

3.16   Maximum power transfer for Example 3.9.

The important fact to be observed in Example 3.9 is that **when maximum power is delivered to a load, the load voltage is one half of the open-circuit voltage.** This information permits us to determine the internal resistance of any voltage source in three steps:

1. Measure the open-circuit voltage of the source.
2. Connect a variable resistor to the battery and adjust until the load voltage is one half of the open-circuit voltage.
3. Measure the value of the variable resistor; this is equal to R_{int}.

This method of determining the internal resistance of a voltage source is called the **half-voltage method.** The half-voltage method is illustrated in Fig. 3.17.

In certain situations it is not practical to reduce the load voltage to one half of the open-circuit voltage. It is still possible to determine internal

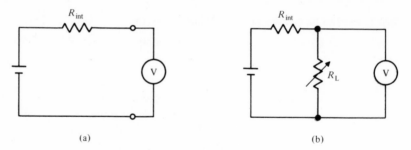

(a)   (b)

3.17 Half-voltage method to determine R_{int}. **(a)** Measure V_{oc}. **(b)** Adjust R_L so that $V_{R_L} = \frac{1}{2}V_{oc}$.

resistance by making measurements and performing a few calculations. Example 3.10 illustrates the determination of internal resistance when the half-voltage method is not practical.

Example 3.10

A certain battery has an open-circuit voltage of 20 V. When a 36-Ω resistor is connected across the battery the load voltage is 18 volts. Find the internal resistance of this battery (see Fig. 3.18).

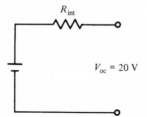

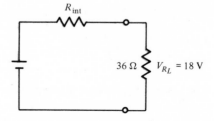

3.18 Conditions for Example 3.10.

Solution Step 1. The load current is

$$I_L = \frac{V_L}{R_L}$$

$$= \frac{18}{36}$$

$$= 0.5 \, \text{Amp.}$$

Since this is a series circuit the current is the same throughout the circuit.

Step 2. Applying Kirchhoff's voltage law to the circuit:

$$V_{oc} = R_{R_{int}} + V_{R_L}$$

$$20 = V_{R_{int}} + 18$$

$$V_{R_{int}} = 2 \text{ volts}$$

Step 3. The internal resistance is equal to the internal voltage divided by the current; both of these values have been determined.

$$R_{int} = \frac{V_{R_{int}}}{I}$$

$$= \frac{2}{0.5}$$

$$= 4 \, \Omega$$

This example illustrates the determination of internal resistance when the half-voltage method is not practical. For example, we might want to determine the internal resistance of a generator in a power plant. The solution is based on obtaining a voltage which is less than the open-circuit voltage and noting the condition under which the measurement is made.

In many situations we wish to achieve maximum power transfer. Obviously this requires knowing the internal resistance of the voltage source. We frequently speak of matching a loudspeaker to a high-fidelity amplifier. This is an example of transferring maximum power.

There are also many situations where we wish to take little or no power from a source. For this case we want to obtain no power transfer to the load instead of maximum power transfer. For example, we purposely use a high-resistance voltmeter if we do not want the act of making a measurement to alter the circuit which is being measured. This is a situation where we need to know the internal resistance of a source to mismatch intentionally. The important point about internal resistance is as follows: **To match properly, or to mismatch properly, a load to a voltage source the internal resistance of the source must be known.**

Summary

1. It is possible to have circuits in which there is no current.
2. Series-parallel circuits are analyzed by reducing to an equivalent series circuit.
3. Superposition can be used to analyze circuits which contain several loops and several batteries.
4. Loop equations can also be used in multiloop, multibattery circuits.
5. The maximum power transfer theorem is important in both matching and mismatching a load to a source.

Questions

1. What is the voltage drop across any resistor in an open circuit?
2. How can there be no current in a closed circuit which contains batteries?
3. What is a series-parallel circuit?
4. Can there be more than one battery in a series-parallel circuit?
5. What is a multiloop circuit?
6. Must there be more than one battery in a multiloop circuit?
7. What is meant by superposition?
8. For what type of circuit is superposition used?
9. Compare superposition and loop equations.
10. What is the meaning of a negative current when using loop equations?
11. What is the difference between an ideal and a real voltage source?
12. Why is the maximum power transfer theorem important?

Problems

1. For the circuit shown in Fig. 3.19, find the voltage drops across the resistors when
   (a) The switch is open
   (b) The switch is closed

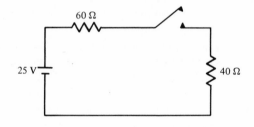

3.19   Circuit for Problem 1.

2. For the circuit shown in Fig. 3.20, find the voltage across the 1-kΩ resistor when V_2 equals
   (a) 10 volts
   (b) 15 volts
   (c) 20 volts
3. For the circuit shown in Fig. 3.21, find the voltage across each resistor.
4. Find the current through the 80-kΩ resistor of the circuit shown in Fig. 3.22.
5. For the circuit shown in Fig. 3.4 (a), $R_1 = 10\ k\Omega$, $R_2 = 40\ k\Omega$, $R_3 = 40\ k\Omega$, $R_4 = 20\ k\Omega$, $R_5 = 5\ k\Omega$, and $V = 100$ volts. Find
   (a) The total current
   (b) The voltage across the parallel combination
   (c) The current through each resistor of the parallel combination

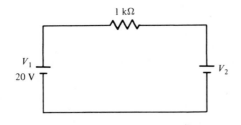

3.20   Circuit for Problem 2.

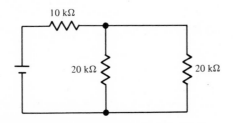

3.21   Circuit for Problem 3.

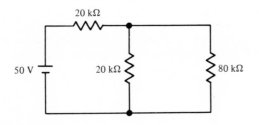

3.22   Circuit for Problem 4.

6. Repeat Problem 5 for the circuit shown in Fig. 3.5 (a). Are there any differences?
7. For the circuit of Example 3.2, all values are the same but the polarity of V_2 is reversed. Find I_{R_2}.
8. For the circuit of Example 3.3, all the values are the same but the polarity of V_2 is reversed. Find the voltage across R_3.
9. Use loop equations to solve Problem 7.
10. Use loop equations to solve Problem 8.
11. For the circuit shown in Fig. 3.23, find V_{R_5} using loop equations.
12. Use the same values as in Problem 11 but reverse all the batteries. Find V_{R_5} using loop equations.
13. For the circuit of Fig. 3.23, find I_{R_1} using superposition.
14. Repeat Problem 13 using loop equations.
15. Use loop equations to find V_{R_2} in Fig. 3.23.

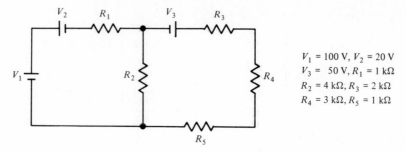

$V_1 = 100$ V, $V_2 = 20$ V
$V_3 = 50$ V, $R_1 = 1$ kΩ
$R_2 = 4$ kΩ, $R_3 = 2$ kΩ
$R_4 = 3$ kΩ, $R_5 = 1$ kΩ

3.23   Circuit for Problem 11.

16. Find the power delivered to the following resistors from a 20-volt ideal voltage source:
    (a) 4 Ω
    (b) 8 Ω
    (c) 12 Ω
17. A voltage source has $V_{oc} = 20$ V. A 2-Ω load resistor reduces the load voltage to 10 volts. Find:
    (a) The maximum power which can be obtained from this load
    (b) The power which this source will deliver to a 10-Ω load
18. A 100-volt source has a 5-Ω internal resistance. Find the load voltage when
    (a) Maximum load power is obtained
    (b) A 50-Ω load is used
19. A 20 volt source has an internal resistance of 2 Ω. What values of load resistance will give half of the maximum power? (There are two such values.)

Chapter 4 Simple Meters

4.1 Introduction

The preceding chapters have discussed current, voltage, and resistance without discussing the principles of making such measurements. In this chapter the methods of making measurements in electronic circuits are introduced and the effect of making measurements is discussed. Since all circuit information is a result of measurements, it is essential that measurements be made properly.

4.2 Electric-Magnetic Interaction

In the 1800's several important experiments were performed which demonstrated that there is interaction between current and the field of force around a magnet.

Hans Christian Oersted performed what now seems a simple experiment He showed that a wire carrying current could deflect a compass needle. In Fig. 4.1, when the switch is closed the compass needle will be deflected

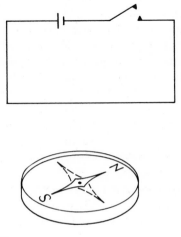

4.1 Oersted's experiment.

from its normal N–S position. Oersted reasoned that **the current through a wire generates a magnetic field around the wire, which interacts with the magnetic field of the compass.** It is the interaction between these two magnetic fields which causes the compass needle to deflect.

At about the same time, Michael Faraday performed another important experiment with a magnet. He passed a magnet through a coil of wire to which an ammeter was connected. As shown in Fig. 4.2, Faraday showed that **when a magnet is moved in or out of a coil of wire a current flows in the wire:** that is, **the moving magnetic field induces a current.**

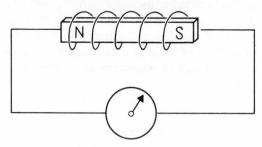

4.2   Faraday's experiment.

As a result of these experiments it is now known that:
1. When a current exists there is a magnetic field of force around the wire.
2. When a magnet is moved past a wire the magnetic field of force induces a current in the wire.

Magnetic fields and currents interact. A current generates a magnetic field and a moving magnetic field generates a current. In one case moving charges (current) generate a magnetic field. In the other case a moving magnetic field generates a current. The interaction between magnetic and electrical fields is the basis of both motors and generators.

In a **motor** a current is used to generate a magnetic field. This magnetic field interacts with another magnet to cause rotation. A motor thus transforms electrical energy into mechanical energy.

In a **generator** the reverse is true. Mechanical energy is used to produce motion between a magnet and a wire. This generates current in the wire.

Motors and generators are of course of great importance in our modern world. In addition the interaction between current and a magnetic field is one basis of electrical measurements.

Figure 4.3 shows a **dynamometer**-type ammeter. The current to be measured generates magnetic fields in three coils which are electrically in series and connected to measure a current. Two of the coils are fixed. The center coil is free to rotate. When a current flows through the dynamometer, magnetic

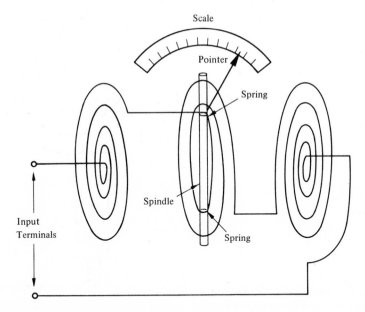

4.3 Dynamometer ammeter.

fields are created. The interaction between the resulting magnetic fields causes the movable coil to rotate. The coil will rotate until the strength of the magnetic field is balanced by the force of the spring. A large current causes a more intense magnetic field and therefore a greater rotation. There is a pointer attached to the spindle which indicates the current by passing over a printed scale.

Very accurate and delicate versions of the dynamometer are used in laboratories as standards against which other ammeters are compared. Calibration is illustrated in Fig. 4.4. The standard meter and the meter being tested are in series, so the current must be the same through both meters. By adjustment of the variable resistor, various current settings can be calibrated on the meter under test.

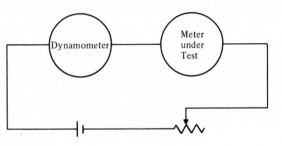

4.4 Ammeter calibration.

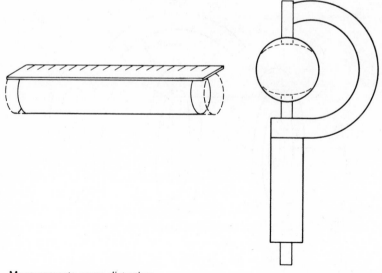

4.5   Measurements cause distortion.

The dynamometer requires relatively large currents to cause deflection. This is not serious as far as calibration is concerned, but it is the reason that dynamometers are not used to make measurements in electronic circuits.

The large power required to cause a dynamometer to deflect is furnished by the circuit which is being measured. This means that the act of measuring the current alters the circuit performance. **A basic principle in making any type of measurement is that the measurement should have little if any effect on the object which is being measured.**

For example, we measure the length of a rod with a ruler and the diameter of the rod with a micrometer, as shown in Fig. 4.5. The weight of the ruler on the rod causes elongation while the micrometer compresses the diameter. It is true that these deformations are negligible if the rod is made of steel. However, we would have to take precautions if the rod were made of rubber. The point is that we must consider the effect of the measurement on whatever is being measured. The effect of making a measurement must always be taken into account in an electrical circuit. If a current measurement reduces the current in the circuit being measured, it is an inaccurate and possibly dangerous situation.

For example, while we measure the current through a flashlight bulb the light will go out if the resistance of the ammeter is comparable to the resistance of the bulb. This is an example of a situation when maximum power transfer is extremely undesirable. We do not want maximum transfer to an ammeter. However, we still need to know the resistance of the ammeter as well as the circuit in which it will be used. This will permit the selection of an ammeter which has negligible effect on the circuit being measured.

4.3   D'Arsonval Meters

The type of ammeter which is commonly used to measure current in electronic circuits is the **D'Arsonval movement.** Figure 4.6 shows a D'Arsonval meter. It is similar to the dynamometer in that both depend on the interaction between a fixed and a movable magnet. In the dynamometer both the fixed and the movable magnets are coils of wire which become magnets when the current which is to be measured flows. In the D'Arsonval meter the fixed magnets are formed by a permanent horseshoe magnet. In this case the current being measured flows only through the movable coil. This creates a magnetic field around the movable coil which interacts with the field of the horseshoe magnet. The movable coil rotates until it balances the force of the restoring spring. Thus the current to be measured by a D'Arsonval movement flows through only one coil, while in a dynamometer the unknown current must flow through three coils. The magnetic strength of a permanent magnet can be much greater than that induced by reasonable currents flowing through a coil. D'Arsonval meters thus require less power to deflect and this is the reason that they are preferred in electronic circuits.

A coil which has a greater number of turns will have a more intense magnetic field when a current is passed through it. However, more turns in the coil require more wire and more wire means more resistance. The resistance of the ammeter coil is in series in any circuit when current is measured (see Fig. 2.1). Once again the making of a measurement causes an error.

This means that trade-offs are required between the strength of the magnetic field and the resistance of an ammeter coil. Meter manufacturers are aware of these requirements, so the resistance of an D'Arsonval ammeter

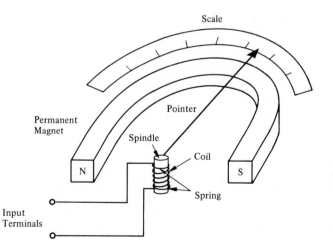

4.6   D'Arsonval movement.

coil for the same range will be about the same regardless of who is the manufacturer. This is true if the meters are physically the same size. Table 4.1 lists the approximate resistances of various ammeters.

Table 4.1   Resistance of Ammeters

Range	Approximate resistance (Ω)
0–10 μA	20,000
0–50 μA	2000
0–1 mA	50
0–10 mA	3
0–100 mA	1
0–1 A	0.1

High-range ammeters have lower resistances than low-range ammeters, because the strength of the magnetic field around a coil is determined by the current as well as the number of turns of wire in the coil (i.e., amperes times turns). Therefore a low current requires more turns to generate the same deflection of a pointer. More turns increase the coil resistance.

Ideally we would like to use high-range ammeters to make measurements. However, a 1-Amp. movement will hardly deflect if it is placed in a circuit where microamperes of current flow. Nevertheless, knowing the resistance of a meter permits us to determine the error introduced by making the measurement. This is illustrated in Example 4.1.

Example 4.1

A 100-kΩ resistor is connected to a 0.5-volt source, as shown in Fig. 4.7. Find the error introduced by measuring the current.

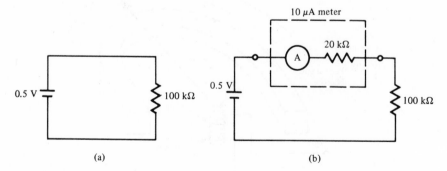

(a)   (b)

4.7 Ammeter resistance affects measurement. **(a)** Before and after measurement. **(b)** During measurement.

Solution Step 1. The theoretical current in this circuit is

$$I_{theor} = \frac{V}{R}$$

$$= \frac{0.5}{10^5} = 5\ \mu A$$

Therefore select a 0–10 μA meter.

Step 2. The resistance of a 10-μA meter from Table 4.1 is 20 kΩ, as shown in Fig. 4.7 (b). The ammeter resistance is in series with the 100-kΩ resistor. Therefore

$$I_{meas} = \frac{V}{R_T} = \frac{0.5}{100 + 20}$$

$$= \frac{0.5}{1.2 \times 10^5} = 4.17\ \mu A$$

Step 3. The theoretical current is 5 μA and the measured current is 4.17 μA. The percent error is

$$\% \text{ error} = \frac{\text{theor} - \text{meas}}{\text{theor}} \times 100\%$$

$$= \frac{5 \times 10^{-6} - 4.17 \times 10^{-6}}{5 \times 10^{-6}} \times 100\% \qquad \textbf{(4.1)}$$

$$\text{error} = 16.6\%$$

In this particular case the act of making the measurement has introduced an error which is greater than 15%. Other current measurements will introduce different errors. In some cases the errors will be less. It is also possible that greater errors will be introduced. In any event, we must always keep in mind that making a current measurement will always give a lower current reading than the actual current which exists when the ammeter is not in the circuit.

In addition to the error caused by adding resistance, ammeters introduce other errors. Manufacturing tolerances and temperature variation will cause errors in readings. Meter manufacturers generally specify meter accuracy in terms of a percentage of **full-scale deflection (FSD)**. Thus a meter movement may be specified as $\pm 3\%$ FSD, $\pm 5\%$ FSD, and so on. This does not mean that in a $\pm 3\%$ meter the error will always be 3%. It means that the error will be no worse than 3% of FSD, high or low. Since the error is given as a percentage of full-scale deflection, the effect will vary at different points on the scale. This is illustrated in Example 4.2.

Example 4.2

Find the error introduced by a 1-mA meter with a $\pm 3\%$ FSD error at (a) full scale, (b) half scale, (c) one tenth scale.

Solution Step 1. Plus or minus 3% of 1 mA is 0.03 mA. At any point on the scale, the meter can be off by as much as 0.03 mA.

Step 2. At full scale the error can be found from Eq. 4.1 :

$$\text{error} = \frac{1 - 0.97}{1} \times 100\% = 3\%$$

This is as expected.

Step 3. At half scale (0.5 mA) the error can be

$$\text{error} = \frac{0.5 - 0.47}{0.5} \times 100\% = 6\%$$

Step 4. At one tenth scale (0.1 mA) the error can be

$$\text{error} = \frac{0.1 - 0.07}{0.1} \times 100\% = 30\%$$

Figure 4.8 shows the possible range of error for these three conditions. The percent error increases as we go lower on a scale. Therefore, **to keep the error to a minimum select a meter which will give a reading as close to full scale as possible.** Read a current of 0.8 mA on a 1-mA meter instead of on a 10-mA meter and so on.

As we have seen, meter resistance and manufacturing tolerances cause errors in a meter reading. There is a third source of error which is not due to

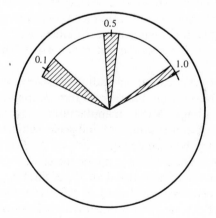

4.8   Effect of FSD meter error.

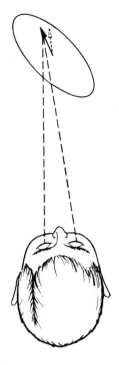

4.9   Parallax error in meter reading.

the meter but frequently introduces the largest error of all. This error is human error caused by not reading the pointer properly and is called **parallax.** As shown in Fig. 4.9, if we do not line our eyes up properly with the pointer we can introduce an error. Parallax errors can be on either the high side or the low side, depending from which side we read the meter. To avoid parallax error we should be directly behind the pointer. This is the reason that a car speedometer reading appears different to a passenger than to the driver. Some meters have mirrors under the scale. In this case the proper reading is obtained when we cannot see the reflection of the pointer in the mirror.

With all these possible errors, a large total error can exist in making a current reading. This does not mean that we should not make current readings. Indeed we have no information about a circuit unless we make measurements. However, we must always keep in mind that making measurements introduces errors. We would prefer to have an ideal ammeter. An ideal ammeter would have no resistance, no errors due to manufacturing, and presumably we would read an ideal ammeter without introducing any human error. In Chapter 3 we described the difference between a real and an ideal voltage source. Just as an ideal voltage source is not possible, an ideal ammeter is not possible. However, by keeping in mind the cause and type of errors which measurements introduce we can act to keep such errors to a minimum.

4.4   Multirange Ammeters

It is possible to have a single-scale ammeter more versatile by having it read over several different ranges. This is accomplished by placing a resistor in parallel **(shunt)** with the ammeter, as shown in Fig. 4.10. This permits a larger current to enter the meter, since a portion of the entering current will be diverted through the shunt resistor.

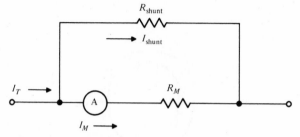

4.10   Shunt resistor extends ammeter range.

The value of the shunt resistor is determined by recognizing that the shunt resistor is in parallel with the resistance of the ammeter. Therefore the conditions which exist in a parallel circuit determine the required value of the shunt resistor. This is illustrated in Example 4.3.

Example 4.3

What value of shunt resistor will convert a 50-μA meter into (a) a 100-μA meter, (b) a 500-μA meter?

Solution Step 1. The shunt resistor is in parallel with the meter resistance. Therefore

$$V_{\text{meter}} = V_{\text{shunt}}$$

Step 2. The voltage drop across the meter is found by Ohm's law. The meter resistance is found from Table 4.1 to be 2000 Ω:

$$V_{\text{meter}} = I_{\text{meter}} \times R_{\text{meter}}$$
$$= 50 \times 10^{-6} \times 2 \times 10^{3}$$
$$= 0.1 \text{ volt}$$

Step 3. From Kirchhoff's current law the current entering the meter terminal must equal the current leaving:

$$I_{T} = I_{\text{meter}} + I_{\text{shunt}}$$

For the 100-μA case:

$$100 \times 10^{-6} = 50 \times 10^{-6} + I_{shunt}$$

$$I_{shunt} = 50 \times 10^{-6} \, Amp.$$

This is the excess current which must be shunted around the meter.

Step 4. From Ohm's law a resistance is the ratio of the voltage to current. Therefore

$$R_{shunt} = \frac{V_{shunt}}{I_{shunt}}$$

$$= \frac{0.1}{50 \times 10^{-6}}$$

$$= 2 \times 10^{3} \, \Omega$$

Step 5. For the 500-μA case the voltage across the ammeter will still be 0.1 volt.

Step 6. The current through the meter itself will still be 50 μA for full-scale deflection. Therefore the excess or shunt current is found from

$$I_T = I_{meter} + I_{shunt}$$

$$500 \times 10^{-6} = 50 \times 10^{-6} + I_{shunt}$$

$$I_{shunt} = 450 \, \mu A$$

Step 7. R_{shunt} for the 500-μA case is

$$R_{shunt} = \frac{V_{shunt}}{I_{shunt}}$$

$$= \frac{0.1}{450 \times 10^{-6}}$$

$$= 222.2 \, \Omega$$

Figure 4.11 shows a schematic for this multirange ammeter. To maintain the accuracy of the basic meter, shunt resistors must be precision resistors rather than ordinary carbon composition resistors.

Shunt resistors cannot be used to produce lower scales than that of the basic meter. The principle of a multirange ammeter is to divert a portion of the total current from the meter movement to a shunt resistor. Therefore shunt resistors can be used only to give ammeter ranges which are higher than those of the basic ammeter.

In multirange ammeters there are typically scales which are multiples of 10 of the basic range as well as other scales. In Example 4.3 the basic meter was 50 μA. With shunts we created a 500-μA range (a multiple of 10) as well as a 100-μA range (a multiple of 2). Generally, using only multiples of

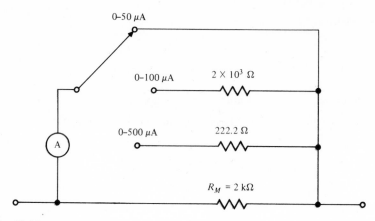

4.11 Multirange ammeter.

10 is avoided. This is because of the effect of the FSD error which has already been discussed.

For example, if there were only 500 μA and, say, a 5000-μA (5 mA) scale, an 80 μA reading would use only a small portion of the 500-μA scale. However, with 1 100-μA range we use 80% of the total scale and therefore minimize the effects of the FSD error.

4.5 Voltmeters

In addition to measuring currents it is also possible to use an ammeter as the basis of a voltmeter. This is accomplished by placing a resistor in series with an ammeter. Knowing the value of the resistor allows us to calibrate the current scale in terms of volts. Figure 4.12 shows a simple voltmeter. Example 4.4 demonstrates how an ammeter can be converted into a volt-meter.

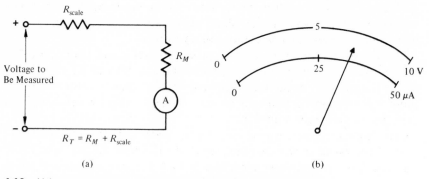

(a)   (b)

4.12 Using an ammeter as a voltmeter. **(a)** Circuit. **(b)** Meter scale.

Example 4.4

Find the value of the resistor which is required to convert a 50-μA meter into a voltmeter with a full-scale reading of 10 volts.

Solution Step 1.   Since the full-scale range is 50 μA, this must be the current which corresponds to 10 volts. The total resistance is therefore

$$R_T = \frac{V}{I} = \frac{10}{50 \times 10^{-6}}$$

$$= 200 \text{ k}\Omega$$

Step 2. The total resistance is the series combination of the meter resistance plus the scaling resistor ($R_M = 2 \text{ k}\Omega$ from Table 4.1):

$$R_T = R_M + R_{\text{scale}}$$

$$200 \times 10^3 = 2 \times 10^3 + R_{\text{scale}}$$

$$R_{\text{scale}} = 198 \text{ k}\Omega$$

By using additional resistors in place of the 198-kΩ resistor, different full-scale voltage ranges are obtained and a multirange voltmeter can be constructed. This is illustrated in Example 4.5.

Example 4.5

What values of scaling are required to use a 50-μA meter as (a) a 50-volt meter and (b) a 100-volt meter?

Solution Step 1.   As in Example 4.4, for the 50-volt range,

$$R_T = \frac{50}{50 \times 10^{-6}} = 1 \text{ M}\Omega$$

Step 2.

$$R_T = R_M + R_{\text{scale}}$$

$$10^6 = 2 \times 10^3 + R_{\text{scale}}$$

$$R_{\text{scale}} = 998 \text{ k}\Omega$$

Step 3. For the 100-volt range,

$$R_T = \frac{V}{I}$$

$$= \frac{100}{50 \times 10^{-6}} = 2 \text{ M}\Omega$$

Step 4.

$$R_T = R_M + R_{scale}$$

$$2 \times 10^6 = 2 \times 10^3 + R_{scale}$$

$$R_{scale} = 1.998 \text{ M}\Omega$$

Figure 4.13 shows the multirange voltmeter schematic for Examples 4.4 and 4.5. As in the case of the multirange ammeter, the multirange voltmeter requires precision resistors to preserve the accuracy of the basic meter movement. The remarks concerning error due to percentage of full-scale deflection and parallax error apply equally to voltmeters.

Voltmeters also introduce an error in the circuit in which they are used. We saw in Chapter 2 that ammeters measure charge flow per unit time and are therefore placed in series in a circuit. In this chapter, placing the ammeter in series was seen to increase the resistance of the circuit. This causes an error in measurement.

In chapter 2 we also saw that voltmeters measure the difference in potential between two points and therefore voltmeters are placed across these two points; that is, voltmeters are placed in parallel with the resistors whose voltage drop we wish to measure. Since placing resistors in parallel reduces

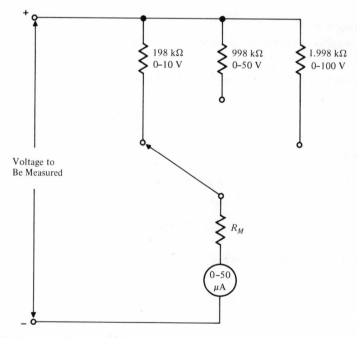

4.13   Multirange voltmeter.

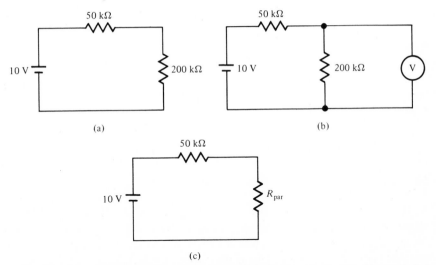

(a)   (b)

(c)

4.14   Measuring voltage introduces an error. **(a)** Actual circuit. **(b)** Circuit during measurement. **(c)** Equivalent circuit during measurement.

the total resistance, making a voltage measurement introduces a measurement error. This is illustrated in Example 4.6.

Example 4.6

Using a voltmeter of the type in Example 4.4, calculate the error introduced by measuring the voltage across the 200-kΩ resistor of Fig. 4.14 (a).

Solution Step 1. Using the voltage divider equation (Eq. 2.14), the theoretical voltage across the 200-kΩ resistor is

$$V_{200} = 20\frac{200}{200 + 50}$$

$$= 16 \text{ volts}$$

Step 2. The voltmeter of Example 4.4 has a total resistance of 200 kΩ. This resistance is in parallel with the 200-kΩ resistor which is in the circuit. The resistance of the parallel combination of 200 kΩ and voltmeter is therefore

$$R_{\text{parallel}} = \frac{R_{200}R_V}{R_{200} + R_V}$$

$$= \frac{200 \times 10^3 \times 200 \times 10^3}{200 \times 10^3 + 200 \times 10^3}$$

$$= 100 \text{ k}\Omega$$

Step 3. Therefore, during measurement the 200-kΩ resistor is replaced by a resistance of 100 kΩ [as shown in Fig. 4.14 (c)] and, using the voltage divider equation, the voltage across this resistor is

$$V_{100} = 10\frac{100}{100 + 50}$$

$$= 13.3 \text{ volts}$$

Step 4. Using Eq. 4.1 the error is

$$\text{error} = \frac{16 - 13.3}{16} \times 100\%$$

$$= 16.67\%$$

The error in Example 4.6 occurs because the voltmeter resistance **"loads down"** the resistor across which the voltage is being measured. The error will be less if the voltmeter resistance is higher since this will not decrease the parallel resistance as much. This is illustrated in Example 4.7.

Example 4.7

Calculate the error introduced by measuring the voltage across the 200-kΩ resistor in Fig. 4.14, using the 100-volt scale of Example 4.5.

Solution Step 1. The total resistance of the 100-volt scale of Example 4.5 is 2 MΩ. Therefore this resistance is in parallel with the 200-kΩ resistor:

$$R_{\text{parallel}} = \frac{2 \times 10^5 \times 2 \times 10^6}{2 \times 10^5 + 2 \times 10^6}$$

$$= 182 \text{ k}\Omega$$

Step 2. In this case the measured voltage will be

$$V_{182} = 20\frac{182}{182 + 50}$$

$$= 15.7 \text{ volts}$$

instead of the theoretical 16 volts.

Step 3. The error in this case is

$$\text{error} = \frac{16 - 15.7}{16} \times 100\%$$

$$= 1.87\%$$

Generally an error of less than 2% is acceptable for many applications in electronics. (Usually we are working with 5% or 10% resistors anyway.) However, trying to read 8 or 10 volts on a 100-volt scale can introduce an

error of as much as 30% (see Example 4.2). So although the answer to reducing voltmeter loading is to use a high-resistance voltmeter, this should not be
accomplished by going to a high voltage range. The answer is to start with a
voltmeter with high-enough resistance.

The actual error introduced by voltmeter loading depends on the voltmeter resistance as well as on what other resistors are in the circuit being
measured. For example, if there were no 50-kΩ resistor in the circuit of

Table 4.2   Effect of Voltmeter Loading

R_V	R_T	Percent change
R	$0.5R$	50
$10R$	$0.91R$	9
$100R$	$0.99R$	1
$10000R$	$0.999R$	0.1

Fig. 4.14 (a), the 200-kΩ resistor would be in parallel with the voltage
source. In this case the voltmeter resistance would not lower the voltage at
all. (However, the voltage source must supply twice as much current.) On
the other hand, if the 50-kΩ resistor were replaced with a 200-kΩ resistor
and a voltmeter with a resistance of 200 kΩ were used, the error would
increase to 33.3%. One way of specifying voltmeter loading is in terms of the
parallel resistance of the voltmeter and resistor being measured. The loading
effect will always be less than the percentage change in resistance. Table 4.2
compares the change in resistance of a resistor in parallel with a voltmeter
as a function of voltmeter resistance (R_V) as shown in Fig. 4.15. From
Table 4.2 we can see that the loading error will always be less than 1%
regardless of what else is in the circuit if the voltmeter resistance is at least
100 times the resistance whose voltage is being measured. For example, on
the 10-volt scale the voltmeter we have been working with has a resistance of
200 kΩ. If we use this meter to measure voltage across resistors which are
less than 2 kΩ (i.e., 1/100 of 200 kΩ) we cannot possibly introduce a voltmeter loading error of more than 1%.

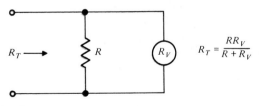

$$R_T \longrightarrow \quad R \quad \quad R_V \quad \quad R_T = \frac{RR_V}{R+R_V}$$

4.15   Voltmeter loading.

Voltmeter resistance is one of the factors which determine voltmeter accuracy. Therefore the resistance of a voltmeter is one of the important factors in selection of the proper voltmeter. Voltmeters are specified in terms of their ohms-per-volt ratio. For the voltmeter we have been using in the illustrative examples:

On the 10-volt scale $R_T = 200,000 \ \Omega$. Therefore

$$\frac{2,000,000 \ \Omega}{10 \ \text{V}} = 20,000 \ \Omega/\text{V}$$

On the 50-volt scale $R_T = 1 \ \text{M}\Omega$. Therefore

$$\frac{1,100,000 \ \Omega}{50 \ \text{V}} = 20,000 \ \Omega/\text{V}$$

On the 100-volt scale $R_T = 2 \ \text{M}\Omega$. Therefore:

$$\frac{2,000,000 \ \Omega}{100 \ \text{V}} = 20,000 \ \Omega/\text{V}$$

Thus on all ranges our voltmeter has a resistance/voltage ratio of 20,000 Ω/V. Since higher voltmeter resistance means less voltmeter loading, our voltmeter is better than a 5000-Ω/V meter or a 10,000-Ω/V meter.

The ohms-per-volt rating is a useful basis for comparing voltmeters. However, we must always remember that the resistance of the voltmeter is constant on any scale. The voltmeter resistance when reading 7 volts on the 10 volt scale is not 140,000 Ω (i.e., 7 volts × 20,000 Ω/V). On the 10-volt scale the voltmeter resistance is always 200,000 Ω. This is the R_T for the 10-volt range. It is the total resistance of the voltmeter which is connected in parallel with the resistor whose voltage we wish to measure.

4.6   Ohmmeters

We have seen that a single ammeter is the basis of the multirange ammeter. The ammeter was also used as the basis of voltmeters. Ammeters are also used as the basis of resistance-measuring meters. Meters which measure resistance are called **ohmmeters.**

An obvious way to determine the value of an unknown resistor is to measure the current through the resistor and the voltage across the resistor, as shown in Fig. 4.16. Ohm's law is then applied to determine the value of the unknown resistor. This is illustrated in Example 4.8.

Example 4.8

For the circuit shown in Fig. 4.16 the ammeter reads 40 μA when the voltage across the unknown resistor is 1 volt. Determine the value of R_x.

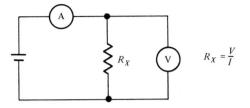

4.16   Ammeter and voltmeter determine R_x.

Solution Step 1. By applying Ohm's law:

$$R_x = \frac{V_x}{I_x}$$

$$= \frac{1}{40 \times 10^{-6}} = 25\,\mathrm{k\Omega}$$

This is a very simple approach. However, it has several drawbacks. Two meters must be read and a calculation must be performed. There are accuracy problems associated with reading any meter. Reading two meters instead of a single meter will not improve accuracy. Also, there is a chance of making an error in performing the calculation. A more satisfactory solution is to use the ammeter as the basis of a direct-reading ohmmeter.

Figure 4.17 shows one approach to using an ammeter as a direct-reading ohmmeter. The circuit consists of a battery in series with three resistors: a variable resistor (R_Z), the resistance (R_M) of the ammeter itself, and the resistor (R_x) to be measured. The variable resistor is used to compensate for the decrease in battery voltage due to aging. To calibrate the ammeter to read directly in ohms we apply the equation for a series circuit:

$$V = I(R_Z + R_M + R_x) \tag{4.2}$$

Example 4.9 illustrates the calibration of an ohmmeter.

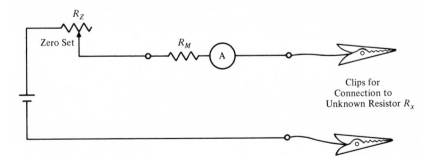

4.17   Direct-reading ohmmeter.

Example 4.9

In the circuit shown in Fig. 4.17 the battery is 3 volts and the meter is a 50-μA movement. Calibrate the meter scale to read ohms directly.

Solution Step 1. When the meter leads are shorted together $R_x = 0$. This condition should give full scale current (from Table 4.1, R_M for a 50-μA meter = 2 kΩ). Therefore by using Eq. 4.1 we can determine R_Z:

$$V = I(R_Z + R_M + R_x)$$
$$3 = 50 \times 10^{-6}(R_Z + 2 \times 10^3 + 0)$$
$$R_Z = 58 \text{ k}\Omega$$

Thus if we have a variable resistor which can reach at least 58 kΩ we can short the leads together to yield maximum current. This means we can engrave 0 Ω over the 50-μA reading on the ammeter scale.

Step 2. If $R_x = \infty$ (i.e., an open circuit) there will be no current since no current can flow in an open circuit. Therefore

$$I = 0$$

This means we can engrave ∞ over the 0-μA reading on the ammeter scale.

Step 3. To find the value of the unknown resistance which corresponds to a current of, say, 10-μA, we again use Eq. 4.2:

$$V = I(R_Z + R_M + R_x)$$
$$3 = 10 \times 10^{-6}(58k + 2k + R_x)$$
$$R_x = 240 \text{ k}\Omega$$

Therefore, engrave 240 kΩ over the 10-μA reading.

Step 4. If we repeat this procedure for 20, 30, and 40 μA we get:

Ammeter reading (μA)	Corresponding resistance (kΩ)
20	90
30	40
40	15

Figure 4.18 shows the scale which results for the values obtained in Example 4.9. This ohmmeter can be converted into a multirange ohmmeter in several different ways. Using different voltages, using different known values of resistance in series with the unknown resistor, and shunting the meter

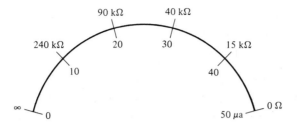

4.18   Ohmmeter scale above ammeter scale.

movement with a known resistor are all practical approaches to creating a multirange ohmmeter.

As has been noted the zero-setting variable resistor offers partial compensation for the decrease in battery voltage with age. This is the reason that an ohmmeter must be zeroed before it is used. Zeroing is accomplished by shorting the leads together and setting the zero-setting variable resistor to read 0 Ω (i.e., full-scale current). The extent to which rezeroing is effective is illustrated by Example 4.10.

Example 4.10

What will be the resistance which corresponds to 40 μA on the ohmmeter which was designed in Example 4.9 when the battery voltage drops to 2.8 volts?

Solution Step 1.   Since the voltage has descreased the ohmmeter must be rezeroed so that 50 μA still corresponds to 0 Ω. Using Eq. 4.2:

$$V = I(R_Z + R_M + R_x)$$
$$2.8 = 50 \times 10^{-6}(R_Z + 2 \times 10^3 + 0)$$
$$R_Z = 54 \times 10^3 \ \Omega$$

Step 2.   The only unknown in the series-circuit equation for the ohmmeter is now the resistance which corresponds to the current of interest (40 μA). Therefore

$$V = I(R_Z + R_M + R_x)$$
$$2.8 = 40 \times 10^{-6}(54 \times 10^3 + 2 \times 10^3 + R_x)$$
$$R_x = 14 \ \text{k}\Omega$$

The original resistance reading for 40 μA when the battery was fresh was 15 kΩ. Thus zeroing is helpful but is not a perfect solution. However, zeroing is better than not doing anything to compensate for the decrease in battery voltage. If we do not rezero at all, the ohmmeter will not read 0 Ω when the leads are shorted together after the battery voltage drops.

Not being able to read 0 Ω is especially serious since one of the important applications of an ohmmeter is to check for circuit continuity. That is, we determine whether or not connecting wires between junctions are proper by measuring the resistance between the junctions. If the ohmmeter does not read 0 Ω under such a situation, the circuit has a malfunction. Therefore an ohmmeter must be able to read 0 Ω. Not zeroing the ohmmeter will lead us to a false conclusion regarding continuity checks. Another consequence of not zeroing an ohmmeter prior to use is that the error will be much larger than the error which occurs when the ohmmeter is zeroed.

As we have seen, calculations are required to design ammeters and voltmeters. Similarly, the design of ohmmeters requires calculations. However, after the ohmmeter is designed it reads directly on the ohm scale. We do not calculate the value of resistance that corresponds to steadily decreasing battery voltage. We simply short the leads together and adjust the zero-setting resistor until the meter reads 0 Ω.

4.7 Multimeters

The ammeter, voltmeter, and ohmmeter have a common basis. In all three cases operation depends on an ammeter movement.

To make a multirange ammeter we used shunt resistors in parallel. A voltmeter uses an ammeter in series with a resistor. An ohmmeter uses an

4.19 Typical VOM. *(Courtesy Simpson Electric Company.)*

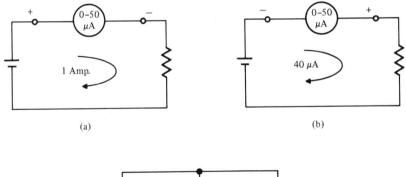

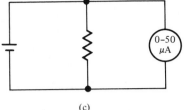

(c)

4.20 Incorrect ammeter methods. **(a)** Excessive current. **(b)** Incorrect meter polarity. **(c)** In parallel with resistor.

ammeter in series with a resistor and a battery. Therefore it is possible to make a multipurpose instrument measuring current, voltage, and resistance which uses the same meter movement.

An instrument of this type is referred to as a **VOM (volt-ohm-milliam-meter)**. Figure 4.19 shows a typical VOM. It is based on the same principles we have discussed for ammeters, voltmeters, and ohmmeters. A selector switch determines what will be measured and also selects the range. Self-contained batteries are used for the ohmmeter scales.

In addition to the comments which have been made concerning meter accuracy and loading, some general statements about test equipment are in order. Meters are used in designing circuits to see if actual measurements agree with calculated values. Meters are also used in trouble shooting equipment which has become defective.

In both of these cases we know what the proper current, voltage, and resistance should be. However, before we make a measurement the actual values are not known. An actual voltage or current may be too high, too low, or within acceptable limits. It is also possible that meters have been connected improperly. Using a scale which is too low for a reading or improperly connecting a meter can cause permanent damage to a meter.

Ammeters may be permanently damaged in several ways, as shown in Fig. 4.20. In Fig. 4.20 (a) the current to be measured greatly exceeds the range of the ammeter. The meter attempts to deflect past its range and the pointer can literally wrap itself around the endpoint. Also, the meter coil can be burned out. This situation is avoided by starting on the highest current range which the VOM has. The selector switch is then rotated to successively lower ranges until the most useful range is found.

In Fig. 4.20 (b) the meter is connected with the polarity reversed. The meter will try to deflect in the opposite direction. This can also cause permanent damage. To avoid an improper polarity connection we need to know which is the more positive portion of the circuit we are measuring.

In Fig. 4.20 (c) the ammeter is connected in parallel with a resistor instead of in series. This also causes excessive current to flow through the meter and results in permanent damage.

In addition using a meter improperly can damage the circuit being measured as well as the meter itself. Proper use of a meter requires both proper attention to the meter scales and an understanding of what is being measured. The concepts of current and voltage were described in Chapter 2. A proper appreciation of the nature of current and voltage will go a long way toward avoiding damage to meters as well as toward making accurate measurements.

Ammeters always are connected in series in a circuit. This means that we must "break into" any circuit when we want to measure current. Voltmeters, on the other hand, are connected in parallel with the component whose voltage is to be measured. This means that voltage measurements can be made without disturbing the circuit. However, we must still be careful to use the voltmeter properly. Excessive voltage or incorrect polarity connections can cause permanent damage to a voltmeter.

As in the case of ammeters, proper polarity connection of a voltmeter requires some knowledge of the circuit being measured. The overvoltage condition is avoided by starting with the highest voltage range and switching downward.

The use of an ohmmeter to check for continuity has already been discussed. But a buzzer or a battery and a flashlight bulb can also be used to check for continuity. In Chapter 1 the resistor color code was described. The ohmmeter, therefore, would seem to have little usefulness since we can determine the resistance by looking at the stripes.

However, there are resistors which do not use the color code. Also colors may fade with age. An important application of ohmmeters is in trouble shooting. When an electronic circuit malfunctions, it is quite possible that excessive current flows through resistors. In such a situation the value of resistance can change permanently. Therefore an important application of an ohmmeter is to check whether resistors have changed value.

For example, a brown-black-red striped resistor should measure in the vicinity of 1000 Ω regardless of the tolerance band. If the ohmmeter indicates, say, 500 Ω or 2000 Ω or values which are even further from 1000 Ω, the resistor should be replaced. However, we cannot use an ohmmeter to make precise resistance measurements because of the errors associated with ohmmeters which have already been discussed.

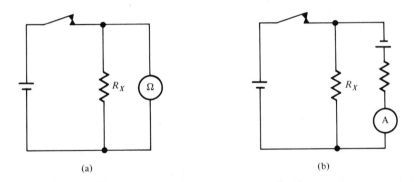

4.21   Incorrect and dangerous ohmmeter use. **(a)** Circuit. **(b)** Equivalent circuit.

Improper use of an ohmmeter can result in permanent damage. As we have seen, an ohmmeter is basically an ammeter in series with a battery and a resistor. If we use an ohmmeter as shown in Fig. 4.21 (a), current from the circuit will flow through the ohmmeter as shown in Fig. 4.21 (b). This means that the ohmmeter scale will read incorrectly since the ohmmeter is calibrated in terms of its own internal battery. The more serious problem is that the normal circuit current can be large enough to permanently damage the meter movement. Therefore the switch in Fig. 4.21 (a) should be opened before an attempt is made to measure resistance. A resistance measurement should never be attempted when a circuit is operating.

Disconnecting voltage from a circuit is necessary to make a resistance measurement. However, this in itself does not ensure that we are measuring the resistor in which we are interested. For example, in Fig. 4.22 (a) we may wish to determine if the 10-kΩ resistor has changed value. If we place an ohmmeter across the resistance as shown it will not read what we are looking for, because the ohmmeter is connected across other resistors as well as the 10-kΩ resistor. In this circuit the ohmmeter is also in parallel with the 5-kΩ

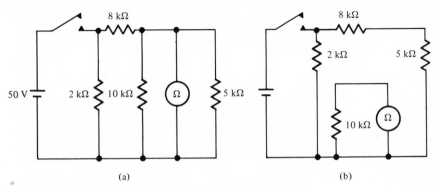

4.22   Measuring a single resistance. **(a)** Incorrect. **(b)** Correct.

resistor, and the series combination of the 8-kΩ and the 2-kΩ (i.e., 10-kΩ) resistors is in parallel with the ohmmeter.

Using the equation for combining resistors in parallel (Eq. 2.19),

$$\frac{1}{R_T} = \frac{1}{R_1} + \frac{1}{R_2} + \frac{1}{R_3}$$

$$= \frac{1}{5 \times 10^3} + \frac{1}{10 \times 10^3} + \frac{1}{10 \times 10^3}$$

$$= 0.2 \times 10^{-3} + 0.1 \times 10^{-3} + 0.1 \times 10^{-3}$$

$$= 0.4 \times 10^{-3}$$

$$R_T = \frac{1}{0.4 \times 10^{-3}} = 2.5 \times 10^3 \ \Omega$$

That is, if all the resistors are correct the ohmmeter will read 2.5 kΩ instead of the 10 kΩ we are interested in measuring.

The only way to measure the value of a single resistor in a circuit is to disconnect one end of the resistor from the rest of the circuit, as shown in Fig. 4.22 (b). In this way the ohmmeter is connected only to the resistor of interest.

The illustrative example in designing an ohmmeter indicated that the ohmmeter scale was not divided uniformly. This means that a compromise between meter accuracy and meter readability must be made. The best place to read an ohmmeter is at midscale, where it is most evenly divided. This is a compromise between the low end, which is well spaced but inaccurate, and the upper end, which is too cramped. Contrast this with reading ammeters and voltmeters as far to the upper end as possible.

VOM's are extremely flexible test instruments. They must be treated with tender loving care if they are to be useful.

Summary

1. Meter movements are based on the interaction between magnetic fields. At least one of the magnetic fields must be a result of the measurement being performed.
2. Ammeters are placed in series in the circuit to measure current. Multirange ammeters are made by placing shunt resistors across the meter movement.
3. Voltmeters are made by placing resistors in series with an ammeter movement. Multirange voltmeters involve switching different resistors in series with the meter.
4. Ohmmeters are made by placing a battery and a resistor in series with the ammeter. Multirange ohmmeters involve switching in different batteries and/or resistors.
5. Meters can be damaged if used improperly. Proper use requires a knowledge of meter principles as well as some information about the circuit being measured.

Questions

1. What do motors, generators, and ammeters have in common?
2. What is the difference between a motor and a generator?
3. How does a dynamometer differ from a D'Arsonval movement?
4. What similarities are there in a dynamometer and a D'Arsonval movement?
5. How should the resistance of an ammeter compare with the resistance of the circuit in which it is used?
6. Why do low-range ammeters have higher resistance than high-range ammeters?
7. Why does using an ammeter to measure current decrease the current?
8. What is the significance of FSD error?
9. Compare a real and an ideal ammeter.
10. What is the principle of a multirange ammeter?
11. How is an ammeter used to construct a voltmeter?
12. What is parallax error?
13. What is the significance of the ohms-per-volt rating of a voltmeter?
14. How is an ammeter used in the construction of an ohmmeter?
15. What is the purpose of the zero-setting resistor of an ohmmeter?

Problems

1. A 10-volt battery is connected to a 1-kΩ resistor. What error results if this current is measured with a 10-mA meter? (Use Table 4.1 to find meter resistance.) Neglect the effect of FSD error.
2. A 1-volt battery is connected to a 100-kΩ resistor. What error results if this current is measured with a 10-μA meter? Neglect the effect of FSD error.
3. A 2-volt battery is connected to a 50-kΩ resistor. Select an appropriate ammeter and determine the error. Neglect the effect of FSD error.
4. A certain 1-mA meter has a ±5% FSD accuracy. What can be the error when the meter reads
   (a) 0.7-mA
   (b) 0.5-mA
   (c) 0.1-mA
5. A bulb for a 3 volt flashlight has a 30-Ω resistance. How much will the current be decreased if the current is measured with a suitable meter?
6. A 10-volt meter has a ±3% FSD. What can the reading be when this meter measures a 3-volt battery?
7. A 1.5-volt battery can be measured using a 3-volt meter and a 10-volt meter. Both voltmeters are ±5% FSD. What can the readings be in both cases?
8. Using a 10-μA meter, design a multirange ammeter which will have 100-μA, 500-μA, and 1-mA ranges. (Use Table 4.1 to find meter resistance.)
9. Repeat Problem 7 using a 50-μA movement. Does either meter offer any advantages, assuming cost is not a factor?
10. Using a 1-mA meter, design a meter which has 0.1-mA, 10-mA, and 100-mA ranges.

11. Use a 0.1-mA meter to design a multirange voltmeter with 10-volt, 50-volt, and 100-volt ranges. Use Table 4.1 to find meter resistance.

12. What is the ohms-per-volt rating of the voltmeter in Problem 11?

13. Use a 10-μA meter to design a multirange voltmeter with 10-volt, 50-volt, and 100-volt ranges.

14. What is the ohms-per-volt rating of the voltmeter in Problem 13? Is a 10-μA meter or a 1-mA meter better for use in a voltmeter?

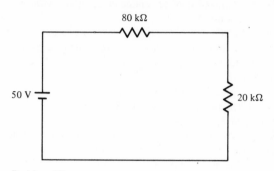

4.23   Circuit for Problem 15.

15. The voltage across the 20-kΩ resistor in Fig. 4.23 is measured on the 10-volt scale of 5000 Ω/V meter. What is the voltmeter reading? What is the percent error?

16. Repeat Problem 15 using the 10-volt scale of a 10,000 Ω/V meter.

17. Repeat Problem 15 using a 20,000 Ω/V meter.

18. Use a 6-volt battery and a 50-μA meter to design an ohmmeter. Determine the unknown resistance which corresponds to 0, 10, 20, ... , 50 μAmps. Compare these values with Example 4.9.

19. Use a 3-volt battery and a 1.0-mA. meter to design an ohmmeter. Determine the resistance which corresponds to each 0.1-mA current reading (i.e., 0.1, 0.2, 0.3, ... , 0.9 mA).

20. Repeat Problem 19 using a 6-volt battery.

Chapter 5 Equivalent Circuits

5.1 Introduction

Basic circuit laws and methods of measuring electronic quantities have been discussed separately; in this chapter the basic circuit laws and measurement techniques are combined. This combination is used to determine the structure of circuits which cannot be observed directly. In addition, advanced measurement techniques are presented which permit more accurate determination of electronic quantities.

5.2 Equivalent Circuits

Two circuits are said to be equivalent if, for the same applied voltage, the identical current results. The principle of an equivalent circuit is illustrated in Example 5.1.

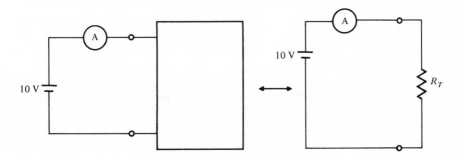

5.1 Simple equivalent circuit.

Example 5.1

A 10-volt battery is connected to a pair of terminals on a closed box which contains an unknown resistive circuit, as shown in Fig. 5.1. The resulting current as measured by the ammeter is 10 mA. Construct a series circuit consisting of two resistors which is equivalent to the original circuit inside the box.

Solution Step 1. Using Ohm's law to determine the total resistance between the two terminals:

$$R_T = \frac{V}{I}$$

$$= \frac{10}{10 \times 10^{-3}} = 1 \text{ k}\Omega$$

Step 2. Any series combination of two resistors will satisfy the requirements for this example if the sum of the resistances is $1000\,\Omega$:

$$R_T = R_1 + R_2$$
$$1 \times 10^3 = R_1 + R_2$$

For example,

$$R_1 = 100\,\Omega, \qquad R_2 = 900\,\Omega$$

or

$$R_1 = 200\,\Omega, \qquad R_2 = 800\,\Omega$$

or

$$R_1 = 500\,\Omega, \qquad R_2 = 500\,\Omega \qquad \text{etc.}$$

We have no way of knowing what is actually inside the box, but we do have an equivalent circuit with any of the above combinations. Any of these combinations is equivalent to the circuit inside the box in the sense that the same current will result if the same voltage is applied. Actually there may be a single 1000-Ω resistor inside. There may be several hundred resistors in series whose total resistance is equal to 1000-Ω. This should not concern us. The important point is that **we can exactly duplicate the conditions which occur at the terminals of the box.** This is what is meant by equivalence. Our two-resistor circuit will have the same resultant current as the circuit inside the box at any voltage level.

If the 10-volt battery which is connected to the box of Example 5.1 is replaced with a 20-volt battery, the resulting current will be 20 mA. The same is true for our two-resistor series circuit. This two-resistor series circuit, therefore, is equivalent to the circuit inside the box.

There is no particular reason why the equivalent circuit must consist of two resistors in series. Instead we could have a single resistor, three resistors in series, four resistors in series, and so on. In fact, we could even construct an equivalent circuit which consists of resistors in parallel. This is illustrated in Example 5.2.

Example 5.2

For the same box as was used in Example 5.1, construct an equivalent circuit which consists of two resistors in parallel. One resistor is to be twice as large as the other.

Solution Step 1. Since the same condition as in Example 5.1 is involved, the total resistance is the same:

$$R_T = 1 \times 10^3 \, \Omega$$

Step 2. For two resistors in parallel we can use the simplified form (Eq. 2.20):

$$R_T = \frac{R_1 R_2}{R_1 + R_2}$$
$$= 1 \times 10^3 \, \Omega$$

Step 3. From the given requirements:

$$R_1 = 2R_2$$

Therefore

$$1 \times 10^3 = \frac{2R_2 R_2}{3R_2}$$
$$R_2 = 1.5 \times 10^3 \, \Omega$$

and since

$$R_1 = 2R_2$$
$$= 3 \times 10^3 \, \Omega$$

Step 4. We can check to see if this parallel combination has a total resistance of 1 kΩ:

$$\frac{1.5 \times 10^3 \times 3 \times 10^3}{4.5 \times 10^3} = \frac{4.5 \times 10^3}{4.5} = 1 \times 10^3 \, \Omega \quad \checkmark$$

As in the case of the series equivalent circuit, there is no particular reason for this exact combination of resistors. Any two other resistors whose parallel combination is 1000 Ω is just as satisfactory. Also, there is no reason to limit the parallel combination to two resistors only. Three resistors in parallel, four resistors in parallel, and so on can also be chosen to satisfy the requirement of Example 5.2. For example, the parallel combination of 2 kΩ, 4 kΩ, and 4 kΩ has a total resistance of 1 kΩ.

In addition to series or parallel equivalent circuits, we could also find additional types of circuits which are equivalent. The circuit of Fig. 5.2

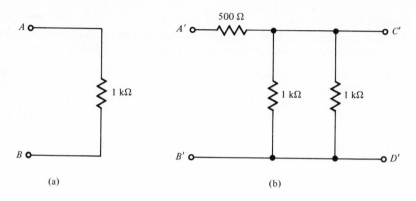

(a)   (b)

5.2   Series–parallel equivalent circuit.

shows a series-parallel circuit which is equivalent to the circuits of Example 5.2.

In fact we have already discussed the concept of equivalent circuits, in Chapter 3, when series-parallel circuits were simplified to equivalent series circuits. An even simpler example of equivalent circuits is the reduction of a parallel circuit to a single "equivalent" resistor, which was introduced in Chapter 2. Equivalence has the same meaning here. Does the same voltage result in the same current? This is the test for equivalence.

The ratio of voltage to current is resistance. This is a consequence of Ohm's law. Thus, if two circuits have the same voltage-to-current ratio both circuits have the same resistance. Therefore, another way of stating circuit equivalence is as follows: **Two resistive circuits are electrically equivalent if they have the same total resistance.**

In specifying circuit equivalence, we must be careful to measure at the corresponding terminals of both circuits. For example, in Fig. 5.2 (b) the series-parallel circuit is equivalent to the 1-kΩ resistor only if A' and B' are considered as the input terminals of the series-parallel circuit. If, on the other hand, a battery and ammeter are connected between terminals C' and D' the total resistance will be only 500 Ω (the parallel combination of two 1-kΩ resistors). Hence, as viewed between terminals C' and D', the series-parallel circuit is not equivalent to the simpler single-resistor circuit.

5.3   Circuit Models

To the extent that two circuits have the same current-voltage relationship there is equivalence. However, unless we actually take the cover off the boxes which have been discussed there is no way of knowing if our equivalent circuit duplicates the circuit on a resistor-to-resistor basis. There may be more resistors inside the box than exist in the equivalent circuit. On the other hand, there may be fewer resistors inside the box than exist in the equivalent circuit. There is also the possibility that we have exactly duplicated the circuit inside the box.

In terms of predicting circuit performance it does not matter which of these conditions exist. As long as the same voltage results in the same current, the box and the equivalent circuit will perform exactly the same. Therefore, what we have done is to construct a model of what is inside the box. This model is electronically equivalent. The concept of a model is extremely useful in the electronic field. Models of transistors, vacuum tubes, amplifiers, computers, and so on are used to design and to analyze performance. There is no reasonable way to design or analyze an electronic circuit without a model which accurately predicts circuit performance of the particular device.

The extent to which our model is an accurate representation of actual operating conditions is the extent to which the model is useful. Once an accurate model exists, **circuit design and analysis involves application of the current and voltage relationships which have already been discussed.** This is the case for circuits which are as simple as a single resistor or as complicated as a computer. The principles of constructing models are most readily understood in terms of circuits which contain only resistors. Later, as more complicated devices are introduced, the same concepts for model making will be used with the necessary refinements.

With the exception of the equivalent series-parallel circuit of Fig. 5.2 (b), the circuits which have been discussed in this chapter had only a single pair of terminals. Most electronic circuits have at least two sets of terminals: **input** and **output**. Generally an electronic circuit accepts some sort of input signal, operates on the signal, and produces some sort of output. This is the situation for simple as well as complicated electronic devices.

An audio amplifier, for example, has a set of input terminals which accept a signal from a tuner, recorder, microphone, and so on. The output terminals of an audio amplifier connect to a loudspeaker. The input terminals on a radio are for the antenna, while the output terminals connect to the speaker. Even as complex a device as a digital computer has no more than input and output terminals. The input terminal accepts data and instructions for processing data. The output terminals present the results of the computations.

There are also electronic circuits which can have more than one set of input as well as output terminals. The telephone system is an example of a multi-input, multi-output system. Another example is electric power generation. Many generators service many customers. At various times there are different numbers of generators and customers.

For our purposes, a model which consists of a single pair of input terminals and a single pair of output terminals will be sufficient. Figure 5.3 shows a **"black box"** with a single pair of input and a single pair of output terminals. A black box is an electronic device which we cannot see. **All the information**

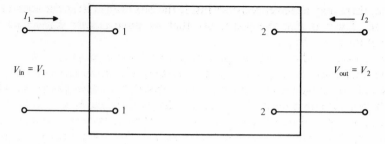

5.3 Black box.

about the black box must be deduced by making measurements at the input and output terminals. Based on these measurements we want to construct a model which is electronically equivalent to the circuit inside the box.

As shown in Fig. 5.3, when dealing with black boxes it is standard to refer to V_1 and V_2 rather than V_{in} and V_{out}. This is more general than V_{in} and V_{out} since the actual input and output terminals may be different under different conditions. For example, consider the previously mentioned case of the telephone. If you initiate a telephone call you are at the input terminals. If you receive a telephone call you are at the output terminals. These roles can be reversed depending on who initiates the call.

Therefore, rather than saying V_{in} and V_{out} it is preferable to use V_1 and V_2 as black-box terminal voltages. Similarly I_1 and I_2 are used as black-box terminal currents. Notice in Fig. 5.3 that both I_1 and I_2 are shown entering the black box. This is to preserve the generality. Particular circumstances may require that one or the other of these currents leave rather than enter the black box. However, choosing both currents as entering the box is flexible enough to allow for any situation, since we can simply make the current negative if necessary.

5.4   Black Box Method

We assume loop equations for the black box of Fig. 5.3 using the terminal voltages and currents:

$$V_1 = I_1 R_{11} + I_2 R_{12} \tag{5.1a}$$

$$V_2 = I_1 R_{21} + I_2 R_{22} \tag{5.1b}$$

At first glance Eqs. 5.1a and 5.1b may appear to be complicated. However, these equations are statements of Kirchhoff's voltage law, and are quite similar to the loop equations which were discussed in Chapter 3. Applied voltages result in voltage drops across resistors. The chief difference is that in Eq. 5.1 all the terms are positive. This is because either terminal pair can inject a current and this has already been discussed.

Equations 5.1 should not be interpreted to mean that there are only two loops inside the box. These equations are equally valid for a black box of any circuit complexity. What Eqs. 5.1 indicate is that what happens at one set of terminals has an effect on the other set of terminals. As long as we use a black box with only two pairs of terminals, Eqs. 5.1 are useful.

By making current and voltage measurements at the 1–1 and 2–2 terminals it is possible to determine the resistance of R_{11}, R_{12}, R_{21}, and R_{22} of Eqs. 5.1. This is the first step in making an equivalent circuit of a black box. Consider the circuit shown in Fig. 5.4. There is a voltage across the 1–1 terminals. Therefore there is an I_1 current. However, there is an open circuit at the 2–2 terminals. Therefore there can be no I_2 current. This is another way of saying that $I_2 = 0$. For this situation Eq. 5.1a becomes

$$V_1 = I_1 R_{11}$$

or   **(5.2a)**

$$R_{11} = \left. \frac{V_1}{I_1} \right|_{I_2 = 0}$$

In Eq. 5.2a the vertical bar with the information to the right indicates the conditions under which the measurement is made.

According to Eq. 5.2a the resistance R_{11} is the ratio of the voltage across the 1–1 terminals to the current which enters at this side. If the 1–1 terminals are considered as input terminals, then R_{11} is the ratio of input voltage to input current under the condition that the output terminals are open circuited. For this reason R_{11} is referred to as the **input resistance**. Notice also in Eq. 5.2a that the subscripts of the input resistance (R_{11}) indicate the voltage (1) and the current (1) which were used to make the measurement. Thus, using the current and voltage values at a pair of external terminals we have determined an equivalent black box resistor.

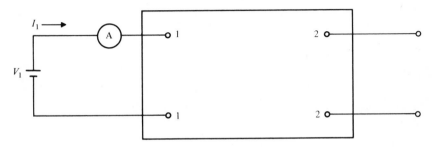

5.4   Circuit for determining R_{11}.

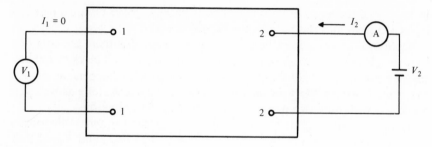

5.5 Circuit for determining R_{12}.

By setting up the appropriate conditions we can similarly determine the value of R_{12} of Eq. 5.1a. The circuit to make this measurement is shown in Fig. 5.5. In this case the voltage source is applied across the terminals 2–2. Therefore a current I_2 enters the box. In Fig. 5.5 there is a voltmeter across the 1–1 terminals. However, since there is no voltage source at the 1–1 terminals there is no I_1 current. In Section 3.2 several instances were presented in which a voltage existed but no current flowed. Therefore we should not be surprised when a situation arises in which there is voltage but no current. For the conditions shown in Fig. 5.5, Eq. 5.1a becomes

$$V_1 = I_2 R_{12}$$

or

$$R_{12} = \frac{V_1}{I_2}\bigg|_{I_1=0} \tag{5.2b}$$

where R_{12} is a resistance which is the ratio of the voltage resulting across the input terminals to the output current. That is, R_{12} is a resistance whose value depends on values at opposite terminals of the black box. Resistance R_{12} is referred to as the **reverse transfer resistance.** Notice again that the R subscripts are the voltage (1) and current (2), in that order. Also notice

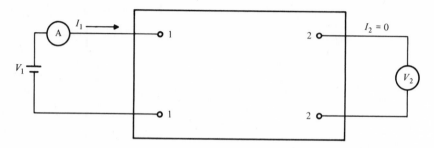

5.6 Circuit for determining R_{21}.

that the current which is missing (I_1 in this case) from the definition is the current which is zero.

Circuits to determine R_{21} and R_{22} make use of Eq. 5.1b. As in the two previous cases, the equivalent R values will be determined by making external voltage and current measurements in the appropriate places. Figure 5.6 shows the configuration for determining R_{21}. As in the previous case, we measure a voltage where there is no current. For the condition that $I_2 = 0$, Eq. 5.1b becomes

$$V_2 = I_1 R_{21}$$

or   (5.2c)

$$R_{21} = \left. \frac{V_2}{I_1} \right|_{I_2=0}$$

where R_{21} is the ratio of the output voltage to input current. Once more the subscripts denote the appropriate voltage (2) and current (1), in that order. Resistance R_{21} is another case of a resistance whose value depends on voltage and current at opposite terminals; R_{21} is referred to as the **forward transfer resistance.**

The remaining black box parameter to be determined is R_{22}. The configuration for determining R_{22} is shown in Fig. 5.7. Since the 1–1 terminals are open, $I_1 = 0$ and Eq. 5.1b becomes

$$V_2 = I_2 R_{22}$$

or   (5.2d)

$$R_{22} = \left. \frac{V_2}{I_2} \right|_{I_1=0}$$

where R_{22} is the ratio of the output voltage to output current when the input is open circuited. Resistance R_{22} is referred to as the **output resistance.**

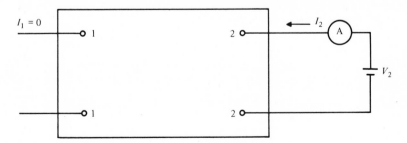

5.7   Circuit for determining R_{22}.

We have used a voltage source, a voltmeter, and an ammeter, at the external terminals of a black box to determine R values. Example 5.3 illustrates this technique.

Example 5.3

A 12-volt battery is used to determine R values of a certain black box.

1. When the battery is connected across the input terminals the input current is 4 mA and the measured output voltage is 4 volts.
2. When the battery is moved to the output terminals the output current is 2 mA and the measured input voltage is 2 volts.

Determine the R_{11}, R_{12}, R_{21}, and R_{22} for this box.

Solution Step 1. The first set of measurements permits us to determine R_{11} using Eq. 5.2a:

$$R_{11} = \frac{V_1}{I_1}\bigg|_{I_2 = 0}$$

$$= \frac{12}{4 \times 10^{-3}} = 3\,\text{k}\Omega$$

Step 2. The second set of measurements permits us to determine R_{22} using Eq. 5.2d:

$$R_{22} = \frac{V_2}{I_2}\bigg|_{I_1 = 0}$$

$$= \frac{12}{2 \times 10^{-3}} = 6\,\text{k}\Omega$$

Step 3. To determine R_{12} using Eq. 5.2b, we use the open-circuit input voltage and the output current from the second measurement:

$$R_{12} = \frac{V_1}{I_2}\bigg|_{I_1 = 0}$$

$$= \frac{2}{2 \times 10^{-3}} = 1\,\text{k}\Omega$$

Step 4. To determine R_{21} using Eq. 5.2c we use the open-circuit output voltage and the input current from the first measurement:

$$R_{21} = \frac{V_2}{I_1}\bigg|_{I_2 = 0}$$

$$= \frac{4}{4 \times 10^{-3}} = 1\,\text{k}\Omega$$

Notice that in this example R_{12} and R_{21} have the same value. This will always be the case if the black box contains only resistors. Therefore, if we know in advance that a particular black box contains only resistors, the fact that $R_{12} = R_{21}$ can be used to check our work.

Thus far we have determined the four values of R as required by Kirchhoff's voltage law (Eq. 5.1). The remaining step is to use these values to select a suitable equivalent circuit. That is, we want **a model of the black box which has the same current-voltage relationships for the same conditions.**

5.5   Models for Black Boxes

The first two examples in this chapter showed that we could construct as many equivalent circuits for a given set of conditions as we needed. We also saw that the equivalent circuits could be relatively simple or rather involved. There is no particular advantage to constructing complicated equivalent circuits. Generally, **we want the simplest equivalent circuit which fulfills all the requirements.**

Thus far we have determined the four R values of a black box by making external voltage and current measurements. The remaining step is to use these values to get a suitable equivalent circuit.

Figure 5.8 shows a possible equivalent circuit which is rather simple. The circuit in Fig. 5.8 is known as a **tee** equivalent circuit because of its resemblance to the letter T. People who work in the electrical power field generally draw the horizontal arms at an angle as shown in Fig. 5.8 (b). This configuration is referred to as a **wye** since it resembles the letter Y. A tee and a wye are equivalent if their corresponding resistors have identical values.

Figure 5.9 shows another possible simple equivalent circuit. The circuit in Fig. 5.9 (a) t known as a **pi** equivalent circuit because of its resemblance to the Greek letter π (pi). People working in the electrical power field generally eliminate the connecting wire at the bottom as shown in Fig. 5.9 (b). This

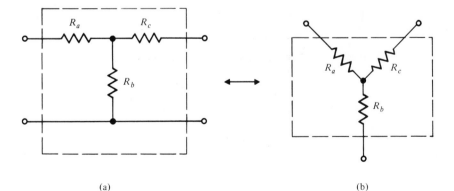

(a)   (b)

5.8   Possible equivalent circuit. **(a)** Tee. **(b)** Wye.

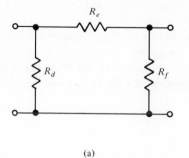

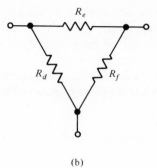

(a)   (b)

5.9   Another equivalent circuit. **(a)** Pi. **(b)** Delta.

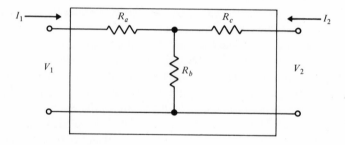

5.10   The tee as a black box.

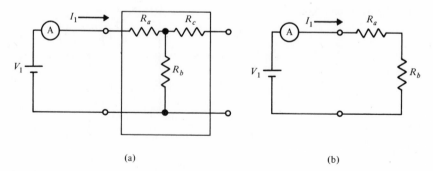

(a)   (b)

5.11   Finding R_{11} for a tee. **(a)** Measurement. **(b)** Equivalent.

configuration is referred to as a **delta** since it resembles the Greek letter Δ (delta).

From the standpoint of number of components there is no advantage between selecting either a tee or a pi as the basis of an equivalent circuit for a black box. Both the tee and the pi contain three resistors. For our applications we shall be better off using tee equivalent circuits of black boxes. This will become apparent in later work.

The method of determining the tee equivalent circuit of a black box is straightforward:

1. Determine R_{11}, R_{12}, R_{21}, and R_{22} for the tee.
2. Set these values equal to R_{11}, R_{12}, R_{21}, and R_{22} of the black box.

The same method would be used if we select a pi or any other model for the black box.

In order to determine the R values of a tee, we imagine the tee to be a black box, as shown in Fig. 5.10. This permits us to determine R_{11}, R_{12}, R_{21}, and R_{22} for the tee. A tee and a black box will be equivalent when their corresponding R values are equal:

$$R_{11_{box}} = R_{11_{tee}}$$

$$R_{12_{box}} = R_{12_{tee}}$$

$$R_{21_{box}} = R_{21_{tee}} \tag{5.3}$$

$$R_{22_{box}} = R_{22_{tee}}$$

We can find R_{11} for a tee by using the circuit shown in Fig. 5.11. Resistance R_{11} has been observed to be the input resistance when the output is an open circuit (Eq. 5.2a); that is, to determine the input resistance we need only find the ratio of input voltage to input current ($V/I = R$) when the output is open. Referring to Fig. 5.11 we see that when the output is open there is no current through R_c. A similar situation of voltage without current has already been discussed in Section 3.2; that is, when the output is an open circuit the input current can flow only through the series combination of R_a and R_b, as shown in Fig. 5.11 (b). Therefore

$$R_{11_{tee}} = R_a + R_b \tag{5.4a}$$

To find R_{21} (Eq. 5.2c) we use the same circuit except that we measure the open-circuit output voltage as shown in Fig. 5.12 (a). Since no current flows through R_c the voltage across R_c is zero ($V = IR$). As shown in Fig. 5.12 (b), if the voltage across R_c is zero, then the output voltage is the same as the voltage across R_b. The only current through R_b is the input current. Therefore

$$R_{21_{tee}} = \frac{V_b}{I_1} = \frac{V_b}{I_b} = R_b \tag{5.4b}$$

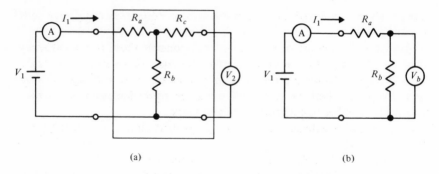

(a)   (b)

5.12   Finding R_{21} for a tee. (**a**) Measurement. (**b**) Equivalent.

To determine R_{22} we must move the external voltage source to the output terminals, as shown in Fig. 5.13. In this case the input current is zero. Resistance R_{22} (Eq. 5.2d) has been seen to be the output resistance when the input is an open circuit. Figure 5.12 (a) shows that when the input is open the output current flows only through the series combination of R_a and R_b. The equivalent circuit for this situation is shown in Fig. 5.13 (b). Thus

$$R_{22_{tee}} = R_b + R_c \tag{5.4c}$$

To find R_{12} we use the circuit of Fig. 5.14 except that we measure the open-circuit input voltage as shown in Fig. 5.14. No current flows through R_a under these circumstances so the voltage drop across R_a is zero. Therefore the input voltage is the same as the voltage across R_b, as shown in Fig. 5.14 (b). The only current through R_b is the output current. Therefore

$$R_{12_{tee}} = \frac{V_1}{I_2} = \frac{V_b}{I_b} = R_b \tag{5.4d}$$

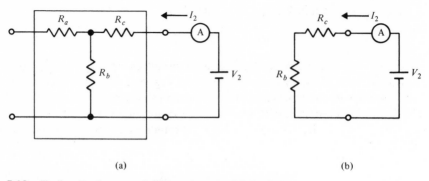

(a)   (b)

5.13   Finding R_{22} for a tee. (**a**) Measurement. (**b**) Equivalent.

As in the case of the black-box example (Example 5.3) we observe that R_{12} is equal to R_{21} for a tee. In a tee which contains only resistors this will always be true. Therefore, to determine R_b in a tee it is not necessary to measure both R_{12} and R_{21}. Either measurement is sufficient. The remaining measurement can be used as a check.

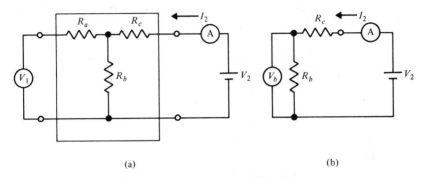

(a)   (b)

5.14   Finding R_{12} for a tee. **(a)** Measurement. **(b)** Equivalent.

In Example 5.3 we determined the R parameters of a certain black box. Example 5.4 shows how to construct the equivalent tee for this black box.

Example 5.4

Find the equivalent tee for the black box in Example 5.3.

Solution Step 1. The R values as determined in Example 5.3 are

$$R_{11} = 3\,\text{k}\Omega$$
$$R_{22} = 6\,\text{k}\Omega$$
$$R_{12} = R_{21} = 1\,\text{k}\Omega$$

Step 3. We know R_b directly by using Eq. 5.4b:

$$R_{21_{\text{tee}}} = R_b$$
$$R_b = 1\,\text{k}\Omega$$

Step 3. The input resistance of a tee is the series combination of R_a and R_b (Eq. 5.4a) and we already know R_b. Therefore

$$R_{11_{\text{tee}}} = R_a + R_b$$
$$3\,\text{k}\Omega = R_a + 1\,\text{k}\Omega$$
$$R_a = 2\,\text{k}\Omega$$

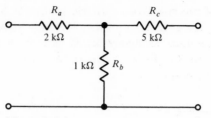

5.15   Tee equivalent of Example 5.4.

Step 4. Similarly, the output resistance of a tee is the series combination R_b and R_c (Eq. 5.4c) and we already know R_b:

$$R_{22_{tee}} = R_b + R_c$$
$$6\,k\Omega = 1\,k\Omega + R_c$$
$$R_c = 5\,k\Omega$$

Figure 5.15 shows this equivalent circuit. We have completed what we set out to do. We have a circuit which duplicates the performance of a box into which we cannot see. Even though there are more components and/or different arrangements inside the black box, we have a model which can be used to predict the performance of the black box. This is what we are after. The actual arrangement inside the black box is unimportant. For example, the pi circuit in Fig. 5.16 bears no apparent resemblence to the tee circuit in Fig. 5.15. However, we can only determine whether or not these circuits are equivalent by comparing their R values. Also, it does not matter what value voltage source is used since resistance is the ratio of voltage to current. The determination of R values for the pi circuit of Fig. 5.16 is shown in Example 5.5.

Example 5.5

Determine if the pi circuit of Fig. 5.16 is equivalent to the tee circuit of Fig. 5.15.

Solution Step 1.

$$R_{11} = \frac{V_1}{I_1}\bigg|_{I_2=0}$$

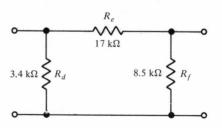

5.16   Pi circuit.

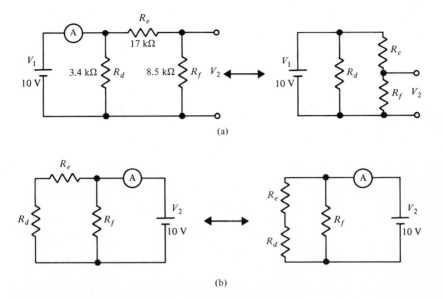

(a)

(b)

5.17   Determining the R's for a Pi. (a) R_{11} and R_{21}. (b) R_{22}.

By referring to Fig. 5.17 (a) we see that when the output is open R_d is in parallel with the series combination of R_e and R_f. We now choose some arbitrary input whose exact value is not too important; for example, if we choose 10-volts,

$$I_{R_d} = \frac{V_1}{R_d}$$

$$= \frac{10}{3.4 \times 10^3} = 2.94 \times 10^{-3} \text{ Amp.}$$

Step 2. Since the current entering the input terminal equals the current leaving the input terminal (Kirchhoff's current law),

$$I_{R_{(e+f)}} = \frac{10}{17 \times 10^3 + 8.5 \times 10^3}$$

$$= \frac{10}{25.5 \times 10^3} = 0.39 \times 10^{-3} \text{ Amp.}$$

Step 3.

$$R_{11} = \frac{V_1}{I_1}\bigg|_{I_2 = 0}$$

$$= \frac{10}{3.33 \times 10^{-3}}$$

$$= 3 \times 10^3 \, \Omega$$

Step 4. As shown in Fig. 5.17 (a), we can determine V_2 when $I_2 = 0$ by using the voltage divider action.

$$V_2 = V_1 \frac{R_f}{R_f + R_e}$$

$$= 10 \frac{8.5 \times 10^3}{8.5 \times 10^3 + 17 \times 10^3}$$

$$= 3.33 \text{ volts}$$

Step 5.

$$R_{21} = \frac{V_2}{I_1}\bigg|_{I_2 = 0}$$

$$= \frac{3.33}{3.33 \times 10^{-3}}$$

$$= 1 \times 10^3 \, \Omega$$

There is no need to detetermine R_{12} since $R_{21} = R_{12}$.

Step 6.

$$R_{22} = \frac{V_2}{I_2}\bigg|_{I_1 = 0}$$

As shown in Fig. 5.17 (b), when the input is open, R_f is in parallel with the series combination of R_e and R_d. If we choose $V_2 = 10$ volts

$$I_{R_f} = \frac{V_2}{R_f}$$

$$= \frac{10}{8.5 \times 10^3} = 1.19 \times 10^{-3} \text{ Amp.}$$

$$I_{R_{(d+e)}} = \frac{V_2}{R_d + R_e}$$

$$= \frac{10}{3.4 \times 10^3 + 17 \times 10^3} = 0.48 \times 10^{-3} \text{ Amp.}$$

Step 7. The current entering the output terminal must equal the current leaving the output terminal:

$$I_2 = I_{R_f} + I_{R_{(d+e)}}$$

$$= 1.19 \times 10^{-3} \times 0.48 \times 10^{-3}$$

$$= 1.67 \times 10^{-3} \text{ Amp.}$$

Step 8.

$$R_{22} = \left.\frac{V_2}{I_2}\right|_{I_1=0}$$

$$= \frac{10}{1.67 \times 10^{-3}}$$

$$= 6 \times 10^3 \, \Omega$$

Step 9. Compare the R parameters of the pi and tee:

	R_{11} (Ω)	$R_{12} = R_{21}$ (Ω)	R_{22} (Ω)
Pi	3×10^3	1×10^3	6×10^3
Tee	3×10^3	1×10^3	6×10^3

Since the corresponding R parameters are equal the circuits of Fig. 5.15 and 5.16 are equivalent.

Thus we see that **circuits which appear to have no similarity as far as appearance is concerned can have identical performance as far as electronic characteristics is concerned.** This is the merit of equivalent circuits. Actually there are easier methods of finding the tee equivalent of a black box which contains only resistors. However, the same general black-box approach is used to make models of transistors and vacuum tubes as well as more complex electronic devices. Therefore, an understanding of a black box at the all-resistor level will make for a better understanding of these more advanced devices.

It is important to specify the conditions under which black-box measurements are made. All our measurements are performed with voltage applied to one set of terminals while the other set of terminals is left open circuited. However, this is not the only set of conditions which is possible. For example, we could apply voltage at one set of terminals and short circuit the other pair of terminals. This technique is equally valid and if used correctly will lead to the identical equivalent circuit. However, the R parameters will not be the same under short-circuit conditions as under open-circuit conditions.

For example, in Fig. 5.15 we have R_{11} as 3 kΩ. This is the condition when the output is an open circuit. However, if the output is a short circuit R_c is in parallel with R_b. Therefore

$$R_{11} = R_a + \frac{R_b R_c}{R_b + R_c}$$

$$= 1 \times 10^3 + \frac{1 \times 10^3 \times 5 \times 10^3}{1 + 10^3 + 5 \times 10^3}$$

$$= 1.833 \text{ k}\Omega$$

Similarly, different values will be obtained for R_{12}, R_{21}, and R_{22} under short-circuit conditions. These R values are just as valid as those obtained under open-circuit conditions. The point is that terms such as input resistance, output resistance, and transfer resistance have meaning only when the conditions under which the measurement is made are specified.

5.6   No-Load Ammeter

The construction of an equivalent tee (or any other equivalent) for a black box requires that current and voltage measurements be made. The accuracy of our model, therefore, depends on the accuracy with which we make current and voltage measurements. The problems associated with making current, voltage, and resistance measurements were discussed in Chapter 4.

The problem associated with making a current measurement is that the addition of the ammeter into the circuit increases the total resistance of the circuit. In Chapter 4 we saw that in many cases the ammeter resistance can be neglected. This is the case when the ammeter resistance is small compared with the resistance of the circuit where it is to be used.

However, when the ammeter resistance is comparable to the circuit resistance, we saw (Example 4.1) that the ammeter introduces excessive error. Figure 5.18 shows a method of making a current measurement without disturbing circuit performance even though the ammeter resistance is significant. The principle is straightforward. The ammeter is in series with the circuit as is required. The only difference is that the voltmeter is placed directly across the circuit input terminals rather than across the voltage source. The voltage source is then adjusted until the proper voltage for normal circuit operation is read on the voltmeter.

In this case the ammeter resistance can be even greater than the circuit resistance. This will not affect either the circuit or the accuracy of the current measurement. As long as the proper voltage appears across the circuit, the ammeter in Fig. 5.18 will read the proper current without loading the circuit. This is illustrated in Example 5.6.

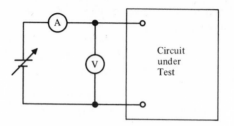

5.18   Compensating for ammeter resistance.

Example 5.6

A certain circuit has a total resistance of 10 kΩ and operates from a 0.1-volt source. Devise a circuit using a 10-μA meter ($R_M = 20\,\text{k}\Omega$) which does not load the circuit.

Solution Step 1. The theoretical current is

$$I = \frac{V}{R_{ckt}}$$

$$= \frac{0.1}{10 \times 10^3} = 10\,\mu\text{A}$$

Step 2. When the ammeter is inserted the total series resistance, as shown in Fig. 5.19, is

$$R_T = R_M + R_{ckt}$$

$$= 20 \times 10^3 + 10 \times 10^3 = 30 \times 10^3\,\Omega$$

The measured current is therefore

$$I = \frac{V}{R_T}$$

$$= \frac{0.1}{30 \times 10^3} = 3.33\,\mu\text{A}$$

Step 3. The error due to ammeter loading is

$$\text{error} = \frac{\text{theor} - \text{meas}}{\text{theor}} \times 100\%$$

$$= \frac{10 \times 10^{-6} - 3.33 \times 10^{-6}}{10 \times 10^{-6}} \times 100\%$$

$$= 67\%$$

which is intolerable.

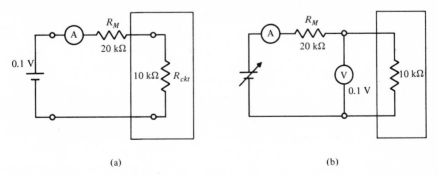

(a) (b)

5.19 Ammeter resistance considerations. **(a)** Uncompensated. **(b)** Compensated.

Step 4. Figure 5.19 (b) shows the solution. The voltage source (V) is adjusted until the input voltage at the circuit reads 0.1 volt. The required battery voltage is the normal current times the total resistance:

$$V = IR_T$$
$$= 10 \times 10^{-6} \times 30 \times 10^3$$
$$= 0.3 \text{ volts}$$

The ammeter now reads $10\ \mu A$ and the circuit is functioning properly. This technique does require a voltage source which is greater than that needed for normal circuit operation, but it permits the circuit to function properly regardless of the resistance of the ammeter.

5.7   No-Load Voltmeters

In Chapter 4 we saw that when a voltmeter is placed across a resistor, the parallel combination of resistance and voltmeter results in a lower effective resistance. Table 4.1 shows to what extent the effective resistance is decreased. To minimize voltmeter loading the voltmeter resistance should be much greater than the resistance across which it is connected.

It is possible to construct a voltmeter which does not load a circuit at all. We have already discussed the principle of a no-load voltmeter when circuits without current were discussed in Section 3.2.

Example 5.7 illustrates the particular zero current circuit which is applicable. The circuit is shown in Fig. 5.20.

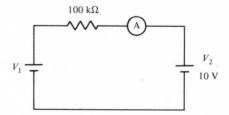

5.20   Two-battery circuit.

Example 5.7

Find the current in the circuit of Fig. 5.20 when $V_1 = 15$ volts, $V_1 = 10$ volts, and $V_1 = 5$ volts.

Solution Step 1. This is a series circuit with the battery polarities opposing. Therefore

$$I = \frac{V_1 - V_2}{R}$$

$$= \frac{V_1 - 10}{100}$$

Step 2. For $V_1 = 15$ volts:

$$I = \frac{15 - 10}{10^5} = \frac{5}{10^5}$$

$$= 50 \ \mu A$$

Step 3. For $V_1 = 10$ volts:

$$I = \frac{10 - 10}{10^5}$$

$$= 0 \ \mu A$$

Step 4. For $V_1 = 5$ volts:

$$I = \frac{5 - 10}{10^5}$$

$$= -50 \ \mu A$$

(i.e., the current flows in the opposite direction).

This problem serves to indicate that in a circuit of the type shown in Fig. 5.20 it is possible to have positive current, no current, or negative current, depending on the values of the two batteries. This is the principle of a voltmeter which does not load a circuit at all. If, for example, V_2 in Fig. 5.20 is a precision 10-volt source, no current will flow when V_1 is exactly 10 volts. When the two voltages are exactly equal it does not matter how much resistance there is between V_1 and V_2. No current will flow because there is no voltage drop across the resistor. Thus the value of ammeter resistance, leads resistance and so on have no effect on the circuit when the voltages balance exactly. The indication of voltage is a null (i.e. zero) current reading on the ammeter. **Since no current flows we are not loading the voltage which we wish to measure.**

Of course the circuit shown in Fig. 5.20 is useful only for finding other 10-volt readings, but the principle of null current is the important point. Once a precision voltage source is available, any unknown voltage can be read which is less than or equal to the precision voltage source. These volt-

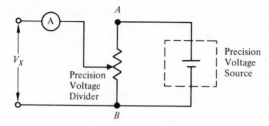

5.21   Simplified potentiometric voltmeter.

ages are measured using the precision voltage, an ammeter, and a precision voltage divider. A simplified version of such a circuit is shown in Fig. 5.21. The unknown voltage is connected at the terminals marked V_x. The unknown voltage can be another battery or the voltage drop across a resistor. A precision variable resistor (potentiometer) is adjusted until the ammeter reads zero current. At this point the voltage between the adjustable arm and the bottom of the potentiometer is exactly equal to the unknown voltage. The precision potentiometer is made of several strings of precision resistors. One possible arrangement is shown in Fig. 5.22. In this way we can read

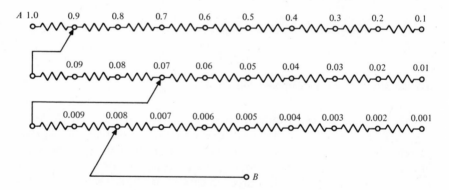

5.22   Simplified three-decade potentiometer.

voltage to several significant figures. This is called a **decade precision resistor.** In this case the resistor readings are directly in volts. If null current occurs with the setting shown in Fig. 5.22, voltage is 0.978 volts. Since this type of voltmeter is based on adjusting a potentiometer, it is referred to as a **potentiometric voltmeter.** The actual value of the resistors in the potentiometer is not critical. However, all the resistors in any decade must have the same value. The reason that the actual value of resistors is unimportant is that no current from the voltage being measured will flow in the potentiometer circuit at balance. However, the resistors must be equal in any decade so that each position of the decade has the same significance.

It is common to use an ammeter with zero reading in the center of the scale for this type of null sensing. A sensitive zero-center meter is called a **galvano-meter.** This tells which way to adjust the potentiometer. If the galvanometer reads positive current, the unknown voltage is higher than the potentiometer setting. If the galvanometer reads negative current, the unknown voltage is lower than the potentiometer setting. In either case we know which way to adjust the potentiometer.

Figure 5.23 shows a practical potentiometric voltmeter. The precision voltage source is a standard cell. This is an accurately manufactured acid

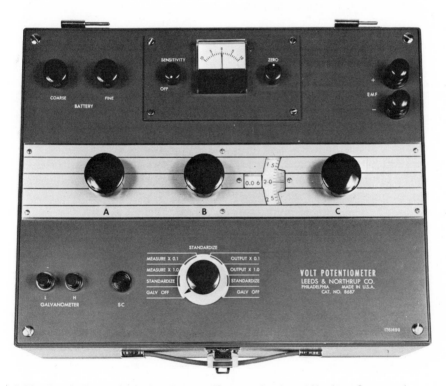

5.23   Practical potentiometric voltmeter. *(Courtesy Leeds and Northrup Company.)*

battery whose voltage is known to at least four significant figures (e.g., 1.018 volts). This type of voltmeter is particularly useful in circuits where the resistance of the leads has a voltage drop comparable to the voltage being measured. Such a situation exists in measuring the output voltage from a thermocouple. Since at current balance the reading is independent of circuit resistance this effect is cancelled. Potentiometric voltmeters may also be used to calibrate other types of voltmeters. Also observe that if the decade potentiometers can be set automatically instead of manually, we have the beginnings of a direct-reading **digital voltmeter.**

It is interesting to note the technique involved in solving this measurement problem. With ingenuity the problems associated with ammeter accuracy, voltmeter loading, and lead resistance have been exchanged for the problems of constructing a precision voltage source and a precision potentiometer. This method of exchanging a certain problem for another type of problem is common in electronics and will occur throughout this book.

5.8   Precision Resistance Measurement

The methods of improving voltmeter and ammeter accuracy to make better black-box determinations and other precision measurements have been discussed. In Section 4.6 the methods of measuring resistance using a volt-meter-ammeter method and the ohmmeter were discussed. Five percent is about the best accuracy to be expected from an ohmmeter. A precision method of measuring resistance would permit R_{11} and R_{22} of a black box to be measured directly. (However, R_{12} and R_{21} cannot be determined by resistance measurements made only at the input and output terminals.) A precision method of measuring resistance is also required in constructing resistors for the potentiometer in a potentiometric voltmeter. Other applica-tions of precision resistance will occur later when transducer-measurements are discussed and other applications.

Precision resistance measurement is another example of exploiting null current sensing. Figure 5.24 (a) shows a circuit called a **Wheatstone bridge.** This name comes about because the circuit is normally drawn to resemble the trusses of a bridge. The circuit in Fig. 5.24 (b) is electrically the same, the only difference is that the resistors are drawn vertically. This configuration may make bridge operation somewhat easier to understand. **A bridge is**

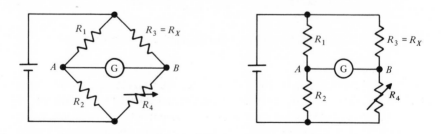

5.24   Wheatstone bridge. **(a)** Basic circuit. **(b)** Redrawn circuit.

said to be balanced when no current flows through the galvanometer. Bridge balance is achieved by adjusting R_4.

To analyze the Wheatstone bridge thoroughly we would have to solve a three-loop circuit. Loop 1 could consist of the battery, R_1 and R_2. Loop 2 could be R_1, R_3, and the galvanometer. Loop 3 could be R_2, R_4, and the galvanometer. While this procedure is correct it is also quite tedious. More important, it obscures the essence of bridge balance. We are interested in the condition which occurs when no current flows through the galvanometer. For this particular situation loop equations are not necessary.

When R_4 of Fig. 5.24 is adjusted so that no current flows through the galvanometer, the current through R_1 is the same current which flows through R_2. This is a consequence of Kirchhoff's current law. The current which enters junction A of Fig. 5.24 is I_{R_1}. The current which leaves junction A is I_{R_2} and I_{galv}. But the galvanometer current has been made zero. Therefore

$$I_{R_1} = I_{R_2} \tag{5.5a}$$

At current balance, a similar situation occurs at junction B. Therefore

$$I_{R_3} = I_{R_4} \tag{5.5b}$$

When no current flows through the galvanometer, it must also be true that the voltage across R_1 is equal to the voltage across R_3. This is a consequence of Kirchhoff's voltage law: Since there is no voltage source in the loop which consists of R_1, R_3, and the galvanometer, the sum of these three voltages must add to zero. However, there is no current through the galvanometer. Therefore there is no voltage drop across the galvanometer and so

$$V_{R_1} = V_{R_3} \tag{5.6a}$$

At current balance a similar situation occurs in the loop which consists of R_2, R_4, and the galvanometer. Therefore

$$V_{R_2} = V_{R_4} \tag{5.6b}$$

If we divide the voltage equation for one loop by the other:

$$\frac{V_{R_1}}{V_{R_2}} = \frac{V_{R_3}}{V_{R_4}} \tag{5.7}$$

From Ohm's law we know that the voltage across any resistor is the product of the current through the resistor and the resistor itself. Therefore

$V_1 = I_1 R_1$, $V_2 = I_2 R_2$, and so on. If these terms are substituted into Eq. 5.7,

$$\frac{V_1 R_1}{V_2 R_2} = \frac{V_3 R_3}{V_4 R_4} \qquad (5.8a)$$

We have already seen that at current balance $I_1 = I_2$ and $I_3 = I_4$ (Eq. 5.5). Therefore

$$\frac{R_1}{R_2} = \frac{R_3}{R_4} \qquad (5.8b)$$

Equation 5.8b gives the relationship between the resistors of a bridge when the bridge is balanced. By cross-multiplying the terms of Eq. 5.8b we get

$$R_1 R_4 = R_2 R_3 \qquad (5.9)$$

Equation 5.9 shows that **at bridge balance the products of the diagonally opposite bridge resistors are equal.** This is a useful way to remember the bridge balance relationship since the bridge arms will not always have the same names.

If R_3 is an unknown resistor and the other three resistors are known we can solve for $R_3(R_x)$ and get

$$R_x = \frac{R_1}{R_2} R_4 \qquad (5.10)$$

Notice that Eq. 5.10 does not depend on what voltage is being used. This means that as the battery voltage drops no compensating adjustment is required, as was the case for the ohmmeter. Another advantage of using a bridge to measure resistance is that a null current indication is used. This eliminates the ammeter errors which were discussed in Chapter 4. With two precision-fixed resistors and one precision-variable resistor we can measure unknown resistors with much greater accuracy than was possible with an ohmmeter.

Referring to Eq. 5.10, we see that if R_1 and R_2 are equal;

$$R_x = R_4$$

that is, the setting of the precision variable resistor is equal to the unknown resistor. If R_1 is 10 times R_2 we get

$$R_x = 10 R_4$$

In this case the unknown resistor is 10 times as great as the precision-variable resistor; that is, the ratio of R_1 to R_2 determines a resistance range and R_4 determines the value. Figure 5.25 shows a laboratory-type bridge.

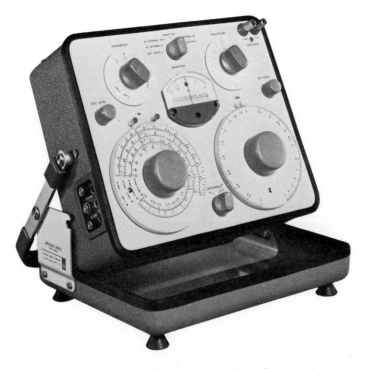

5.25   Practical wheatstone bridge. *(Courtesy General Radio Company.)*

This particular bridge also measures other quantities besides resistance. However, all bridge measurements are based on adjusting the bridge until no current flows through the galvanometer.

Carbon composition resistors, which were described in Chapter 1, are not sufficiently accurate for bridge applications. Precision resistors are made from **resistance wire.** Resistance wire is wire with a very uniform composition and diameter. The same equation (Eq. 1.4) as was used for carbon composition resistors determines the value of precision resistors:

$$R = \rho \frac{L}{A}$$

Since the composition is uniform, the resistivity is constant along the wire. The resistivity of a carbon composition resistor is not as constant since the carbon resistor is a mixture of carbon and flour. Also, the diameter of the resistance wire is more uniform than for a carbon resistor. Therefore the area of the resistance wire is constant and thus, various values of precision resistance will be determined by selecting the appropriate length. This is illustrated in Example 5.8.

Example 5.8

A certain type of resistance wire has a resistivity of 10^{-4} Ω-cm and a cross-sectional area of 10^{-5} cm^2. What length of wire is required to make a 1000-Ω resistor?

Solution Step 1.   Equation 1.4 is applicable directly:

$$R = \rho \frac{L}{A}$$

Step 2.   Insert the known values:

$$10^3 = 10^{-4} \frac{L}{10^{-5}}$$

Step 3.   Solve for L:

$$L = \frac{10^3 \times 10^{-5}}{10^{-4}} = 10^2$$

$$= 100 \text{ cm} = 1 \text{ meter}$$

The answer to Example 5.8 is realistic for typical resistance wire material. However, a resistor which is one meter long is not realistic. For this reason resistance wire is wound around a coil until the proper length is reached. Figure 5.26 (a) shows a fixed-precision resistor and Fig. 5.26 (b) shows how a

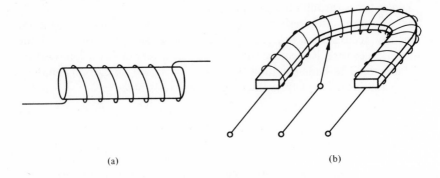

(a)   (b)

5.26   Wirewound precision resistors. **(a)** Fixed. **(b)** Variable.

precision-variable resistor is made. A calibrated dial as was shown in Fig. 2.15 can be placed under the pointer so that the resistance may be read directly. Using wirewound resistors it is possible to mass produce resistors which are accurate to within 0.1 %. Using resistors with this accuracy it is possible to determine the basic accuracy of a Wheatstone bridge. This is illustrated in Example 5.9.

Example 5.9

Determine the possible error in a bridge which uses 0.1 % resistors.

Solution Step 1. For a bridge,

$$R_x = \frac{R_1}{R_2} R_4$$

One error situation occurs when all three resistors are maximum:

$$R_x = \frac{R_1(\cancel{1.001})}{R_2(\cancel{1.001})} R_4(1.001)$$

In this case the error is 0.1 %.

Step 2. Maximum error will occur when R_1 and R_4 are maximum and R_2 is minimum, or vice versa:

$$R_x = \frac{R_1(1.001)}{R_2(0.999)} R_4(1.001)$$

$$= 1.003 \frac{R_1}{R_2} R_4$$

Therefore the maximum error is 0.3 %.

Using 0.1 % resistors the worst error will be only 0.3 %. Since the most that can be expected from an ohmmeter is 5 %, this bridge is at least 15 times more accurate. Also, it is possible to use resistors which are better than 0.1 % and further increase bridge accuracy.

The Wheatstone bridge has been discussed only in terms of measuring the value of the unknown resistors. However, the bridge circuit has many other applications in electronics.

For example, a **strain gauge** is usually connected into a bridge circuit. In this case the "unknown" resistor is the one which is deformed due to pressure being exerted.

Another example might be a circuit in which the "unknown" resistor is a light-sensitive resistor and the galvanometer is replaced by a lamp, as shown in Fig. 5.27. When the bridge is balanced initially, no current flows through

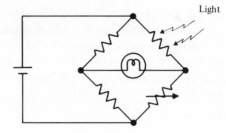

5.27   Bridge used to control lamp intensity.

the lamp. When the light level changes so does the resistance of the light-sensitive resistor. This unbalances the bridge and current flows through the lamp. Further changes in light level cause more current to flow through the lamp. In this way the lamp intensity can be made to follow changes in light level.

Similar types of circuits may be envisioned using a temperature-sensitive resistor in an oven or refrigerator. In this case the temperature changes which affect the temperature-sensitive resistor operate the heating coil in an oven or the compressor in a refrigerator. It is clear, therefore, that in addition to measuring resistance the bridge circuit may be used in **automatic control circuits.**

Summary

1. Circuits need not be made of the same components to be equivalent electronically. Two circuits are equivalent if, for the same applied voltage, identical currents result.
2. A model of a circuit is used to analyze and to predict performance of the circuit. The extent to which a model is useful depends on the accuracy of the model.
3. A black box is a circuit which cannot be viewed directly. The characteristics of a black box are determined by making current and voltage measurements at available terminals under specified conditions.
4. Based on black-box measurements, a circuit model which is electronically equivalent can be devised. There is no single model which is unique. However, simple models are more preferable than complicated models.
5. If necessary, the increase in circuit resistance due to an ammeter may be compensated for by increasing the source voltage.
6. Voltmeter loading can be eliminated completely by using a potentiometric voltmeter. Such voltmeters measure voltages by precisely bucking an unknown voltage with a known voltage. The indication of proper voltage occurs when no current flows through an ammeter placed between the unknown voltage and the known bucking voltage.

7. Precision resistance measurements are made using a Wheatstone bridge. The indication that a bridge is balanced is also a no-current reading on an ammeter. The bridge is direct reading if precision resistors are used. The bridge principle is also useful in automatic control circuits.

Questions

1. What is meant by circuit equivalence?
2. What is a circuit model?
3. What difference can exist between a circuit and its model?
4. In what way must a circuit and its model be the same?
5. What is meant by a black box?
6. Describe in terms of input and output terminals:
   (a) Battery charger
   (b) Phonograph
   (c) Television set
   (d) Voting machine
7. How can we determine whether two circuits are equivalent?
8. Describe how ammeter resistance can be taken into account in a circuit in which
   (a) The ammeter resistance is much smaller than the circuit resistance.
   (b) The ammeter resistance is the same as or greater than the circuit resistance
9. Describe how a voltmeter which does not load a circuit operates.
10. What determines the maximum voltage which can be measured by a potentiometric voltmeter?
11. What is meant by null current sensing?
12. Describe the factors which make a Wheatstone bridge more accurate than an ohmmeter.
13. Why are precision resistors required in a bridge but not in an ohmmeter?
14. Describe how a bridge can be used to control a process automatically instead of measuring resistance.

Problems

1. A 20-volt battery is connected to a box which has only an input pair of terminals. The input current is 5 mA. Construct an equivalent circuit which consists of two resistors in series. One resistor should be three times larger than the other.
2. The conditions are the same as in Problem 1. Construct an equivalent circuit which consists of two resistors in parallel. One resistor should be three times larger than the other.
3. A 10-volt battery is connected to a box which has only an input pair of terminals. The input current is 1 mA. Construct an equivalent circuit which consists of a single resistor.
4. The conditions are the same as in Problem 3. Construct an equivalent circuit which consists of two resistors in series. One resistor should be three times as large as the other.

5. The conditions are the same as in Problem 3. Construct an equivalent circuit which consists of two resistors in parallel. One resistor should be twice as large as the other.

6. A 10-volt battery is used to make black-box measurements.
   (a) When the battery is placed across the input terminals the input current is 2 mA and the open-circuit output voltage is 2 volts.
   (b) When the battery is connected across the output terminals the output current is 2.5 mA and the open-circuit input voltage is 2.5 volts.
   Find R_{11}, R_{12}, R_{21}, and R_{22}.

7. Construct a tee equivalent for the black box in Problem 6.

8. A 15-volt battery is used to determine the R parameters of a certain black box.
   (a) When the battery is placed across the input terminals the input current is 3 mA and the open-circuit output voltage is 3 volts.
   (b) When the battery is connected across the output terminals the output current is 3.75 mA and the open-circuit input voltage is 3.75 volts.
   Determine if this black box is equivalent to the black box in Problem 6.

9. A 10-volt battery is used to make black-box measurements.
   (a) When the battery is connected across the input terminals the input current is 2 mA and the open-circuit output voltage is 2 volts.
   (b) When the battery is connected across the output terminals the output current is 5 mA and the open-circuit input voltage is 5 volts.
   Is this box equivalent to the box of Problem 6?

10. Construct a tee equivalent of the box in Problem 9.

11. Construct a tee which is equivalent to the pi shown in Fig. 5.28.

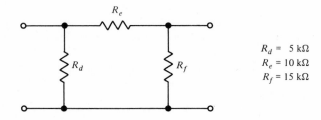

$$R_d = 5 \text{ k}\Omega$$
$$R_e = 10 \text{ k}\Omega$$
$$R_f = 15 \text{ k}\Omega$$

5.28   Circuit for Problem 11.

12. Construct a tee which is equivalent to the pi shown in Fig. 5.29.

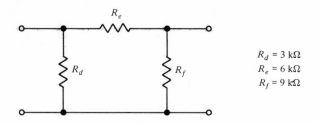

$$R_d = 3 \text{ k}\Omega$$
$$R_e = 6 \text{ k}\Omega$$
$$R_f = 9 \text{ k}\Omega$$

5.29   Circuit for Problem 12.

13. A certain circuit has a total resistance of 5 kΩ. The circuit requires 10 μAmps. to operate properly. If the current is to be measured with a 10-μA meter which has a meter resistance of 20 kΩ, what voltage is required to measure current and permit the circuit to function properly?

14. A potentiometer is made with a precision voltage source and a precision-variable resistor, as shown in Fig. 5.30. No current flows through the ammeter when $R_a = 1$ kΩ and $R_b = 4$ kΩ. Find V_{R_2}.

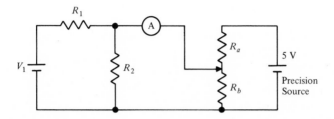

5.30   Circuit for Problem 14.

15. For the same conditions as in Problem 14, find V_1 if $R_1 = 10$ kΩ and $R_2 = 20$ kΩ.
16. Repeat Problem 14 except that a 1-MΩ resistor is inserted in series with the ammeter.
17. For the circuit shown in Fig. 5.31, a current null occurs when $R_4 = 3.16$ kΩ. Find R_3.

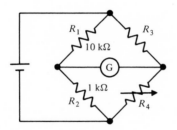

5.31   Circuit for Problem 17.

18. For the circuit shown in Fig. 5.32, current balance occurs when $R_1 = 4$ kΩ. Find R_x. (Hint: Eq. 5.9 not applicable. Use the opposite-arm condition.)

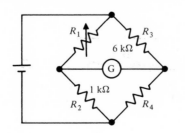

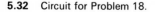

5.32   Circuit for Problem 18.

19. Determine what errors are possible in a bridge which uses 0.5% resistors.
20. Determine what errors are possible in a bridge which uses 0.05% resistors.
21. A precision resistor is to be made from resistance wire which is 0.01 cm^2 in area and has $\rho = 2 \times 10^{-4}$ Ω-cm. What length should be used if a 150-Ω resistor is required?
22. A 1-kΩ precision resistor is to be made from resistance wire. The available wire is 0.015 cm in diameter and has $\rho = 5 \times 10^{-5}$ Ω-cm. How much wire is needed?

Chapter 6 Waveforms, Motors, and Generators

6.1 Introduction

In this chapter we shall discuss voltages which are different from those which have been described. Terms used to describe such voltages are introduced. Methods of generating some important voltage waveforms are described. In addition, methods of generating electricity and using electricity to produce rotary motion are covered.

6.2 Direct Current

Voltage sources discussed in the previous chapters have been batteries. Battery voltage remains constant for a long period of time, and the current which flows when a battery is connected to a circuit will also be constant. This type of current is referred to as **direct current (DC).** Through usage it has become acceptable to say DC current (direct current current). Similarly it is acceptable to say DC voltage (direct current voltage) for a steady voltage. We say the voltage of a certain battery is 1.5 volts DC, the current through a resistor is 10 mA DC, and so on.

Figure 6.1 shows a graph of DC voltage versus time. In this particular case the vertical axis represents voltage. Each division on the vertical axis is $\frac{1}{2}$ volt, so a DC voltage which is three divisions above the zero volt line represents 1.5 volts. The horizontal axis in Fig. 6.1 represents time. In this particular case each division represents 10 seconds. At, say $\frac{1}{2}$ min (three divisions of 10 sec each) we can see that the voltage is 1.5 volts. In fact the voltage is 1.5 volts at any time shown on the graph. **DC voltage remains constant regardless of the time at which it is measured.** Similarly, DC current is constant regardless of time.

Figure 6.2 is an **oscilloscope** photograph of DC voltage. An oscilloscope is a device used to measure or observe voltages at different times. It presents its information on a screen similar to that of a television set. We can photograph this picture for a permanent record. It is quite similar to the graph in Fig. 6.1. In the oscilloscope photograph the vertical line at the extreme left is the voltage axis. The horizontal line in the center is the time axis. Thus an oscilloscope photograph is also a graph of voltage versus time. In fact the vertical scales in both Fig. 6.1 and Fig. 6.2 happen to be 0.5 V per division.

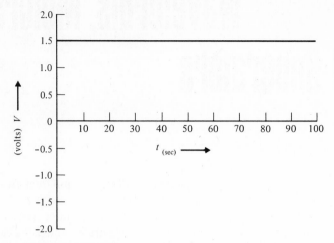

6.1   Graph of voltage versus time.

On the oscilloscope, the scale divisions are at 1 cm intervals. For this situation we say that the vertical scale is 0.5 V/cm.

The horizontal axis in Fig. 6.2 is also divided into 1 cm intervals. For this particular situation each horizontal centimeter represents 10 sec. In this case we say that the horizontal scale is 10 sec/cm. Typically, the center horizontal line represents zero volts. An oscilloscope photograph is a permanent record of the conditions which existed during the time when the photograph was taken. It is quite legitimate to consider an oscilloscope as a voltmeter with a picture tube. Just as a voltmeter has several voltage ranges, an oscilloscope has several volt/cm ranges. For example, we can select ranges so that each vertical centimeter represents 50 mV/cm, 0.5-volts/cm, 10-volts/cm, as well as other higher and lower ranges.

Similarly, a variety of time scales may be selected for the horizontal axis. Scales from tenths of a microsecond all the way up to seconds per centimeter are available on most quality oscilloscopes.

If we had taken oscilloscope photographs of voltages in any of the circuits described in previous chapters, they would all look the same. All we would have had to do would be to select different voltage ranges for different situations. In other words, all our previous circuits have been DC circuits, since DC voltage sources were used. The only difference between oscilloscope photographs of DC circuits is that different voltage sources require different volt-per-centimeter ranges. This is similar to the situation which we encountered with the VOM.

We would not expect to read 0.2 volts on the 100-volt scale of a VOM. We could not read 50 volts on the 10-volt scale of a VOM. The same type of reasoning is applicable when using an oscilloscope. We select the particular range which is most appropriate for our circuit conditions.

As yet nothing has been said about how an oscilloscope operates. We have merely stated that it is available to be used. This is similar to the voltage and

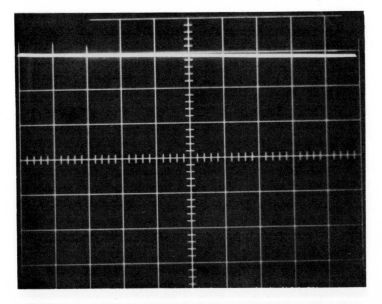

6.2 Oscilloscope photograph of voltage versus time. Vertical scale = 0.5 v/cm; horizontal scale = 10 sec/cm.

voltmeter situation. A good deal was said about voltage before the operating principles of voltmeters were described. Similarly we shall make use of oscilloscope photographs before actually describing how an oscilloscope operates.

An oscilloscope voltage reading can be used to determine current just as a voltmeter can be used to determine current. In both cases we need to know the resistance across which the voltage reading is taken. When both the voltage and resistance are known, the current is determined by using Ohm's law.

6.3 Pulsating DC

A different type of voltage waveform is shown in Fig. 6.3. This particular voltage is not constant with time. By referring to the information about the voltage and time scales given in Fig. 6.3 we can determine the voltage at particular times. For example, between zero seconds and 2 msec the voltage is 2 volts. Between 2 msec and 5 msec the voltage is zero, and so on.

Usually the extreme left point on the time axis of an oscilloscope photograph is referred to as zero seconds. Generally this point corresponds to closing or opening a switch to initiate circuit action. The expression, "at $t = 0 \ldots$ " is used to indicate what condition is used as the reference point for the time axis.

The voltage at a particular instant of time is referred to as the **instantaneous voltage.** For example, in Fig. 6.3 the instantaneous voltage at $t = 1$ msec is

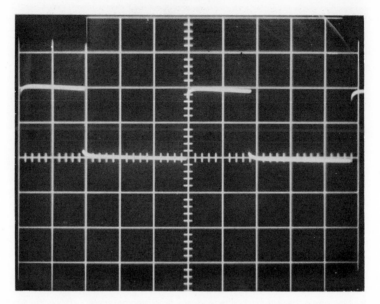

6.3 Pulsating DC voltage waveform. Vertical scale = 1 v/cm; horizontal scale = 1 msec/cm.

2 volts, the instantaneous voltage at t = 4 msec is zero and so on. Generally, DC voltages and currents are denoted by capital letters (V and I). Instantaneous voltages and currents are denoted by lowercase letters (v and i). Example 6.1 illustrates how instantaneous current is determined from an oscilloscope photograph.

Example 6.1

The voltage shown in Fig. 6.3 is connected across a 1 kΩ resistor. Determine the instantaneous current at t = 1 msec and at t = 3 msec.

Solution Step 1.   From the scale data given in Fig. 6.3, determine the instantaneous voltages at the required times:

$$v(t = 1 \text{ msec}) = 2 \text{ volts}$$

$$v(t = 3 \text{ msec}) = 0 \text{ volts}$$

Step 2.   Using Ohm's law, find i at t = 1 msec:

$$i(t = 1 \text{ msec}) = \frac{v(t = 1 \text{ msec})}{R}$$

$$= \frac{2}{10^3} = 2 \times 10^{-3} \text{ Amp.}$$

$$= 2 \text{ mA}$$

Step 3.   Similarly, to find $i(t = 3 \text{ msec})$

$$i(t = 3 \text{ msec}) = \frac{v(t = 3 \text{ msec})}{R}$$

$$= \frac{0}{10^3}$$

$$= 0 \text{ Amp.}$$

Example 6.1 shows that when the voltage across a resistor varies, the current through the resistor also varies. The voltage waveform shown in Fig. 6.3 varies in amplitude but not in polarity. Such a waveform is referred to as **pulsating DC.** It is also possible for a pulsating DC voltage to be negative. A negative pulsating DC waveform is shown in Fig. 6.4. In this case the voltage is either -2 volts or zero. As long as the voltage amplitude changes but the voltage polarity remains the same we have pulsating DC.

We have seen that instantaneous voltage and instantaneous current must be used to describe a pulsating waveform. Similarly, instantaneous power (p) must be used to describe power dissipation when a pulsating DC voltage source is used; that is,

$$p = iv = \frac{v^2}{R} = i^2 R \tag{6.1}$$

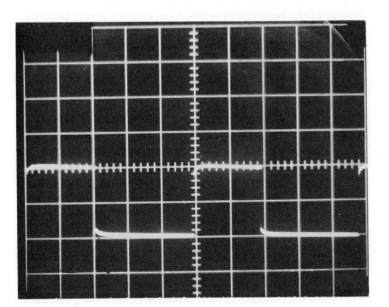

6.4 Negative pulsating DC voltage waveform. Vertical scale $= 1$ v/cm; horizontal scale $= 1$ msec/cm.

Example 6.2

Determine the instantaneous power dissipation for the instantaneous currents determined in Example 6.1.

Solution Step 1.   Any form of Eq. 6.1 is equally valid. Therefore, at $t = 1$ msec,

$$p(t = 1 \text{ msec}) = v(t = 1 \text{ msec}) \times i(t = 1 \text{ msec})$$

$$= 2 \times 2 \times 10^{-3}$$

$$= 4 \times 10^{-3} \text{ watts}$$

$$= 4 \text{ mW.}$$

Step 2.   Similarly, for $t = 3$ msec,

$$p(t = 3 \text{ msec}) = v(t = 3 \text{ msec}) \times i(t = 3 \text{ msec})$$

$$= 0 \times 0$$

$$= 0 \text{ Watts}$$

What we really have been saying is that **the equations which are used for DC are also applicable to pulsating DC.** The only modification necessary is that we work with instantaneous values instead of constant values. Thus concepts such as Ohm's law, Kirchhoff's voltage and current laws, loop equations, black boxes, and so on are used in pulsating DC situations just as in constant DC situations.

The voltage waveforms shown in Figs. 6.3 and 6.4 repeat every 5 msec. The time required for a complete repetition of a waveform is called the **period** (T). Thus, in Figs. 6.3 and 6.4 we say that the period is 5 msec. In 10 msec there will be two complete waveform repetitions. In 15 msec there will be three complete waveform repetitions, and so on. The number of times a waveform repeats itself in 1 sec is called the **pulse repetition frequency** (PRF). To find the PRF we divide the period into 1 sec:

$$\text{PRF} = \frac{1}{T} \tag{6.2}$$

Example 6.3

Determine the PRF of the pulsating DC waveform shown in Fig. 6.4.

Solution Step 1.   From Fig. 6.4 we observe that the period of the waveform is 5 msec:

$$T = 5 \text{ msec}$$

Step 2. Equation 6.2 is used to find the PRF:

$$\text{PRF} = \frac{1}{T}$$

$$= \frac{1}{5 \times 10^{-3}}$$

$$= 0.2 \times 10^3$$

$$= 200 \text{ pps} \quad \text{(pulses per second)}$$

We have used the oscilloscope photograph to determine voltage levels and, with the aid of calculations, also to determine the number of times a waveform occurs in 1 sec. Additional information may also be obtained from the oscilloscope and these situations will be covered as they arise.

6.4   Alternating Current

Figure 6.5 shows a waveform which is not pulsating DC. In Fig. 6.5 we see that the maximum voltage (V_{max}) is 20 volts, and that the minimum voltage (V_{min}) is -20 volts. In this case the **peak-to-peak voltage** ($V_{\text{p}-\text{p}}$) will be 40 volts. The interesting thing about this waveform is that the voltage changes

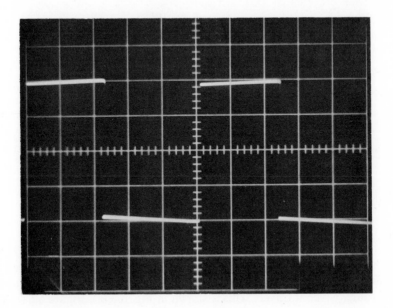

6.5   AC symmetrical square wave. Vertical scale = 10 v/cm; horizontal scale = 1 msec/cm.

in polarity as well as in amplitude. **A waveform which changes in polarity and in amplitude is referred to as alternating current (AC).** We use terms such as AC voltage and AC current in describing these waveforms.

In an AC waveform power dissipation in a resistor will be positive even when the voltage is negative. This has already been discussed (Chapter 2). In fact, with the same provision as was mentioned regarding pulsating DC (working with instantaneous values), all our previous electrical laws and concepts may be extended to AC.

Example 6.4

Determine (a) the PRF and (b) $p(t = 1 \text{ msec})$ for the waveform shown in Fig. 6.5 if this voltage is connected across a 100-Ω resistor.

Solution Part (a) Step 1. The period is a complete waveform excursion which for AC must include both the positive and negative voltage portions. Therefore

$$T = 5 \text{ msec}$$

Step 2.

$$\text{PRF} = \frac{1}{T}$$

$$= \frac{1}{5 \times 10^{-3}}$$

$$= 0.2 \times 10^3$$

$$= 200 \text{ pps}$$

Part b Step 1. At $t = 1 \text{ msec}$, $v = 20 \text{ V}$.

Step 2.

$$p = \frac{v^2}{R}$$

$$p(t = 1 \text{ msec}) = \frac{v^2(t = 1 \text{ msec})}{R}$$

$$= \frac{(20)^2}{100}$$

$$= 4 \text{ watts}$$

When we whistle or strike a tuning fork a sound wave is produced. A sound wave is heard because it produces compression and expansion of the air through which it travels. This is shown in Fig. 6.6 (a). Figure 6.6 (b) is a graph of the air pressure at a fixed point as the sound wave passes this point. "Zero" pressure level represents normal air pressure. Positive pressure levels on the graph represent increases in air pressure. Negative values represent decreases in air pressure. The waveform shown in Fig. 6.6 (b) is a **sine wave.**

There are other mechanical motions which produce sine waves. For example, the motion described by a clock pendulum is approximately a sine wave. By attaching a pen to the pendulum and moving a roll of paper perpendicular to the pendulum, we can graph the sine wave as shown in Fig. 6.7. Spring motion, vibrating rods, and so on also generate sine waves. In addition to generating sine waves mechanically, it is also possible to generate sine waves electrically. An electrical sine wave is often called a **sinusoidal** wave. In fact the voltage which power companies generate and deliver to homes, factories, and so on is sinusoidal AC. Sinusoidal AC is important in all phases of electricity as a voltage waveform. In addition, sinusoidal AC is used as an analysis tool to predict the circuit performance of other types of waveforms.

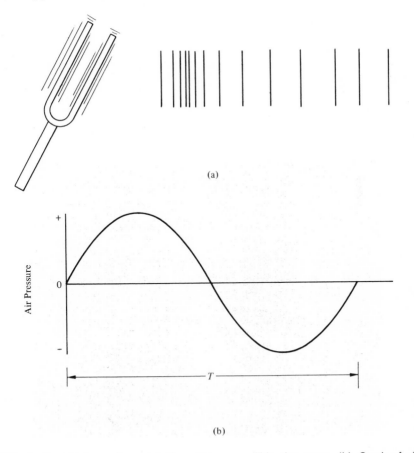

(a)

(b)

6.6 A sinusoidal waveform. (a) Generating an audible sine wave. (b) Graph of air pressure at a fixed point.

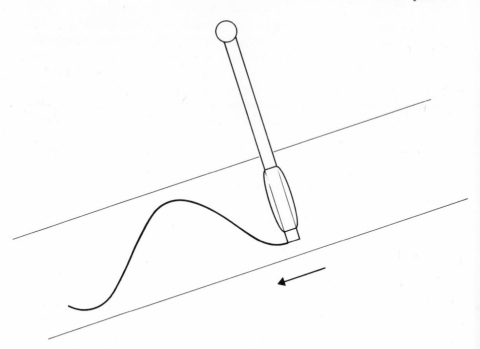

6.7 Pendulum generating a sine wave.

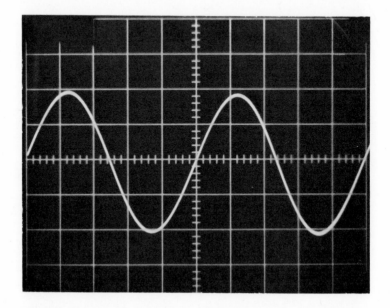

6.8 Sinusoidal AC voltage waveform. Vertical scale = 50 v/cm; horizontal scale = 0.2 msec/cm.

There is an important difference between sinusoidal AC and other wave-forms which have been discussed in this chapter. All the previous waveforms were composed of straight lines. The sine wave, however, is a continuous curve which contains no straight lines. This makes analysis of sinusoidal waveforms somewhat different, although some concepts are similar. Figure 6.8 shows a sine wave. We can continue to use the notions of V_{max}, V_{min}, and V_{p-p},

$$V_{p-p} = V_{max} - V_{min} \qquad (6.3)$$

as illustrated in Example 6.5.

Example 6.5

For the sinusoidal AC waveform shown in Fig. 6.8 find V_{max}, V_{min}, and V_{p-p}.

Solution Step 1.   From the scale data given for Fig. 6.8, the vertical scale is 50 volt/cm.

Step 2.   The maximum voltage is 2 cm high. Therefore

$$V_{max} = 50 \, \frac{volt}{\cancel{cm}} \times 2 \, \cancel{cm}$$

$$= 100 \text{ volts}$$

Step 3.   Similarly, the minimum voltage is 2 cm "low." Therefore

$$V_{min} = 50 \, \frac{volt}{\cancel{cm}} \times (-2 \, \cancel{cm})$$

$$- 100 \text{ volts}$$

Step 4.

$$V_{p-p} = V_{max} - V_{min}$$

$$= 100 - (-100)$$

$$= 200 \text{ volts}$$

As in the case of other waveforms we are also interested in the repetition rate. For sinusoidal voltages different terms are used:
Hertz (Hz) replaces pulses per second (pps).
Frequency (*f*) replaces pulse repetition frequency (PRF).
Thus

$$f = \frac{1}{T} \qquad (6.4)$$

Example 6.6

Find the frequency of the sinusoidal voltage shown in Fig. 6.8.

Solution Step 1.   From the scale data given for Fig. 6.8, the time scale is 0.2 msec/cm. One complete repetition of the wave (called a **cycle**) is 5 cm wide. Therefore

$$T = 0.2 \frac{\text{msec}}{\text{cm}} \times 5 \text{ cm}$$

$$= 1 \text{ msec}$$

$$= 10^{-3} \text{ sec}$$

Step 2.

$$f = \frac{1}{T}$$

$$= \frac{1}{10^{-3}} = 1000 \text{ Hz}$$

$$= 1 \text{ kHz}$$

The symbol kHz, pronounced "kilo-Hertz," means 1000 Hertz. As in the case of "straight-line" AC, sinusoidal AC voltages continue to repeat. For example, in Fig. 6.8 $V(t = 0.1 \text{ msec})$ is about 53 volts. This is the same voltage that occurs at 1.1 msec, 2.1 msec, 3.1 msec, and so on. The point is that in many cases we are not interested in the exact time at which a particular voltage occurs. Instead we need to know at what portion of the period the particular waveform occurs.

For this purpose it is useful to compare the correspondence between a sine wave and a point on a rotating wheel, as shown in Fig. 6.9. In fact, the position of the point on the rotating wheel can be used to generate the sine wave. By plotting the ratio of y values of the rotating point to the wheel radius for each point the result is a sine wave. Also, if we go past one complete

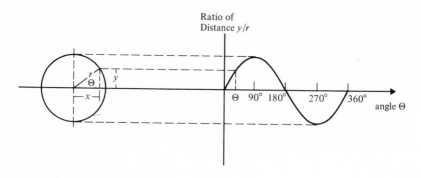

6.9   A rotating point generates a sine wave.

wheel rotation, the values will continue to repeat. Thus, instead of speaking of the precise time at which a specific voltage occurs, we can speak of the angle at which the voltage occurs.

For example, in Fig. 6.8 we see that regardless of the particular sinusoidal, AC will have its maximum value at 90° and the minimum value at 270°. Also observe that except for V_{max} and V_{min} any instantaneous voltage will occur twice during each period; that is, the voltage will be the same at 45° as at 135°. The voltage at 190° will be the same as at 350°, and so on.

If we know the period for a sinusoidal voltage and need to know the angle (θ) which corresponds to a specific instant, this can be found:

$$\theta = \frac{t}{T} 360°$$ (6.5a)

Example 6.7

For the sinusoidal voltage shown in Fig. 6.8, find the angle which corresponds to 0.4 msec.

Solution Step 1.   We have already seen (Example 6.6) that this waveform has a period of 1 msec:

$$T = 10^{-3} \text{ sec}$$

Step 2.   Therefore

$$\theta = \frac{t}{T} 360°$$

$$= \frac{0.4 \times 10^{-3}}{10^{-3}} 360°$$

$$= 144°$$

We can also solve Eq. 6.5a for t and use this result to find the instant of time which corresponds to a particular angle:

$$t = \frac{\theta}{360°} T$$ (6.5b)

This is illustrated in Example 6.8.

Example 6.8

Find the instant of time at which a 400-Hz voltage will correspond to a 90° angle.

Solution Step 1.   We must find the period of a 400-Hz sine wave:

$$f = \frac{1}{T}$$

$$400 = \frac{1}{T}$$

$$T = 2.5 \times 10^{-3} \text{ sec}$$

Step 2.   Therefore

$$t = \frac{\theta}{360°} T$$

$$= \frac{90°}{360°} 2.5 \times 10^{-3} \text{ sec}$$

$$= 0.625 \times 10^{-3} \text{ sec}$$

The correspondence between a sine wave and a rotating point has already been discussed. Frequently in electricity it is necessary to work with **radian frequency** (ω) rather than frequency. The relationship between radian frequency and frequency is

$$\omega = 2\pi f \tag{6.6a}$$

The voltage (v) at any instant is written as

$$v = V_{max} \sin \omega t \tag{6.6b}$$

Example 6.9

Find the radian frequency for the frequency used in Example 6.8.

Solution Step 1.   In Example 6.8,

$$f = 400 \text{ Hz}$$

Step 2.

$$\omega = 2\pi f$$

$$= 2\pi 400$$

$$\simeq 2,512 \text{ rad/sec}$$

6.5   Comparing Waveforms

It is useful to have a method of comparing the effect of DC, pulsating DC, and AC waveforms. One such method is based on comparing average voltages.

The average value of ordinary DC is equal to that particular DC value. For example, the DC voltage shown in Fig. 6.2 is 1.5 volts. But some additional effort is required to find the average voltage of a waveform which varies. This is how a regular DC voltmeter measures average DC voltage. If the voltage is constant, the meter measures this constant value. If, on the other hand, the voltage changes quickly enough the meter needle cannot follow the changes. In this case the needle will settle at some intermediate value, which is the **average voltage.**

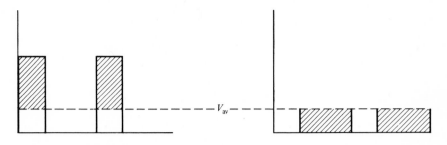

6.10   Averaging a pulsating DC waveform.

Consider the voltage illustrated in Fig. 6.10. Think in terms of using the area above the average voltage line to "fill in" the area below the average voltage line where there is no voltage.

To find the average value of a quantity which varies, find the total area (A_T) and divide by the total time.

$$\text{average} = \frac{A_T}{T} \tag{6.7}$$

Example 6.10 illustrates how average voltage of a pulsating DC waveform is determined.

Example 6.10

Find the average voltage of the voltage waveform shown in Fig. 6.4.

Solution Step 1.   To find the average voltage we must average over a complete period:

$$A_T = (-2 \text{ volts})(2 \times 10^{-3} \text{ sec}) + (0 \text{ volts})(3 \times 10^{-3} \text{ sec})$$

$$= -4 \times 10^{-3} \text{ volt-sec} + 0 \text{ volt-sec}$$

$$= -4 \times 10^{-3} \text{ volt-sec}$$

Notice that the area comes out in units of volts times seconds, called volt-seconds.

Step 2.

$$\text{average} = \frac{A_T}{T}$$

$$= \frac{-4 \times 10^{-3} \text{ volt-sec}}{5 \times 10^{-3} \text{ sec}}$$

$$V_{av} = -0.8 \text{ volts}$$

Similarly, since the voltage shown in Fig. 6.3 is the positive mirror image, the average voltage for this waveform is +0.8 volts.

An interesting situation arises when the average voltage of the AC waveform shown in Fig. 6.5 is computed.

Example 6.11

Find the average value of the AC voltage waveform shown in Fig. 6.5.

Solution Step 1.   The total volt-seconds for a complete period of an AC waveform consists of the positive voltage area plus the negative voltage area.

$$A_T = A_{(+)} + A_{(-)}$$

Step 2.   From the scale data given in Fig. 6.5:

$$A_{(+)} = 20 \text{ volts} \times 2.5 \times 10^{-3} \text{ sec}$$

$$= 50 \times 10^{-3} \text{ volt-sec}$$

Step 3.   Similarly,

$$A_{(-)} = -20 \text{ volts} \times 2.5 \times 10^{-3} \text{ sec}$$

$$= -50 \times 10^{-3} \text{ volt-sec}$$

Step 4.

$$\text{average} = \frac{A_T}{T} = \frac{A_{(+)} + A_{(-)}}{T}$$

$$= \frac{50 \times 10^{-3} - 50 \times 10^{-3}}{5 \times 10^{-3}} = \frac{0}{5 \times 10^{-3}}$$

$$V_{av} = 0 \text{ volts}$$

This answer is mathematically correct. The average value of the voltage waveform shown in Fig. 6.5 is zero volts. Although this answer is correct it is also useless. We can see from Example 6.11 that **the average value of any symmetrical waveform is zero.** This is because, regardless of the actual voltage involved, there will be equal but opposite polarity voltage areas. Whether the maximum voltage is 20 volts, 100 volts, or 1000 volts, the average voltage will be zero as long as the waveform is symmetrical.

However, based on our experience with DC and pulsating DC we know that higher voltages result in higher currents and greater power dissipation. The same situation will be true for AC voltages. While we might not even notice the shock from a 20-V_{p-p} voltage source, we would certainly be aware of the shock from a 200-V_{p-p} source. The conclusion is that we must use something instead of average voltage for AC situations. This is accomplished by inverting (in principle only) the negative portion of the voltage waveform as shown in Fig. 6.11.

The previous waveforms, except for sinusoidal AC, have been composed of straight lines so that averaging was relatively easy. In the case of a sinusoidal waveform we must first invert and then determine the resulting average. One approach would be to count boxes on the graph paper to find the area. Naturally our answer would become more and more accurate as we used graph paper with finer and finer scales. The precise answer to the average

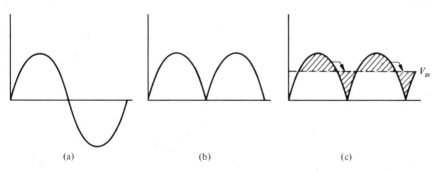

6.11 Averaging an AC waveform. (a) Original waveform. (b) Inverting the negative portion. (c) "Filling in" the spaces.

value of a sinewave with the negative portion inverted requires more mathematics.

$$V\begin{pmatrix} \text{average} \\ \text{sine wave} \\ \text{inverted} \end{pmatrix} = \frac{2}{\pi} V_{\text{max}} \simeq 0.636\ V_{\text{max}} \qquad \textbf{(6.8)}$$

Example 6.12

The average value of a certain sinusoidal AC voltage is 10 volts when the negative portion is inverted. Find the corresponding peak-to-peak voltage.

Solution Step 1.   Inverting the negative half,

$$V\begin{pmatrix} \text{average} \\ \text{sinewave} \\ \text{inverted} \end{pmatrix} = \frac{2}{\pi} V_{\text{max}}$$

$$10 = \frac{2}{\pi} V_{\text{max}}$$

$$V_{\text{max}} = \frac{\pi}{2} 10$$

$$\simeq 15.7 \text{ volts}$$

Step 2.   Since this is a symmetrical waveform,

$$V_{\text{min}} \simeq -15.7 \text{ volts}$$

Step 3.

$$V_{\text{p-p}} = V_{\text{max}} - V_{\text{min}}$$

$$= 15.7 - (-15.7)$$

$$\simeq 31.4 \text{ volts}$$

There are many devices whose equivalent circuits are essentially resistors. Heaters, irons, incandescent lamps, and certain types of motors are examples of such devices. These devices perform equally well on DC, pulsating DC, and AC. As we have seen, average value is one method of comparing different voltage waveforms. Another useful method is to compare voltages on the basis of equal power dissipation. We must not make the mistake of thinking that two voltages which have the same average will deliver the same power.

As was discussed in Chapter 2, power is a nonlinear quantity. Power depends either on current squared or on voltage squared. Thus, we do not obtain the same result if we average a varying waveform and then square the average as we do if we square the waveform itself and then average. Thus we can compare waveforms on the basis of average values, but this is not the same as comparing voltage waveforms based on equivalent power capability. Voltages which deliver the same power to a load are called **effective voltages** (V_{eff}). This is illustrated in Example 6.13.

Example 6.13

Compare the average voltage and effective voltage if the waveform shown in Fig. 6.4 is connected across a 1-Ω resistor.

Solution Step 1. For 2 msec,

$$p = \frac{V^2}{R}$$

$$= \frac{4}{1}$$

$$= 4 \text{ watts}$$

For 3 msec,

$$p = \frac{V^2}{R}$$

$$= \frac{0^2}{1}$$

$$= 0 \text{ watts}$$

Step 2.

$$P_{average} = \frac{A_T}{T}$$

$$= \frac{4 \times 2 \times 10^{-3} - 0 \times 3 \times 10^{-3}}{5 \times 10^{-3}}$$

$$= 1.6 \text{ watts}$$

Step 3. The voltage required from a DC supply to furnish the same power is

$$P = \frac{V^2}{R}$$

$$1.6 = \frac{V^2}{1}$$

$$V = \sqrt{1.6}$$

$$V_{eff} = 1.26 \text{ volts}$$

Step 4. Since $V_{av} = 0.8$ volts and $V_{eff} = 1.26$ volts we can see that $V_{eff} \neq V_{av}$ that is **the effective voltage is the DC voltage which will deliver the same power as the AC source.** Since sinusoidal AC is the waveform transmitted by power companies, it is of special interest to determine the effective value of a sinusoidal voltage. Again we require additional mathematical background, but the precise result for a sinewave is

$$V_{eff} = \frac{V_{max}}{\sqrt{2}} \simeq 0.707 V_{max} \tag{6.9}$$

Example 6.14

What peak-to-peak sinusoidal voltage has the same effect as a 10-volt battery?

Solution Step 1. From the given data,

$$V_{eff} = 10 = \frac{V_{max}}{\sqrt{2}}$$

$$V_{max} = \sqrt{2} \times 10$$

$$\simeq 14.14 \text{ volts}$$

Step 2. Since $V_{max} = 14.14$, $V_{min} = -14.14$.

Step 3.

$$V_{p-p} = V_{max} - V_{min}$$

$$= 14.14 - (-14.14)$$

$$= 28.28 \text{ volts}$$

The effective voltage is also called the **root-mean-square voltage,** V_{rms}. This term describes the mathematical method used to determine the effective value. Figure 6.12 relates the important voltage levels used to describe sinusoidal AC voltages. Each waveform has its own value of V_{av} and V_{rms}. The values listed in Fig. 6.12 apply only to sinusoidal AC.

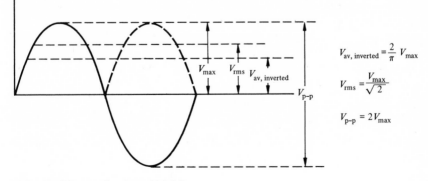

$$V_{av, \text{ inverted}} = \frac{2}{\pi} V_{max}$$

$$V_{rms} = \frac{V_{max}}{\sqrt{2}}$$

$$V_{p-p} = 2 V_{max}$$

6.12 Useful terms for sinusoidal AC.

The concepts of peak-to-peak, average, and root-mean-square values apply to current as well as to voltage.

6.6   Generating Waveforms

In Chapter 4 we saw that the ammeter is based on interaction between a magnet and a coil of wire in the magnetic field. The same principle is used by power companies to generate voltage.

Figure 6.13 shows the general principle. In Fig. 6.13 (a) the coil is parallel to the magnetic field. Under this condition the coil intercepts or "cuts" the minimum flux of the magnetic field, but the change in flux is maximum. **Flux** is the term used to describe the magnetic lines of force between the poles of the magnet. In Fig. 6.13 (b) the coil is rotated so that it is perpendicular to the magnetic field. Under this condition the coil cuts maximum magnetic flux but the change in flux is minimum. At intermediate positions the amount of flux cut will be proportional to the angle between the coil and the magnetic field. When the coil is rotated 180° from the position shown in Fig. 6.13 (a), the magnetic flux which is cut is again a maximum, but the coil is now in the opposite direction.

Faraday's law gives the value of the voltage generated across the ends of the coil:

$$V = N \times \text{magnetic flux} \times \text{rps} \qquad \textbf{(6.10)}$$

where N is the number of coils and rps is the speed in revolutions per second. Equation 6.10 shows how the generated voltage may be increased:
1. N may be increased by connecting additional coils in series.
2. Magnetic flux may be increased by using stronger magnets.
3. The speed of rotation (revolutions per second) may be increased.

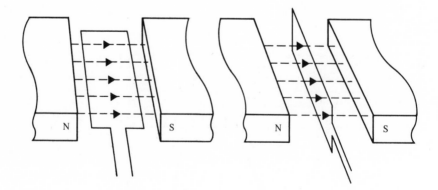

6.13   Wire coil in a magnetic field. (a) Parallel to field. (b) Perpendicular to field.

Example 6.15

A certain generator consists of 350 coils of wire connected in series. The flux is 1.2×10^{-2} magnetic units and the coil rotates at 30 rps. Find (a) the voltage which is generated, and (b) the new voltage if the speed of rotation is increased to 2400 rpm (40 rps).

Solution Part (a) Step 1.   From the given data, $N = 350$, magnetic flux $= 1.2 \times 10^{-2}$, and rps $= 30$.

Step 2.   Therefore

$$V = N \times \text{magnetic flux} \times \text{rps}$$
$$= 3.5 \times 10^2 \times 1.2 \times 10^{-2} \times 3 \times 10^1$$
$$= 126 \text{ volts}$$

Part (b) Step 1.   The data for the new conditions are $N = 350$, magnetic flux $= 1.2 \times 10^{-2}$, and rps $= 40$.

Step 2.   Therefore

$$V = N \times \text{magnetic flux} \times \text{rps}$$
$$= 3.5 \times 10^2 \times 1.2 \times 10^{-2} \times 4 \times 10^1$$
$$= 168 \text{ volts}$$

Figure 6.14 shows the principle of a basic generator. **Slip rings** are attached to the ends of the coil. Carbon brushes make contact with these rotating

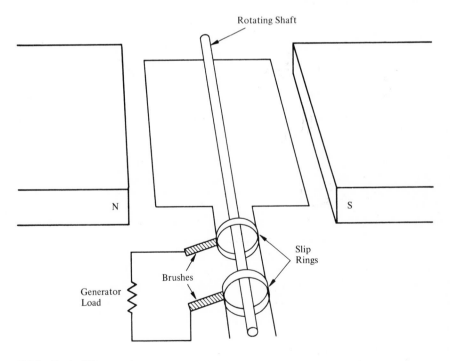

6.14   Basic AC generator.

rings so the voltage which is generated can be connected to a load. Mechanical work must be used to keep the shaft to which the coil is attached rotating. Steam turbines, water wheels, and so on are commonly used methods of rotating the shaft. A generator converts mechanical energy into electrical energy.

The speed of rotation of the turbine, water wheel, and so on directly affects the generator voltage and frequency since this speed is the rps term in Faraday's law. Therefore the turbine speed must be kept constant. Unfortunately, the voltage developed by a generator fluctuates as the load varies. Increased power demand lowers the generated voltage. By keeping the generator shaft speed constant, power companies can guarantee the frequency of the generated voltage but not amplitude.

Figure 6.15 (a) shows the relationship between the position of the coil in the magnetic field and the voltage being generated. When the coil is right under the north pole [this is the parallel position of Fig. 6.13 (a)] minimum flux is cut but the change is maximum and the generated voltage is a maximum. When the coil is between the poles [this is the perpendicular position

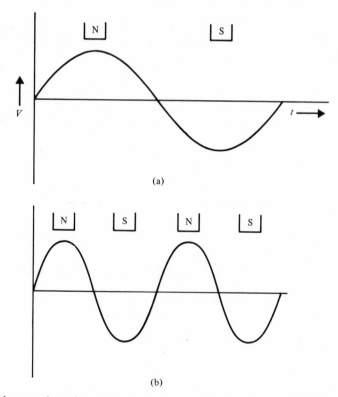

(a)

(b)

6.15 Magnets determine generator frequency. (a) One magnet. (b) Two magnets double the frequency.

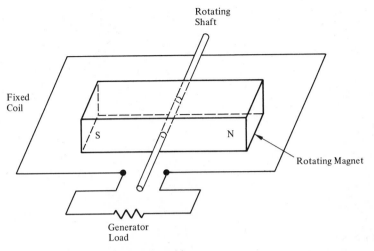

6.16   Interchanging coil and magnet positions.

of Fig. 6.13 (b)] maximum flux is cut but the change is minimum and the generated voltage is zero. As the coil continues to rotate, the side of the coil which was originally opposite the north pole approaches the south pole and the voltage becomes negative. The most negative voltage occurs when the coil is again parallel to the field and the coil has rotated 180° from the position shown in Fig. 6.13 (a). The voltage output of this generator is sinusoidal AC.

Practical AC generators in use today generate voltages above 10,000 volts. At such voltages, arcing between the rotating collector rings and the fixed brushes is a severe problem. Therefore in actual AC generators it is common practice to use a rotating magnet and a fixed coil, as shown in Fig. 6.16. The principle is still the same. Faraday's law applies since there is still relative motion between a coil and a magnetic field. However, since the coil is fixed the generated voltage is obtained from nonrotating contacts and there is no arcing problem. That is, in a practical AC generator the rotor (rotating part) contains the magnetic poles, and the stator (stationary part) contains the coil. Figure 6.17 shows the size of a modern generator.

As shown in Fig. 6.15, the frequency of a generator also depends on the number of magnets:

$$f = M \times \text{rps} \qquad \qquad \textbf{(6.11a)}$$

where M is the number of magnets (each magnet has an N pole and an S pole).

Example 6.16

At what speed must a two-magnet AC generator rotate if the required frequency is 60 Hz.

6.17   Modern AC generator. (*Courtesy of General Electric Company.*)

Solution Step 1.   The given data are

$$M = 2, \quad f = 60\,\text{Hz}$$

Step 2.   Therefore

$$f = M \times \text{rps}$$
$$60 = 2 \times \text{rps}$$
$$\text{rps} = 30$$

and since rpm = rps × 60,

$$\text{rpm} = 1800$$

It is possible to place independent windings on an armature and thus obtain several voltages which have the same frequency but differ as to when the peaks occur. Voltages of the same frequency which peak at different times are said to be **out of phase.** Figure 6.18 shows the principle of a three-phase generator. In a three-phase generator the voltages are 120° out of phase with each other. The principal advantages of three-phase power are the following:

1. More power can be delivered for the same amount of wire.
2. Power of the waveform is more uniform over a cycle.

Phase A   Phase B   Phase C

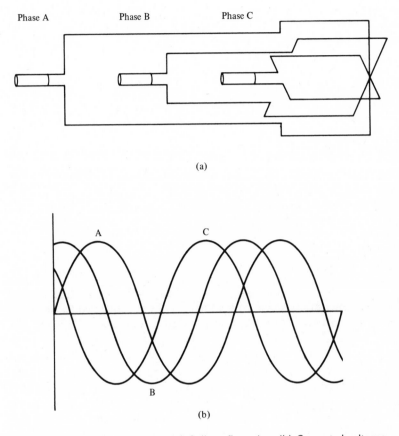

(a)

(b)

6.18 Basic three-phase generator. (a) Coil configuration. (b) Generated voltages.

For these reasons three-phase power is generally used for high-power load requirements. Most residential wiring is single phase, while industrial applications are generally multiple phase.

Although power companies generate and deliver sinusoidal AC, there are industrial applications for which generation of DC is required. The principle of a DC generator is the same as that of an AC generator; that is, **voltage is generated when there is a relative motion between a magnetic field and a coil of wire.** Thus Faraday's law also applies to DC generators. The basic difference between AC and DC generators is the method by which the voltage generated in the coil is delivered to an external load.

In the case of an AC generator, slip rings were connected to opposite ends of the coil. As the coil rotates so do the slip rings. Thus, as the polarity of the generated voltage reverses, the polarity of the voltage between the slip rings also reverses. In this way sinusoidal AC is delivered to the load.

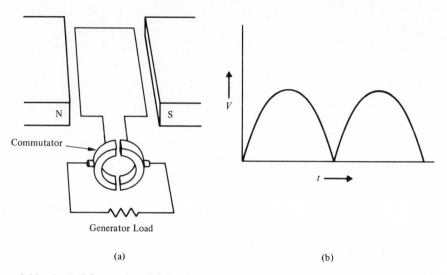

Commutator

Generator Load

(a)   (b)

6.19 Basic DC generator. (a) Configuration. (b) Load voltage for one rotation.

In a DC generator a single ring which is split is connected to the coil as shown in Fig. 6.19 (a). The split ring is called a **commutator.** It is the commutator which changes AC into the pulsating DC shown in Fig. 6.19 (b). During the initial half of a rotation, the voltage is one half of a sinewave, just as in the case of an AC generator. During the alternate half-rotation the voltage developed in the coil will reverse polarity. However, **at the instant of polarity reversal the commutator reverses connection to the brushes.** In this way the current always flows in the same direction through the external load.

In one rotation of the coil in a DC generator, two complete pulsating DC waveforms are generated. In one rotation of an AC generator, only one complete sinewave is generated. That is, the frequency of a DC generator is twice that of an AC generator and Eq. 6.11 (a) must be modified:

$$f_{DC} = 2M \times \text{rps} \qquad \qquad \text{(6.11b)}$$

Example 6.17

The generator is the same as in Example 6.16 except that the slip rings are replaced by a commutator. What is the frequency of the pulsating DC?

Solution Step 1. From Example 6.16, $M = 2$ and rps $= 30$.

Step 2. Therefore

$$f_{DC} = 2 \times 2 \times 30$$

$$= 120 \qquad \text{(twice that of Example 6.16)}$$

As in the case of AC generators, it is possible to have independently wound coils. In a DC generator these coils are connected together at the

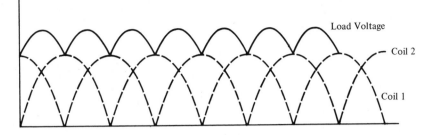

6.20   Combining coils in a DC generator.

commutator and the voltages combine and approach battery-type DC. This is illustrated in Fig. 6.20 for a two-coil generator. Notice that the load voltage has a maximum and a minimum but that the minimum is above zero volts. As more coils are used the range between V_{max} and V_{min} decreases.

DC voltage generators typically deliver lower voltages than AC generators. Therefore arcing between ring and brush does not present much of a problem. In a DC generator the **rotor** is the armature and the **stator** is the field structure.

It is interesting to note that permanent magnets as such are rarely used in generators. **Electromagnets,** which are coils of wire wrapped around an iron core, replace the permanent magnet. The electromagnet provides a magnetic field as long as current flows.

6.7   Electric Motors

A generator, as we have seen, converts mechanical energy into electrical energy. An electrical motor functions in the opposite manner; that is, a motor converts electrical energy into mechanical energy. The input to an electrical motor is electrical power and the output is a shaft rotation.

Motors are made in a variety of ratings ranging from small fractions of a horsepower to operate electric clocks to thousands of horsepower to pull trains. Regardless of the power rating or application all electrical motors are based on the same principle.

In fact ammeters, generators, and motors are all based on the interaction between a fixed and a rotating magnetic field. In the ammeter the rotating magnetic field works against a spring. In both the generator and the motor there is no spring and rotation is continuous; that is, the generator functions as long as a mechanical force keeps the shaft rotating and the motor functions as long as electrical power is supplied.

As shown in Fig. 6.21, there are two basic DC motor types. In the **induction** motor shown in Fig. 6.21 (a) there is no electrical connection between the rotor and the stator. The rotor can be a copper disc. When AC is connected to the stator an electromagnet exists. This varying magnetic field generates a

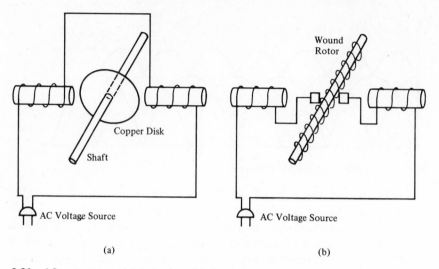

6.21   AC motor types. (a) Induction. (b) Conduction.

current in the copper rotor. Since there is a current in the rotor this in turn generates a magnetic field around the rotor. The interaction between the rotor and stator magnetic fields causes the motor shaft to rotate. That is, in an induction motor there are no brushes or rings. The rotor voltage is said to be induced.

In Fig. 6.21 (b) there is a conduction motor. A **conduction** motor has brushes and rings just as in a generator. The interaction between the stator and rotor magnetic field produces shaft rotation.

There are several characteristics which determine the type and rating of motor to be selected:

1. Ability to control speed.
2. Ability to keep speed constant as load changes
3. Ability to withstand overload conditions
4. Torque

Torque is the ability to produce rotation. The relationship between torque (in foot-pounds) and horsepower is

$$T = \frac{\text{hp} \times 550}{2\pi \times \text{rps}} \tag{6.12}$$

Example 6.18

A vacuum cleaner motor rotating at 1800 rpm is rated at $\frac{1}{2}$ hp. Assuming that no power is wasted, determine the torque of this motor.

Solution Step 1.   The given information is hp = 0.5 and rpm = 1800. Thus

$$\text{rps} = \frac{1800}{60} = 30$$

Step 2.   Therefore

$$T = \frac{\text{hp} \times 550}{2\pi \times \text{rps}}$$

$$= \frac{0.5 \times 550}{2\pi \times 30}$$

$$= 1.46 \text{ ft-lb}$$

In Chapter 2 the relationship between watts and horsepower was estab-lished (Eq. 2.7), so we are now able to calculate the motor current if the source voltage is known.

Example 6.19

The motor in Example 6.18 is operated from a 115-volt line. Assuming that no power is lost, calculate the motor current.

Solution Step 1.   From Eq. 2.7,

$$1 \text{ hp} \simeq 746 \text{ watts}$$

Step 2.   Therefore

$$0.5 \text{ hp} \simeq 373 \text{ watts}$$

Step 3.   Since $P = VI$ and V is given as 115 volts

$$373 = 115 \times I$$

$$I = 3.25 \text{ Amp.}$$

As a practical matter it is impossible to build a motor which has frictionless bearings, no heat losses, and so on. Therefore more current than was calculated will have to be supplied to operate the motor at rated capacity.

Motor torque is determined by magnetic flux and armature current. Armature current is determined by the type of motor connection and resistive losses in the windings.

Heavy motor loads usually require polyphase motors. Polyphase motors, of course, must be driven from polyphase generators. Two-phase and three-phase motors are the most common types for heavy-duty applications.

All DC motors are conduction motors since it is not possible to transfer energy through a magnetic field which does not vary with time. DC motors are classified by the method of connecting the field and armature windings. These methods are shown in Fig. 6.22.

In the **shunt** connection [Fig. 6.22 (a)] the field winding and the armature winding are connected in parallel. Since the field winding is across the source voltage the magnetic flux remains constant. The torque is therefore deter-mined only by varying the armature current.

In the **series** motor connection [Fig. 6.22(b)] the field current is the same as the armature current. This permits **series motors to operate on both AC**

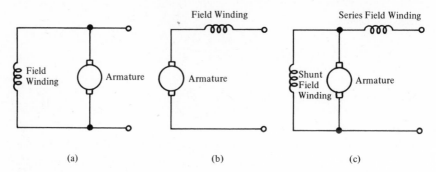

6.22   DC motor connections. (a) Shunt. (b) Series. (c) Compound.

and DC, and this type is sometimes called a **universal motor.** Series motors can be destroyed when operated without a load connected to the shaft.

The **compound** motor [Fig. 6.22 (c)] has characteristics which are a combination of the shunt and series configuration. Detailed analysis of specific applications are required to decide properly between AC and DC motors, and also to decide actual motor type.

Summary

1. Direct current remains constant with respect to time. An oscilloscope can be used to measure DC, just as a voltmeter can be used.
2. Pulsating DC varies in amplitude but not in polarity. DC circuit can be analyzed using Ohm's law, and so on, provided that instantaneous values are used.
3. Alternating current varies in both amplitude and polarity. Sinusoidal AC is a particularly important waveform in electricity.
4. The minimum, maximum, and peak-to-peak voltages are parameters used to describe AC. Frequency has the same meaning as PRF but refers specifically to sinusoidal AC.
5. The average voltage is a method of comparing different waveforms. The true average value of any symmetrical AC waveform is zero.
6. The effective voltage compares waveforms to DC voltage on an equivalent power basis. Since power is a nonlinear quantity the average value of a waveform is different from its effective value.
7. Voltage generators are based on relative motion between a magnetic field and a coil of wire. Faraday's law relates the quantities which determine the output of the voltage generator.
8. In an AC generator the voltage is delivered to a load through slip rings. In a DC generator the commutator reverses the output polarity on alternate halves of each rotation.
9. Motors use electrical energy to produce torque. Torque is determined by magnetic flux intensity and armature current.
10. AC motors can be either induction or conduction motors; DC motors must be conduction motors.

Questions

1. What is the difference between DC and pulsating DC?
2. How can an oscilloscope be used to find current?
3. How is an oscilloscope used to find PRF?
4. What is the difference between pulsating DC and AC?
5. What is the difference between PRF and frequency?
6. How is the average value of a quantity which varies with time determined?
7. What is the difference between average and effective value?
8. Explain why the average value of any symmetrical AC waveform is zero.
9. What is the principle of voltage generators?
10. Why is the rotor the armature in a DC generator, while in an AC generator the stator is the armature?
11. How does a commutator convert AC into pulsating DC?
12. What is the difference between an induction and a conduction motor?
13. Why must all DC motors be conduction type?
14. What factors termine motor torque?

Problems

1. The voltage shown in Fig. 6.23 is connected across a 50-Ω resistor. Determine the instantaneous power at $t = 0$, $t = 1$ msec, and $t = 2$ msec.
2. Determine the PRF of the triangular waveform in Fig. 6.23.

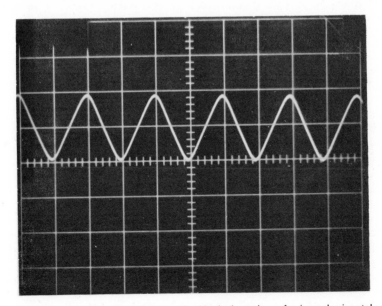

6.23 Voltage waveform for Problem 1. Vertical scale = 1 v/cm; horizontal scale = 1 msec/cm.

3. The waveform shown in Fig. 6.5 is connected across a 100-Ω resistor. Find (a) $p(t = 1\ \text{msec})$ and (b) $p(t = 3\ \text{msec})$.

4. A sinusoidal AC voltage has $V_{max} = 50$ volts. Find V_{min} and V_{p-p}.

5. In the United States the powerline frequency is 60 Hz. Find the period.

6. Assuming that the voltage of Problem 5 is 0 at $t = 0$, how long will it take to reach (a) V_{max} and (b) V_{min}?

7. What is the radian frequency of the U.S. powerline frequency?

8. Compute the average value of the sawtooth voltage shown in Fig. 6.24.

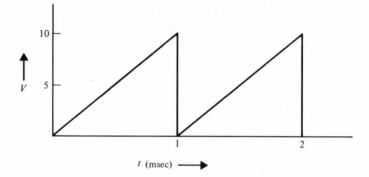

6.24   Voltage waveform for Problem 8.

9. The powerline V_{rms} in the United States is nominally 115 V. Find V_{p-p}.

10. What must be the peak-to-peak voltage of a sinusoidal AC which can deliver the same power as a 1.5-volt battery?

11. Compute the average and effective voltage of the waveform shown in Fig. 6.25.

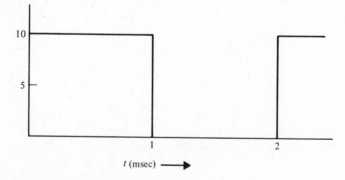

6.25   Voltage waveform for Problem 11.

12. A one-magnet AC generator has a coil with 300 turns and the magnetic flux is 1.5×10^{-2} units. How fast should the shaft rotate to generate 135 volts?

13. What is the frequency of the generator in Problem 12?

14. How fast must the shaft in Problem 13 rotate if the generated frequency is to be 60 Hz? What will be the generated voltage in this case?

15. A two-magnet DC generator is to generate 115 volts. The magnetic flux is 1.2×10^{-2} units. How many turns should the armature have if the rotor turns at 1800 rpm?

16. Find the frequency of the pulsating DC of the generator described in Problem 15.

17. A $\frac{1}{20}$-hp clock motor operates at 60 rpm. What torque is developed to operate the clock mechanism?

18. If the clock motor in Problem 17 is connected to a 115-volt source, what current is drawn, assuming no losses?

19. An electric drill must supply 2.0 ft-lb of torque when operating at 1800 rpm. What must be the motor horsepower?

20. What current will the motor in Problem 19 draw when operating from a 115-volt source?

Chapter 7 Alternating Current Fundamentals

7.1 Introduction

In this chapter components other than resistors are introduced and the effect of varying voltages on such components is investigated. The relationship between such components and voltages to previously discussed equations also will be treated.

7.2 Capacitors

A **capacitor** is formed by separating two metal plates by an insulator, as shown in Fig. 7.1. In the case of capacitors the insulator is called a **dielectric.** Air, mica, paper and Teflon are examples of capacitor dielectrics. Since the dielectric is an insulator, no current can flow through a capacitor.

However, an interesting effect occurs when a capacitor is connected across a variable DC voltage source. The capacitor is in parallel with the voltage source. Thus as the source voltage is varied the capacitor voltage must follow the source voltage. The same condition results if we use a

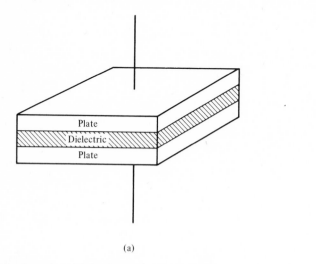

(a)   (b)

7.1   Capacitor. (a) Configuration. (b) Symbol.

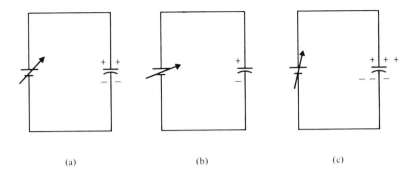

7.2   Capacitor voltage follows source voltage. (a) Voltage. (b) Lower voltage. (c) Higher voltage.

resistor in place of the capacitor, but there is an important difference. In the case of the resistor a current results in accordance with Ohm's law. In the case of the capacitor no current can flow since the dielectric is an insulator. Yet the capacitor voltage must follow the source voltage because this is a parallel circuit.

The voltage across the capacitor plates appears as a charge build-up. As shown in Fig. 7.2, higher voltage results in more charge and lower voltage results in less charge. This follows the initial discussion of voltage presented in Chapter 1, where voltage was defined as joules per coulomb or work per unit charge. Thus as source voltage changes, the amount of charge on the capacitor plates changes.

As the source voltage increases, the capacitor plate connected to the positive side of the voltage source becomes more positively charged. A decrease in source voltage results in a decrease in charge build-up. Thus as the source voltage decreases, charge flows from the capacitor plate back to the voltage source. In fact, it is observed that **the charge stored on the capacitor plates is directly proportional to the applied voltage.** The constant of proportionality that makes this statement into an equation is **capacitance** (C):

$$Q = CV \qquad\qquad (7.1a)$$

The dimensions of capacitance can be determined by solving Eq. 7.1a for C:

$$C = \frac{Q}{V} = \frac{\text{coulombs}}{\text{volt}} \qquad\qquad (7.1b)$$

A coulomb per volt is called a **farad** (F) in honor of Michael Faraday, who worked on electricity in England during the mid 1800's.

A farad of capacitance is an extremely large unit. In fact, a one farad air dielectric capacitor whose plates were 1 cm apart would be approximately

100 stories high and 2300 miles long. Typically, practical values of capacitance are expressed in microfarads (μF) which are a millionth (10^{-6}) of a farad, and picofarads (pF), which are equal to 10^{-12} F.

Example 7.1

It is observed that when the voltage across a certain capacitor is 100 volts, the stored charge is 0.0012 coulomb. Determine the capacitance.

Solution Step 1.   From Eq. 7.1b:

$$C = \frac{Q}{V}$$

Step 2.   Using the given data,

$$C = \frac{1.2 \times 10^{-3}}{10^2}$$

$$= 1.2 \times 10^{-5}$$

$$= 12 \times 10^{-6}$$

$$= 12 \ \mu F$$

In the case of a resistor, the resistance value depends on geometry and a property of the material (resistivity). A similar situation exists for a capacitor. The actual value depends on geometry and a property of the dielectric called the **dielectric constant** (κ):

$$C = \kappa \frac{A}{d} \tag{7.2}$$

is the relationship for a parallel plate capacitor, where A is the area of one of the plates and d is the distance between the plates (i.e., the thickness of the dielectric) in centimeters. Table 7.1 lists dielectric constants of some important materials.

Table 7.1   Typical Dielectric Constants

Material	κ (F/cm)
Air	8.85×10^{-14}
Ceramic	6.65×10^{-10}
Insulating oil	3.54×10^{-13}
Mica	4.42×10^{-13}
Paper	2.21×10^{-13}
Teflon	1.77×10^{-13}

Example 7.2

Determine the capacitance of a ceramic capacitor. The rectangular plates are 2 cm wide by 3 cm long. The ceramic is 0.001 cm thick.

Solution Step 1.   From the given data,

$$d = 10^{-3} \text{ cm}$$

$$A = 3 \times 2 = 6 \text{ cm}^2$$

Step 2.   From Eq. 7.2,

$$C = \kappa \frac{A}{d}$$

$$= 6.65 \times 10^{-10} \frac{6}{10^{-3}}$$

$$= 39.9 \times 10^{-7}$$

$$= 3.99 \ \mu\text{F}$$

The knowledge which we have already acquired about series and parallel circuits can be used to determine how capacitors combine in series and also in parallel. Figure 7.3 (a) shows a series circuit consisting of a voltage source

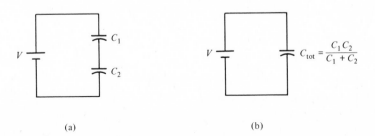

(a)   (b)

7.3   Combining capacitors in series. (a) Actual circuit. (b) Equivalent circuit.

and two capacitors. The Kirchhoff's voltage law statement for this circuit is

$$V = V_{C_1} + V_{C_2} \tag{7.3a}$$

If Eq. 7.1a is solved for the voltage across a capacitor,

$$V = \frac{Q}{C} \tag{7.1c}$$

This statement allows us to replace the voltages in Eq. 7.3a with their corresponding charge-to-capacitance ratios:

$$\frac{Q_T}{C_T} = \frac{Q_1}{C_1} + \frac{Q_2}{C_2} \tag{7.3b}$$

Since we have a series circuit the charge must be the same throughout the circuit:

$$Q_T = Q_1 = Q_2 = Q \tag{7.4a}$$

When this statement is used in Eq. 7.3b we get

$$\frac{\not{Q}}{C_T} = \frac{\not{Q}}{C_1} + \frac{\not{Q}}{C_2}$$

or
$$\tag{7.3c}$$

$$\frac{1}{C_T} = \frac{1}{C_1} + \frac{1}{C_2}$$

$$C_T = \frac{C_1 C_2}{C_1 + C_2}$$

This is the same relationship as was developed for resistors in parallel; that is, **capacitors connected in series combine the same way as resistors connected in parallel.**

Example 7.3

For the circuit shown in Fig. 7.3 (a), $C_1 = 1\ \mu F$, $C_2 = 2\ \mu F$, and $V = 30$ volts. Find (a) the total capacitance; (b) the voltage across each capacitor.

Solution Part (a) Step 1.   From the given data,

$$C_1 = 1 \times 10^{-6}\ F \qquad C_2 = 2 \times 10^{-6}\ F$$

Step 2.   From Eq. 7.3c,

$$C_T = \frac{C_1 C_2}{C_1 + C_2}$$

$$= \frac{1 \times 10^{-6} \times 2 \times 10^{-6}}{3 \times 10^{-6}}$$

$$= 0.67\ \mu F$$

Part (b) Step 1.   Use this total of C_T to find

$$Q = C_T V$$

$$= 0.67 \times 10^{-6} \times 3 \times 10^{1}$$

$$= 2 \times 10^{-5}\ \text{coulomb}$$

Step 2.   Since this is a series circuit the charge is everywhere the same:

$$Q = Q_1 = C_1 V_1$$
$$2 \times 10^{-5} = 10^{-6} V_1$$
$$V_1 = \frac{2 \times 10^{-5}}{10^{-6}}$$
$$= 20 \text{ volts}$$

Step 3.   Similarly,

$$Q = C_2 V_2$$
$$2 \times 10^{-5} = 2 \times 10^{-6} V_2$$
$$V_2 = \frac{2 \times 10^{-5}}{2 \times 10^{-6}}$$
$$= 10 \text{ volts}$$

Step 4.   As a check,

$$V_T \overset{?}{=} V_1 + V_2$$
$$30 = 20 + 10$$
$$30 = 30 \quad \checkmark$$

We can also determine how capacitors in parallel combine by using our previous knowledge and the available information. In a parallel capacitor situation the total stored charge is the sum of the charges on the individual capacitors. This statement, combined with the fact that the voltage across parallel components is equal, leads to

$$C_T = C_1 + C_2 \tag{7.4b}$$

as the condition for capacitors in parallel. This is illustrated in Fig. 7.4. Of course it is also possible to have capacitors connected in series-parallel configurations. Such a circuit is handled in a manner similar to series-

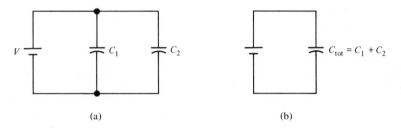

(a)   (b)

7.4   Combining capacitors in parallel. (a) Actual circuit. (b) Equivalent circuit.

parallel resistor circuits. Basically, we first reduce the circuit to a simple series circuit and then work back to the actual circuit.

Figure 7.5 shows several types of capacitors.

7.5 Typical capacitors. (*Courtesy of P. R. Mallory & Co., Inc.*)

7.3   Current in a Capacitive Circuit

Although no current can flow through a capacitor, we have seen that the charge on the capacitor plates changes whenever the applied voltage changes. Thus during the time that a capacitor voltage changes, charge flows in the wires which connect the capacitor to the voltage source. A flow of charge constitutes current, so we have a situation in which wires in series with the capacitor are passing a current and at the same time no current can flow through the capacitor.

In the case of resistive circuits, if current flows in any part of a series circuit, current must flow through the entire series circuit. In fact, the current is the same throughout a series resistive circuit. Capacitive circuits, as we have just seen, are quite different. The wire in series with a capacitor can carry current while the capacitor itself can never pass current since the dielectric is an insulator.

From the standpoint of circuit analysis it is convenient to ascribe the same characteristics to series and parallel circuits regardless of whether we are considering resistors or capacitors. That is, we would like to say that the current is the same everywhere in any type of series circuit, total current is the sum of the individual currents in any type of parallel circuit, and so on. For this reason we make use of a mythical quantity called **displacement current.** Displacement current is the current which would need to flow through the dielectric so that the current in the connecting wires would appear to have a complete path. This is illustrated in Fig. 7.6.

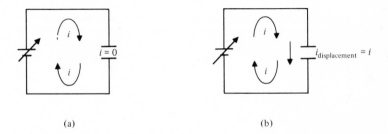

(a)   (b)

7.6 Notion of displacement current. (a) Actual condition. (b) "Equivalent" circuit using displacement current.

We should keep in mind that the concept of displacement current is a mathematical convenience which permits us to retain the notion of a complete path for current flow. Using displacement current the description of current flow in a capacitive circuit is as follows:

1. As the source voltage increases, current flows from the positive terminal of the voltage source through the connecting wire of the positive plate of the capacitor.
2. A displacement current which has the same value as in step 1 "flows" through the capacitor dielectric.
3. This same value flows from the negative plate of the capacitor through the connecting wire to the negative terminal of the voltage source.
4. This same value of current also flows through the voltage source and out of the positive terminal.

Thus we see that with the notion of displacement current we can continue to think in terms of a complete path for current flow even though this is not actually the case.

It is necessary to determine the value of current that flows in a capacitive circuit. The basic relationship between charge, capacitance, and voltage (Eq. 7.1a) is the starting point:

$$Q = CV$$

During the time (t) that the voltage changes, we have seen that there is a change in charge. When this condition is combined with Eq. 7.1a,

$$\frac{Q}{t} = C\frac{V}{t} \tag{7.5a}$$

It is convenient to describe this condition in terms of final and initial values during the time that there is a voltage change:

$$\frac{Q_f - Q_i}{t_f - t_i} = C\frac{V_f - V_i}{t_f - t_i} \tag{7.5b}$$

where f and i refer to final and initial values. The left-hand side of Eqs. 7.5a and 7.5b is charge per second. This is the basic definition of current. Thus:

$$i = C\frac{V_f - V_i}{t_f - t_i} \tag{7.5c}$$

This equation allows us to predict the current in a capacitive circuit. In fact, Eq. 7.5c is even correct when the applied voltage happens to be DC. In a DC situation the final and initial values of voltage are the same, so $V_f - V_1$ must be zero. Since the right-hand side of Eq. 7.5c is zero, the left-hand side must also be zero.

Conclusion: **No current flows in a capacitor when DC voltage is used.** This is a conclusion which we had already reached based on the previous description of the conditions under which charge would flow in a capacitive circuit. As we have just seen, Eq. 7.5b verifies this conclusion. Example 7.4 illustrates how current in a capacitive circuit is determined.

Example 7.4
The voltage shown in Fig. 7.7 is connected across a 1-μF capacitor. Determine the current in this circuit.

Solution Step 1. From the given data $C = 1\ \mu$F.

$$i = C\frac{V_f - V_i}{t_f - t_i} = 10^{-6}\frac{V_f - V_i}{t_f - t_i}$$

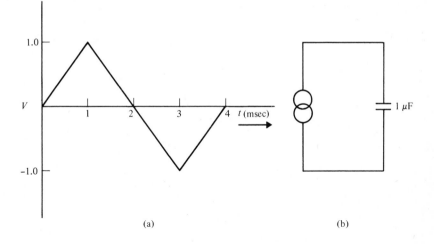

(a)   (b)

7.7   Conditions for Example 7.4. (a) Voltage waveform. (b) Circuit.

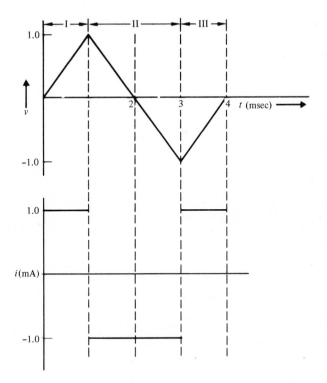

7.8   Voltage and current, v and i, in a capacitive circuit.

Step 2.   It is convenient to divide this waveform into three regions as shown in Fig. 7.8:

In region I: $V_f = 1$ volt, $V_i = 0$ volt, $t_f = 10^{-3}$ sec, and $t_1 = 0$ sec. Therefore

$$i_1 = 10^{-6}\frac{1-0}{10^{-3}-0}$$

$$= 10^{-3}\,\text{Amp.}$$

$$= 1\,\text{mA.}$$

Step 3.   In region II; $V_f = -1$ volt, $V_1 = 1$ volt, $t_f = 3 \times 10^{-3}$ sec, and $t_i = 1 \times 10^{-3}$ sec. Therefore

$$i_{II} = 10^{-6}\frac{-1-(+1)}{3 \times 10^{-3} - 1 \times 10^{-3}}$$

$$= -10^{-3}\,\text{Amp.}$$

$$= -1\,\text{mA.}$$

Step 4.   In region III: $V_f = 0$ volt, $V_i = -1$ volt, $t_f = 4 \times 10^{-3}$ sec, and $t_i = 3 \times 10^{-3}$ sec. Therefore

$$i_{III} = 10^{-6}\frac{0-(-1)}{4 \times 10^{-3} - 3 \times 10^{-3}}$$

$$= 10^{-3}\,\text{Amp.}$$

$$= 1\,\text{mA.}$$

By comparing the voltage and current waveforms shown in Fig. 7.8 we observe several interesting features:
1. The current and voltage waveforms are not similar. In fact, the current is constant while the voltage varies.
2. During a positive voltage portion it is possible to have negative current (first part of region II of Fig. 7.8, for example).
3. During a negative voltage portion it is possible to have positive current (region III of Fig. 7.8, for example).

These results are quite consistent with the capacitor current equation (Eq. 7.5c):
1. The voltage and current are not similar because **capacitor current depends on the change in voltage** and not on the value of voltage.
2. Since current depends on voltage change, current will be negative if V_f is less than V_i, even though both values are positive.
3. Similarly, even when voltage is negative current will be positive if V_f is less negative than V_i.

Another method of explaining these relationships between capacitor current and voltage is in terms of our initial description of capacitor action. The only time current can flow in a capacitive circuit is when voltage is changing, because the dielectric does not pass current. During the period that the source voltage is increasing, charge flows from the positive source terminal toward the capacitor. During the period that the source voltage is decreasing, charge flows from the capacitor to the positive terminal of the voltage source. This is a negative current.

There is a reason for current behaving differently in a capacitive circuit than in a resistive circuit. Current in a resistive circuit is in accordance with Ohm's law, which depends on voltage. Current in a capacitive circuit is determined by the capacitor current equation, which depends on a voltage change.

7.4   Inductors

The fact that a magnetic field exists around a wire which carries current has already been mentioned in connection with meter movements, motors, and generators. If we form a piece of wire into a coil, as shown in Fig. 7.9, we

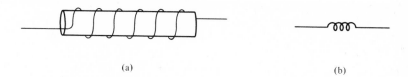

(a)   (b)

7.9   An inductor. (a) Configuration. (b) Symbol.

concentrate the magnetic field. Such a device is called an **inductor. An inductor is a component which stores energy in a magnetic field** just as **a capacitor is a component which stores energy in an electric field.** There is a very important difference in the manner in which inductors and capacitors store energy. In the case of an inductor the magnetic field vanishes when the current through the wire ceases. A capacitor, on the other hand, continues to store charge after the source voltage is removed.

In Fig. 7.10 an ideal inductor is connected to a variable voltage source. An ideal inductor has no resistance; of course it is not possible to form a coil out

7.10   Current in an ideal inductor.

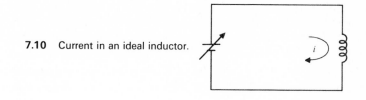

of wire which has no resistance at all. It is possible, however, to build inductors which have very little resistance and thus approximate ideal inductors. Since we are considering ideal inductors there is no Ohm's-law voltage drop across an inductor because R is zero; that is, there is no DC voltage across an inductor.

Consider what happens when the source voltage across the inductor varies. When the source voltage increases, the magnetic field around the inductor also increases. The direction of the magnetic field is such that it tends to oppose any change in current. As the source voltage decreases, the magnetic field releases some of its energy. In this case current flows back to the source voltage.

There will be a voltage drop across an inductor only when the current through the inductor is changing. The unit of inductance (L) is the henry (H), in honor of Joseph Henry, an American who worked in the field of electricity during the middle of the last century. A 1-H inductor is such that a current which changes at the rate of 1 Amp/sec will produce a voltage drop of 1 V across the inductor:

$$1 \text{ H} = \frac{1 \text{ V}}{1 \text{ Amp/sec}}$$

or   (7.6a)

$$L = \frac{v}{(i_f - i_i)/(t_f - t_i)}$$

This statement may be solved for voltage:

$$v = L \frac{i_f - i_i}{t_f - t_i} \qquad \text{(7.6b)}$$

Equation 7.6b is the inductor voltage equation, just as Eq. 7.5c is the capacitor current equation. Observe that in both cases something must vary with time for any effect to be noticed. However, the roles are reversed: In the case of a capacitor there is no current unless voltage changes with time; in the case of an inductor there is no voltage unless current changes with time.

Example 7.5

A trapezoidal current waveform as shown in Fig. 7.11 (a) is connected to a 50-mH inductor. Determine the voltage versus time.

Solution Step 1.   For the current waveform shown it is convenient to consider three distinct regions, as shown in Fig. 7.11 (a).

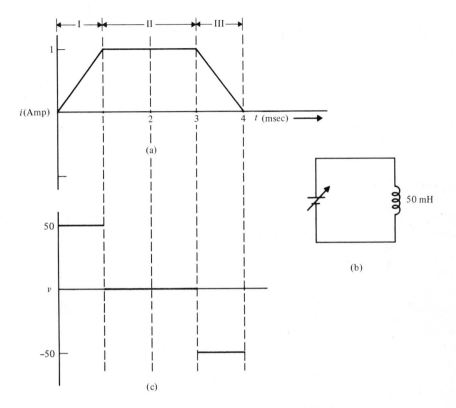

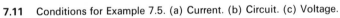

7.11   Conditions for Example 7.5. (a) Current. (b) Circuit. (c) Voltage.

Step 2.   From the given data $L = 50 \times 10^{-3}$ H:

$$v = L\frac{i_f - i_i}{t_f - t_i}$$

$$= 50 \times 10^{-3}\frac{i_f - i_i}{t_f - t_i}$$

Step 3.   In region I: $i_f = 1$ Amp, $i_i = 0$ Amp, $t_f = 10^{-3}$ sec, $t_i = 0$ sec.

$$v = 50 \times 10^{-3}\frac{1 - 0}{10^{-3} - 0}$$

$$= 50 \text{ volts}$$

Step 4.   In region II: $i_f = 1$ Amp, $i_i = 1$ Amp, $t_f = 3 \times 10^{-3}$ sec, and $t_i = 1 \times 10^{-3}$ sec.

$$v = 50 \times 10^{-3}\frac{1 - 1}{3 \times 10^{-3} - 1 \times 10^{-3}}$$

$$= 0 \text{ volts}$$

Step 5.   In region III: $i_f = 0$ Amp, $i_i = 1$ Amp, $t_f = 4 \times 10^{-3}$ sec, $t_i = 3 \times 10^{-3}$ sec.

$$v = 50 \times 10^{-3} \frac{0 - 1}{4 \times 10^{-3} - 3 \times 10^{-3}}$$

$$= -50 \text{ volts}$$

Step 6.   The resultant voltage waveform is shown in Fig. 7.11 (c).

This basic technique for determining the voltage across an inductor is thus seen to be quite similar to that used for finding the current through a capacitor; that is, the waveform is divided into convenient regions and the appropriate formula is used. The important distinction has already been mentioned: In a capacitor voltage change determines current and in an inductor current change determines voltage.

We have already seen that for both resistors and capacitors, these values are determined by the geometry of the component and also by a property of the material. For the resistor the property is resistivity and for the capacitor the property is dielectric constant. A similar condition applies to inductors. The material on which the coil is wound is called the core. The property of the core material is called permeability (μ). Permeability is the ability of a material to sustain a magnetic field. Table 7.2 lists some permeabilities of interest.

Table 7.2   Some Typical Permeabilities

Material	Permeability, μ (H/cm)
Air	1.26×10^{-8}
Alnico	1.5×10^{-4}
Iron	1.6×10^{-5}
Steel	5.0×10^{-5}

The geometric factors which affect inductance are the length (l) in centimeters, the cross-sectional area (A) in square centimeters and the number of turns (N) in the coil. The inductance is given by

$$L = \mu \frac{N^2 A}{l} \tag{7.7}$$

Example 7.6 illustrates how inductance is determined.

Example 7.6

A coil with an iron core is 1 cm in diameter and 5 cm long. If the coil has 200 turns of wire, what is the inductance?

Solution Step 1.   Use the diameter to determine the area:

$$A = \frac{\pi}{4} d^2$$

$$= \frac{\pi}{4} 1^2$$

$$= 0.785 \text{ cm}^2$$

Step 2.   The other necessary data are also given: $l = 5$ cm, $N = 200$ turns, and, from Table 7.2,

$$\mu_{\text{iron}} = 1.6 \times 10^{-5} \text{ H/cm}$$

Step 3.   Thus Eq. 7.7 is directly applicable:

$$L = \mu \frac{N^2 A}{l}$$

$$= 1.6 \times 10^{-5} \frac{(2 \times 10^2)^2 \times 0.785}{5} = 0.1 \text{ H}$$

$$= 100 \text{ mH}   \text{(millihenries)}$$

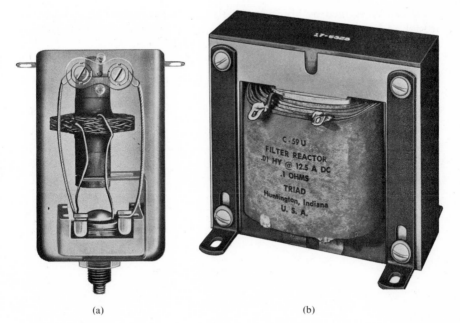

(a)   (b)

7.12   Practical inductors. (a) Powdered iron core, variable. (*Courtesy of T. W. Miller Co.*) (b) Steel core, fixed value. (*Courtesy of Triad-Utrad Distributor, Inc.*)

Practical values of inductance range from microhenries to tens of henries. Figure 7.12 shows two actual inductors. In Fig. 7.12 (a) the powdered iron core can be inserted into the coil to various lengths. In this way the effective value of permeability depends on the ratio of air to iron core and thus the inductance is variable. Inductors of this type are used in adjusting high-frequency circuits. Figure 7.12 (b) shows a steel-core, fixed inductor. This type is used in DC power supplies which operate from an AC line.

It is possible to combine inductors by connecting them in either series or parallel. If inductors are connected in series, the total inductance is the sum of the individual inductors:

$$L_T = L_1 + L_2 \qquad (7.8a)$$

Equation 7.8a can be verified by observing that in a series circuit the change in current must be the same throughout the circuit. This statement, combined with Kirchhoff's voltage law, is all that is needed to verify Eq. 7.8a.

For two inductors connected in parallel the total inductance is equal to the product of the inductors divided by the sum:

$$L_T = \frac{L_1 L_2}{L_1 + L_2} \qquad (7.8b)$$

This can be verified by observing that in a parallel circuit the voltages are equal and that the total change in current is the sum of the individual changes. This is actually Kirchhoff's current law.

Equations 7.8a and 7.8b assume that there is no interaction between the magnetic fields of the two inductors. If the magnetic fields do interact, then mutual inductance (M) will have to be considered. Interaction of magnetic fields is illustrated in Fig. 7.13. If the magnetic fields are in a

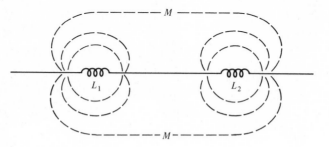

7.13   Interaction of magnetic fields

direction to aid each other, the mutual inductance will increase the total inductance. If the magnetic fields are in a direction to oppose each other, mutual inductance will decrease the total inductance. For inductors in series,

$$L_T = L_1 + L_2 \pm 2M$$

A plus sign before $2M$ indicates that the magnetic fields aid each other. A minus sign indicates that the magnetic fields oppose each other.

Example 7.7

A 100-mH inductor is connected in series with another inductor. When the magnetic fields add, the total inductance is 250 mH. If one coil is reversed so that the magnetic fields oppose, the total inductance becomes 200 mH. Find (a) the inductance of the second inductor, and (b) the mutual inductance.

Solution Part (a) Step 1.   For the flux aiding condition,

$$L_T = L_1 + L_2 + 2M$$
$$0.25 = 0.1 + L_2 + 2M$$

(1)

Step 2.   For the flux opposing condition,

$$L_T = 0.1 + L_2 - 2M$$
$$0.2 = 0.1 + L_2 - 2M$$

(2)

Step 3.   Add (1) and (2) to find L_2:

$$0.25 = 0.1 + L_2 + 2M$$
$$0.20 = 0.1 + L_2 - 2M$$

$$\overline{}$$

$$0.45 = 0.2 + 2L_2$$
$$2L_2 = 0.25 \text{ H}$$
$$L_2 = 125 \text{ mH}$$

Part (b) Step 1.   Since L_2 has been determined either (1) or (2) may be used to determine M.

Step 2.   Using (1):

$$0.25 = 0.1 + 0.125 + 2M$$
$$= 0.225 + 2M$$
$$2M = 0.025$$
$$M = 12.5 \text{ mH}$$

A very important application of mutual inductance is the **transformer.** Figure 7.14 shows a transformer. A transformer is constructed by winding two (or more) coils on a common core. Since the core is common, it is a reasonable assumption to state that all the magnetic flux from one winding

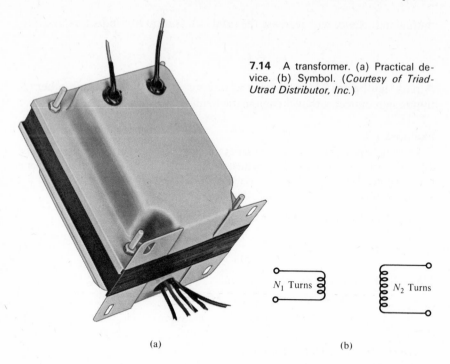

7.14 A transformer. (a) Practical device. (b) Symbol. (*Courtesy of Triad-Utrad Distributor, Inc.*)

N_1 Turns

N_2 Turns

(a)   (b)

couples to the other winding. Combining this statement with Faraday's law (Eq. 6.10) allows us to determine how a transformer operates.

If a generator with voltage V_1 is connected to the transformer winding with N_1 turns, as shown in Fig. 7.15, we get Eq. 6.10:

$$V_1 = N_1 \frac{\phi_f - \phi_i}{t_f - t_i} \tag{7.9a}$$

(which will be referred to as Eq. 7.9a in this chapter) where ϕ is the magnetic flux.

Since we have said that the flux is the same in both windings and a changing flux will generate a voltage across the other winding,

$$V_2 = N_2 \frac{\phi_f - \phi_i}{t_f - t_i} \tag{7.9b}$$

If we divide Eq. 7.9a by Eq. 7.9b:

$$\frac{V_1}{V_2} = \frac{N_1}{N_2} \tag{7.9c}$$

Equation 7.9c shows that the voltage across a winding is related to the number

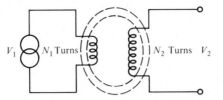

7.15   Analyzing transformer action.

of turns in the winding. Thus if N_2 is greater than N_1 the output voltage will be greater than the input voltage (step-up transformer). Similarly, if N_2 is less than N_1 the output voltage will be less than the input voltage (step-down transformer). Both of these types have important applications.

Example 7.8

A transformer with 100 turns on the input side is connected to a 10-volt generator. If the desired output voltage is 50 volts how many turns must the output winding have?

Solution Step 1.   From the given data,

$$V_1 = 10 \qquad V_2 = 50 \qquad N_1 = 100$$

Step 2.   Only N_2 is unknown and Eq. 7.9c is directly applicable,

$$\frac{V_1}{V_2} = \frac{N_1}{N_2}$$

$$\frac{10}{50} = \frac{100}{N_2}$$

$$N_2 = 500 \text{ turns}$$

Example 7.8 shows that a transformer may be used as a voltage amplifier. However, at best the output power of a transformer will almost equal the input power:

$$P_{out} \simeq P_{in} \tag{7.10}$$

so that a transformer cannot amplify current and voltage simultaneously.

Example 7.9

If the input current in Example 7.8 is 1 Amp. What current would flow in a resistor connected across the transformer output terminals?

Solution Step 1.   The data are $V_1 = 10$ volts, $I_1 = 1$ Amp, and $V_2 = 50$ volts.

Step 2. Equation 7.10 is directly applicable:

$$P_{\text{out}} \simeq P_{\text{in}}$$
$$V_2 I_2 = V_1 I_1$$
$$I_2 = 0.2 \text{ Amp.}$$

It should also be recalled that no voltage will exist across an inductor unless the current is changing (Eq. 7.6b). Therefore unless a varying current flows through the input side of a transformer, there will not be an output voltage. Thus, **a transformer cannot operate from a DC source.**

7.5 Transients

Thus far we have discussed ideal capacitor and inductor circuits. One reason is that we have not considered the resistance of the connecting wires. Since the resistance in such cases is quite negligible, our calculations are accurate. However, if an actual resistor is used with a capacitor or inductor, our previous discussion must be modified to conform to observation.

Figure 7.16 shows a circuit in which a series combination of resistor and capacitor is connected to a battery. This appears to be a "pure" DC circuit in which no current can flow. Although ultimately this will be the case, current will flow for some time after the switch is closed; that is, it takes time for the capacitor to charge up to the battery voltage. This can be seen from Kirchhoff's voltage law for the circuit in Fig. 7.16:

$$V_{\text{battery}} = V_R + V_C \qquad\qquad \textbf{(7.11a)}$$

Since there was no voltage across the capacitor prior to switch closure, there can be no voltage across the capacitor at the instant of switch closure; that is, at $t = 0$, $V_C = 0$. Therefore at $t = 0$:

$$V_{\text{battery}} = V_R \qquad\qquad \textbf{(7.11b)}$$

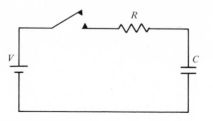

7.16   Resistor added to a capacitive circuit.

This means that at the instant of switch closure the entire battery voltage is across the resistor and the capacitor acts as a short circuit. As current flows through the resistor, charge builds up on the capacitor plates until V_C equals the battery voltage. When this occurs Eq. 7.11a becomes

$$V_{battery} = V_R + V_{battery}$$

or

(7.11c)

$$V_R = 0$$

that is, when the voltage across the capacitor equals the battery voltage, there is no voltage across the resistor. Since the voltage across the resistor is zero the current must be zero (Ohm's law).

Another way of saying the same thing is as follows: **In a series RC (resistor-capacitor) circuit current flows until the capacitor voltage equals the source voltage.** At this time the capacitor voltage exactly bucks the source voltage so that no further current flows. The time between switch closure and reaching the steady-state condition is called the **transient** time. Figure 7.17 (a) is an oscilloscope photograph of the current in an RC circuit. As predicted, the current is a maximum at $t = 0$ since the entire battery voltage is across the resistor. As time increases the current decreases since capacitor voltage [Fig. 7.17 (b)] is increasing. Finally, when the capacitor charges to the full battery voltage, the current drops to zero.

The equation for current in a series RC circuit is

$$i = \frac{V}{R}\varepsilon^{-t/RC}$$

(7.12)

where

V = applied voltage
R = resistance in ohms
C = capacity in farads
ε = base of natural logarithms $\simeq 2.72$
t = time in seconds

While we need greater mathematical background to derive Eq. 7.12, we can show that the RC product has the dimension of seconds:

1. From Ohm's law we have

$$R = \frac{V}{I}$$

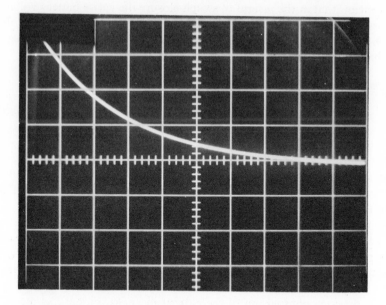

(a)

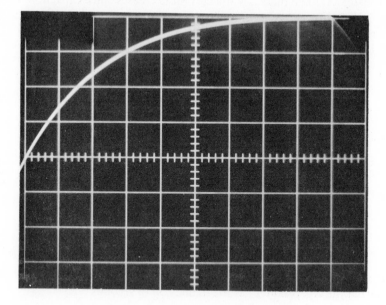

(b)

7.17   Transient in an *RC* circuit. (a) Current. (b) Capacitor voltage.

2. From the capacitor current equation (Eq. 7.5c)

$$C = i\frac{t_f - t_i}{v_f - v_i}$$

3. Thus the dimensions of RC are

$$RC = \frac{\cancel{V}}{\cancel{A}} \times \cancel{A}\frac{t_f - t_i}{\cancel{v_f - v_i}} = t_f - t_i = \text{seconds}$$

Example 7.10

A 10-μF capacitor connected in series with a 100-kΩ resistor is charged from a 100-volt DC source. Determine:

(a) The current at the instant of switch closure
(b) The current 1 sec after switch closure
(c) The capacitor voltage 1 sec after switch closure

Solution Part (a) Step 1.   Determine RC:

$$RC = 10^5 \times 10 \times 10^{-6}$$
$$= 1 \text{ sec}$$

Step 2.   Therefore, from Eq. 7.12,

$$i = \frac{V}{R}\varepsilon^{-t/RC}$$

$$= \frac{10^2}{10^5}\varepsilon^{-0/1}$$

$$\varepsilon^{-0} = 1$$

$$i(t = 0) = \frac{10^2}{10^5} \times 1$$

$$= 1 \text{ mA.}$$

Part (b) Step 1.

$$i = \frac{V}{R}\varepsilon^{-t/RC}$$

Step 2.   For $t = 1$ sec,

$$i(t = 1 \text{ sec}) = \frac{10^2}{10^5}\varepsilon^{-1/1}$$

$$= 10^{-3}\varepsilon^1$$

$$= 10^{-3} \times 0.368$$

$$= 0.368 \text{ mA.}$$

Part (c) Step 1.   From Part (b),

$$1(t = 1 \text{ sec}) = 0.368 \text{ mA}.$$

$$V_R(t = 1 \text{ sec}) = IR = 0.368 \times 10^{-3} \times 10^5$$

$$= 36.8 \text{ volts}$$

Step 2.   From Kirchhoff's voltage law for a series RC circuit (Eq. 7.11):

$$V_{\text{battery}} = V_R + V_C$$

At $t = 1$ sec,

$$100 = 36.8 + V_C$$

$$V_C(t = 1 \text{ sec}) = 63.2 \text{ volts}$$

We have already seen that the RC product has the dimension of seconds. RC is called the circuit **time constant.** Thus we say that the circuit in Example 7.10 has a 1-sec time constant. Similarly, a circuit consisting of a 1-μF capacitor and a 1-kΩ resistor would have a $(10^3 \times 10^{-6} = 10^{-3})$ 1-msec time constant, and so on. Table 7.3 shows how the ε^{-tRC} term of Eq. 7.12 varies as time increases.

Table 7.3   Some values of $\varepsilon^{-tR}C$

t (RC)	$\varepsilon^{-t/RC}$	$\varepsilon^{-t/RC}$ (evaluated)
0	ε^{-0}	1.000
1	ε^{-1}	0.368
2	ε^{-2}	0.135
3	ε^{-3}	0.050
4	ε^{-4}	0.018
5	ε^{-5}	0.007

Notice that at the end of five time constants, the current, although not zero, is less than 1% of its initial value. Thus we say that **at the end of five time constants the transient has ended and steady-state conditions exist.** A circuit which consists of a battery connected to an RC network has a steady-state condition of zero current. This is not the only circuit of interest. If, for example, the source voltage is pulsating DC or AC, there will be current under steady-state conditions. Also there will be a transient time which exists for five time constants, before steady-state conditions are established. Thus regardless of voltage waveform, **transient time is the interval between switch operation and attaining steady-state conditions.**

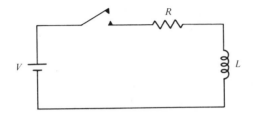

7.18 Series RL circuit.

A circuit consisting of a series RL combination as shown in Fig. 7.18 will also experience a transient condition upon switch closure. Since inductors and capacitors have different characteristics, the nature of the transient will be different. In an RL circuit, if there is no current prior to switch closure there will be no current at the instant of switch closure. At this instant the inductor acts like an open circuit. If there is no current there can be no voltage drop across the resistor (Ohm's law). Since there is no voltage across the resistor, the entire battery voltage appears across the inductor at the instant of switch closure (Kirchhoff's voltage law). At first it may seem odd that there can be voltage across an inductor even though there is no current. However, we must remember that the voltage across an inductor depends not on the value of current but on the change in current. At switch closure the current changes from zero current to some current value, and the change from nothing to something is indeed a dramatic change. After switch closure the current begins to increase and therefore a voltage appears across the resistor. As the voltage across the resistor increases the voltage across the inductor must decrease, so that at the end of the transient period there is no voltage across the inductor and the entire source voltage is across the resistor. This means that **the steady-state current condition in an RL circuit is one of maximum current.** In an RC circuit we saw the exact opposite. The steady-state current is zero. The equation which describes the current in a series RL circuit is

$$i = \frac{V}{R}(1 - \varepsilon^{-tR/L}) \qquad\qquad (7.13)$$

Example 7.11

A 10-Ω resistor and a 10-H inductor are connected in series to a 5-volt DC source. Determine (a) V_R and V_L at the instant of switch closure, and (b) V_R and V_L 2 sec after switch closure.

Solution Part (a) Step 1.

$$\frac{R}{L} = \frac{10}{10} = 1$$

For $t = 0$,

$$i = \frac{5}{10}(1 - \varepsilon^{-0 \times 1})$$

$$i(t = 0) = 0 \text{ Amp.}$$

Step 2. For this circuit Kirchhoff's voltage law is

$$V_{\text{battery}} = V_R + V_L$$

but at $t = 0$,

$$V_R = 0 \quad \text{since} \quad i = 0$$

At $t = 0$,

$$V_{\text{battery}} = V_L = 5 \text{ volts}$$

Part (b) Step 1.

$$i = \frac{V}{R}(1 - \varepsilon^{-tR/L})$$

At $t = 2$ sec,

$$i = \frac{5}{10}(1 - \varepsilon^{-2 \times 1})$$

$$= 0.5(1 - 0.135)$$

$$i(t = 2 \text{ sec}) = 0.433 \text{ Amp.}$$

Step 2. Therefore at $t = 2$ sec,

$$V_R = iR$$

$$= 0.433 \times 10$$

$$V_R(t = 2 \text{ sec}) = 4.33 \text{ volts}$$

Step 3. Again, using Kirchhoff's voltage law,

$$V_{\text{battery}} = V_R + V_L$$

At $t = 2$ sec,

$$5 = 4.33 + V_L$$

$$V_L = 0.67 \text{ volts}$$

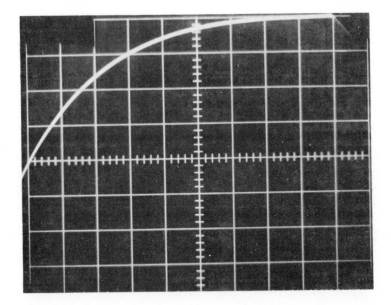

(a)

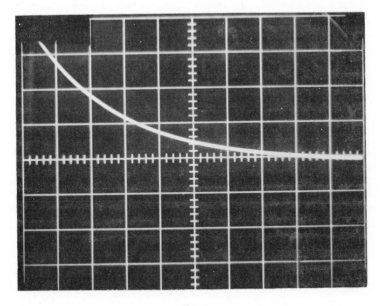

(b)

7.19   Transient in an *RL* circuit. (a) Current. (b) Inductor voltage.

Figure 7.19 shows the current and voltage across an inductor in an RL circuit. As predicted, the current is zero at $t = 0$ and becomes a maximum at the end of the transient time. Also we see that the voltage across the inductor is a maximum at $t = 0$ and goes to zero as the transient disappears.

7.6   Sinusoidal L and C Behavior

Thus far we have considered the behavior of inductors and capacitors to waveforms which are composed of straight lines. Other waveforms are also of interest. In particular, we are interested in sinusoidal voltages and currents. Strictly speaking, the inductor voltage equation (Eq. 7.6b) and the capacitor current equation (Eq. 7.5c) apply only to waveforms which are composed of straight lines.

Suppose we are interested in determining, say, the voltage across an inductor when a sinusoidal current, (where I_m is maximum current)

$$i_L = I_m \sin \omega t \qquad (7.14)$$

is applied. The best we can do with our available technique (Eq. 7.6b) is to approximate the correct voltage; that is, we can consider the sine wave shown in Fig. 7.20 (a) as consisting of a series of linear segments. These linear segments can then be used to find the voltage across the inductor as we have done in previous cases. This method is only as good as our approximation. If we use smaller and smaller linear segments our approximation will become increasingly accurate.

Using a more powerful technique than we have available, it turns out that the voltage across an inductor which results from a current given by Eq. 7.14 is

$$v_L = \omega L I_m \cos \omega t \qquad (7.15)$$

Comparing Eq. 7.15 with Eq. 7.14 we see that if the current is a sine wave the voltage will be a cosine wave. This is shown in Fig. 7.21. The difference between a sine wave and a cosine wave is a matter of 90°; that is, as shown in Fig. 7.21 at $t = 0$, the cosine is a maximum and the sine is zero. This difference of 90° will continue over the entire cycle. Since the inductor voltage is a cosine when the current is a sine we say that **in an inductor the voltage leads the current by**

$$v_L = \omega L I_m \sin \left(\omega t + \frac{\pi}{2} \right) \qquad (7.16)$$

For a resistor the ratio of voltage to current (ohms) is of interest. In the case of an inductor the ratio of voltage to current is also of interest. If we

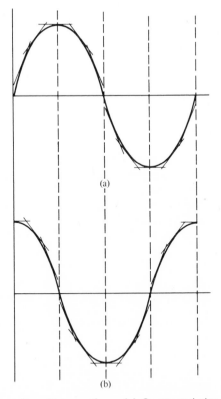

(a)

(b)

7.20 Approximating a sinusoidal waveform. (a) Segmented sine wave. (b) Resultant inductor voltage.

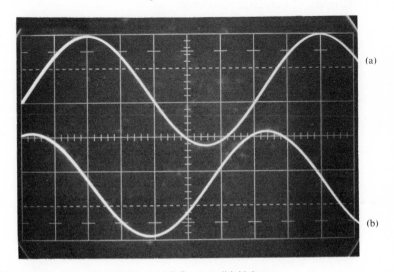

(a)

(b)

7.21   Inductor current and voltage. (a) Current. (b) Voltage.

divide Eq. 7.15 by Eq. 7.14,

$$\frac{v_L}{i_L} = \frac{\omega L I_m \cos \omega t}{I_m \sin \omega t} = \omega L \frac{\cos \omega t}{\sin \omega t} \qquad (7.17a)$$

Since Eq. 7.17a is a ratio of voltage to current, it must have the dimension of ohms. The ohms presented by an inductor are somewhat different from the ohms presented by a resistor. Equation 7.17a shows that **inductive ohms increase as frequency increases and ohms vary over the entire cycle.** Neither of these conditions is true for a resistor.

We know that the maximum value of $\sin \omega t$ is 1, as is the maximum value of $\cos \omega t$. Hence if $i_L = I_m \sin \omega t$, its maximum value is I_m. Similarly, the maximum value of v_L is $\omega L I_m$ (this is similar to Eq. 6.6b). This means that the maximum value of the ratio of Eq. 7.17a is

$$\frac{V_{L(\text{max})}}{I_{L(\text{max})}} = \frac{V_L}{I_L} = \frac{\omega L I_m}{I_m} = \omega L = X_L \qquad (7.17b)$$

In a linear resistor, current and voltage are proportional. But in an inductor, as we have seen in Fig. 7.21, the maximum values of voltage and current occur at slightly different times. Nevertheless Eq. 7.17b is correct. This is important since Eq. 7.17b resembles Ohm's law, since it is a ratio of voltage to current. Because ωL is a ratio of voltage to current it must be measured in ohms. But rather than call it resistance, we call it **inductive reactance** and label it X_L, where X stands for reactance and L indicates that we are talking about inductive reactance.

Example 7.12

At what frequency will a 1-H inductor have the inductive reactance equal to a 1000-Ω resistor?

Solution Step 1.   From the given data we have

$$X_L = 1000 \, \Omega$$

$$L = 1 \text{H}$$

Step 2.   By using Eq. 7.17b

$$X_L = \omega L$$

$$1000 = \omega \times 1$$

$$\omega = 1000$$

Step 3.   By using Eq. 6.6,

$$\omega = 2\pi f$$

$$2\pi f = 1000$$

$$f = \frac{1000}{2\pi}$$

$$= 159 \text{ Hz}$$

Equation 7.17b is also applicable to zero Hertz (i.e., DC). At this frequency $\omega = 0$ and thus $X_L = 0$. This is the same conclusion we came to earlier when an ideal inductor was discussed.

We also need to know the **capacitive reactance (X_c)** to a sinusoidal waveform. When the voltage across a capacitor is

$$v_C = V_m \sin \omega t \tag{7.18}$$

the current will then turn out to be

$$i = \omega C V_m \sin \omega t \tag{7.19}$$

Thus in a capacitor the current and voltage are also 90° apart, just as in an inductor. However, **in a capacitor the current leads the voltage** since the current depends on the cosine if the voltage is a sine. This is shown in Fig. 7.22.

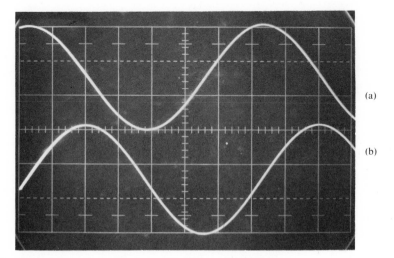

(a)

(b)

7.22   Capacitor current and voltage. (a) Current. (b) Voltage.

The capacitive reactance can be determined in a similar manner to that used to determine inductive reactance:

$$X_C = \frac{v_C}{i_C} \tag{7.20a}$$

Therefore

$$X_C = \frac{V_m \sin \omega t}{\omega C V_m \cos \omega t} = \frac{1}{\omega C} \frac{\sin \omega t}{\cos \omega t} \tag{7.20b}$$

If we again use the maximum values for $\sin \omega t$ and $\cos \omega t$ we obtain the capacitive reactance:

$$X_C = \frac{1}{\omega C} \tag{7.20c}$$

X_C depends on frequency just as X_L does, but with a most significant difference: **As frequency increases capacitive reactance decreases;** that is, as frequency increases the ohms presented by a capacitor decreases.

Example 7.13

    (a) At what frequency will a 1 μF capacitor have a capacitive reactance equal to a 200-ohm resistor?

    (b) What will be the capacitive reactance if this frequency is doubled?

Solution Part (a) Step 1.   From the given data $X_c = 2000 \, \Omega$ and $C = 1 \times 10^{-6}$ F.

Step 2. Therefore

$$X_C = \frac{1}{\omega C}$$

$$2000 = \frac{1}{\omega \times 10^{-6}}$$

$$\omega = \frac{1}{2 \times 10^{-3}} = 2\pi f$$

$$f = 79.5 \text{ Hz}$$

Part (b) Step 1.   In this case $f = 2 \times 79.5 = 159$ Hz.

Step 2.   Since

$$X_C = \frac{1}{\omega C} = \frac{1}{2\pi f c}$$

$$= \frac{1}{2\pi \times 159 \times 10^{-6}}$$

$$= 1000 \, \Omega$$

7.7   Sinusoidal Ohm's Law

Both X_L and X_C have the dimensions of ohms. Thus Ohm's law can be extended to include sinusoidal waveforms:

$$i_L = \frac{V_L}{X_L} \qquad (7.21a)$$

$$i_C = \frac{V_C}{X_C} \qquad (7.21b)$$

Example 7.14

A 1-H inductor is connected across a 10 V_{rms} generator. Find the current when the generator frequency is (a) 100 Hz; (b) 1 kHz; (c) 10 kHz.

Solution Part (a) Step 1. $X_L = \omega L = 2\pi f L = 2\pi f \times 1 = 6.28 f$

for 100 Hz. $X_L = 6.28 \times 10^2 \Omega$

Step 2.

$$I_L = \frac{V_L}{X_L}$$

$$= \frac{10}{6.28 \times 10^2}$$

$$= 15.9 \, mA_{rms}$$

Part (b) Step 1.   For 1 kHz,

$$X_L = 6.28 \times 10^3$$

Step 2.

$$I_L = \frac{V_L}{X_L}$$

$$= \frac{10}{6.28 \times 10^3}$$

$$= 1.59 \, mA_{rms}$$

Part (c) Step 1.   For 10 kHz,

$$X_L = 6.28 \times 10^4$$

Step 2.

$$I_L = \frac{V_L}{X_L}$$

$$= \frac{10}{6.28 \times 10^4}$$

$$= 0.159 \, \text{mA}_{\text{rms}}$$

Example 7.14 shows that if the voltage is kept constant but the frequency is varied, current through an inductor decreases as frequency increases; that is, **the higher the frequency, the more an inductor blocks current.** For this reason an inductor is often called a **choke.** Also since X_L is zero at DC (0 Hz) there will be no voltage drop across an inductor at DC.

Example 7.15

A 1-μF capacitor is connected across a 10-V_{rms} generator. Find the current when the generator frequency is (a) 100 Hz; (b) 1 kHz; (c) 10 kHz.

Solution Part (a) Step 1.

$$X_C = \frac{1}{\omega C} = \frac{1}{2\pi f C}$$

$$= \frac{1}{6.28 \times 10^2 \times 10^{-6}}$$

$$= 1.59 \times 10^3 \, \Omega$$

Step 2.

$$I_C = \frac{V}{X_C}$$

$$= \frac{10}{1.59 \times 10^3}$$

$$= 6.28 \, \text{mA}_{\text{rms}}$$

Part (b) Step 1.

$$X_C = \frac{1}{2\pi f C}$$

$$= \frac{1}{6.28 \times 10^3 \times 10^{-6}}$$

$$= 1.59 \times 10^2 \, \Omega$$

Step 2.

$$I_C = \frac{V}{X_C}$$

$$= \frac{10}{1.59 \times 10^2}$$

$$= 62.8 \text{ mA}_{\text{rms}}$$

Part (c) Step 1.

$$X_C = \frac{1}{2\pi f C}$$

$$= \frac{1}{6.28 \times 10^4 \times 10^{-6}}$$

$$= 15.9 \, \Omega$$

Step 2.

$$I_C = \frac{V}{X_C}$$

$$= \frac{10}{15.9}$$

$$= 628 \text{ mA.} = 0.628 \text{ Amp}_{\text{rms}}$$

Example 7.15 shows that if the voltage is kept constant but the frequency is varied, current through a capacitor increases as frequency increases. That is, **the higher the frequency the more a capacitor approaches a short circuit.**

Figure 7.23 shows the relationship between current and voltage in an inductor which has already been described. If we multiply the current waveform by the voltage waveform we get the power waveform. When the voltage and current are 90° apart **the power dissipated in an ideal inductor will be zero.** During half of the cycle the inductor will absorb power from the generator and store it in the magnetic field. However, during the other half of the cycle, the energy stored in the magnetic field will be returned to the generator. Similarly, a capacitor will store energy in an electrical field over half a cycle and return this energy during the other half-cycle. Thus, **the power dissipated in an ideal capacitor will be zero.**

Figure 7.24 (a) shows a series *RL* circuit connected to a generator. Since Kirchhoff's voltage law may be used, it must be true that the generator voltage is the sum of the voltages across the resistor and inductor. However, the **phase difference** between current and voltage in an inductor complicates the situation. This is a series circuit so that the current is the same throughout. In a resistor the voltage and current are in phase. Waveforms of the same frequency are **in phase** if their maximum, minimum, zero, and other values occur at the same time. If this is not the case the waveforms are **out of phase.**

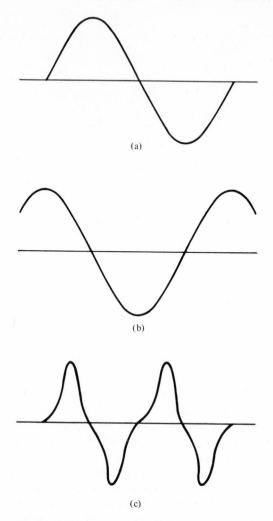

(a)

(b)

(c)

7.23   Determining power in an inductor. (a) Voltage. (b) Current. (c) Power.

In an inductor the voltage leads the current by 90° so that the voltage across the inductor is 90° ahead of the voltage across the resistor, as shown in Fig. 7.24 (b). Therefore the resistor and generator voltages must be added geometrically instead of algebraically. This is the same situation as occurs in adding the sides of a right triangle which are also 90° apart. That is,

$$V_{\text{gen}} = \sqrt{V_R^2 + V_L^2} \qquad\qquad \textbf{(7.22a)}$$

is the modified form of Kirchhoff's voltage law for sinusoidal RL circuits.

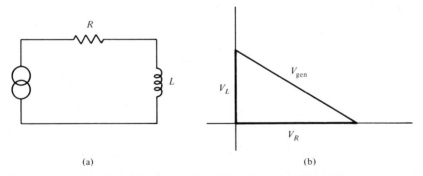

7.24   AC generator with series *RL* circuit. (a) Schematic. (b) Voltage diagram.

We are using the **Pythagorean theorem** for right triangles to add voltages.

Since inductive and resistive voltages are separated by 90°, resistance and inductive reactance must also be separated by 90°. R and X_L must also be added geometrically:

$$Z = \sqrt{R^2 + X_L^2} \qquad\qquad \text{(7.22b)}$$

The combination of resistive ohms and reactance (X) is called **impedance** (Z), so that Ohm's law becomes

$$I = \frac{V}{Z} = \frac{V}{\sqrt{R^2 + X_L^2}} \qquad\qquad \text{(7.22c)}$$

Notice that if X_L is zero, Eq. 7.22c reverts to the more familiar DC version of Ohm's law.

Example 7.16

For the circuit shown in Fig. 7.24, $V_{\text{gen}} = 50\ \text{V}_{\text{rms}}$, $X_L = 4\ \text{k}\Omega$, and $R = 3\ \text{k}\Omega$. Find V_R and V_L.

Solution Step 1.   Use Eq. 7.22b to find Z:

$$Z = \sqrt{R^2 + X_L^2}$$

Step 2.   Using the given data,

$$Z = \sqrt{(3 \times 10^3)^2 + (4 \times 10^3)^2} = 5 \times 10^3\ \Omega$$

Step 3.   Using Eq. 7.22c, find the current:

$$I = \frac{V}{Z}$$

$$= \frac{50}{5 \times 10^3} = 10\ \text{mA}_{\text{rms}}$$

Step 4.   Use Ohm's law to find V_R:

$$V_R = IR$$
$$= 10^{-2} \times 3 \times 10^3$$
$$= 30\ \text{V}_{\text{rms}}$$

Step 5.   Use Ohm's law to find V_L:

$$V_L = IX_L$$
$$= 10^{-2} \times 4 \times 10^3$$
$$= 40\ \text{V}_{\text{rms}}$$

Step 6.   As a check, use Kirchhoff's voltage law (Eq. 7.22a):

$$V_{\text{gen}} \overset{?}{=} \sqrt{V_R^2 + V_L^2}$$
$$50 = \sqrt{30^2 + 40^2}$$
$$= 50 \quad \checkmark$$

If we keep in mind that we are working with geometric rather than algebraic quantities when dealing with sinusoidal waveforms, all the properties of series and parallel circuits are still valid.

Figure 7.25 (a) shows a series RC circuit connected to a sinusoidal generator. Once more there is a 90° phase difference. This time the voltage across the capacitor is 90° behind the current through the capacitor. Since the current and voltage for a resistor are in phase, the voltage across the capacitor lags the voltage across the resistor by 90° as shown in Fig. 7.25 (b). In this case we get

$$V_{\text{gen}} = \sqrt{V_R^2 + (-V_C)^2} \tag{7.23a}$$

$$Z = \sqrt{R^2 + (-X_C)^2} \tag{7.23b}$$

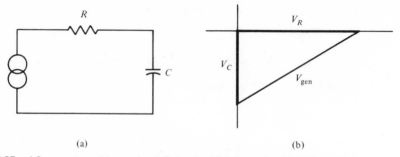

(a)   (b)

7.25   AC generator with a series RC circuit. (a) Schematic. (b) Voltage diagram.

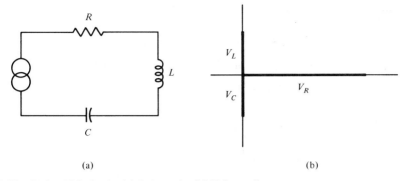

7.26 Series *RLC* circuit. (a) Schematic. (b) Voltage diagram.

The minus sign indicates that the capacitive voltage and capacitive reactance lag the resistive voltage and resistive ohms.

The voltage across an inductor leads the voltage across a resistor by 90°. The voltage across a capacitor lags the voltage across a resistor by 90°. Therefore, **there is a 180° difference between the voltage across an inductor and capacitor** in a circuit which contains *R*, *L*, and *C*. Such a circuit is shown in Fig. 7.26. Since there is a 180° difference between V_L and V_C there must also be a 180° difference between X_L and X_C so that the impedance of a series *RLC* circuit is given by

$$Z = \sqrt{R^2 + (X_L - X_C)^2} \qquad (7.24)$$

Notice that if the circuit contains no X_C we get Eq. 7.22b, which is the *RL* circuit. Similarly, if $X_L = 0$ we get Eq. 7.23b, which is the *RC* case. If both X_C and X_L are zero, Eq. 7.24 reduces to the DC case (i.e., $Z = R$).

Example 7.17

For the circuit shown in Fig. 7.26, $R = 12\ k\Omega$, $L = 1.59\ H$, $C = 0.0318\ \mu F$, $V_{gen} = 13\ V_{rms}$, and $f = 1\ kHz$. Find V_R, V_L, and V_C.

Solution Step 1. Find X_L:

$$X_L = \omega L = 2\pi f L$$

$$= 2\pi \times 10^3 \times 1.59$$

$$= 10 \times 10^3\ \Omega$$

Step 2. Find X_C:

$$X_C = \frac{1}{\omega C} = \frac{1}{2\pi f C}$$

$$= \frac{1}{2\pi \times 10^3 \times 3.18 \times 10^{-8}}$$

$$= 5 \times 10^3\ \Omega$$

Step 3.   Find Z using Eq. 7.24:

$$Z = \sqrt{R^2 + (X_L - X_C)^2}$$

$$= \sqrt{(12 \times 10^3)^2 + (10 \times 10^3 - 5 \times 10^3)^2}$$

$$= 13 \times 10^3 \, \Omega$$

Step 4.   Find I_{rms}:

$$I_{rms} = \frac{V_{rms}}{Z}$$

$$= \frac{13}{13 \times 10^3}$$

$$= 1 \text{ mA.}$$

Step 5.

$$V_R = IR$$

$$= 10^{-3} \times 12 \times 10^3$$

$$= 12 \text{ volts}$$

Step 6.

$$V_L = IX_L$$

$$= 10^{-3} \times 10 \times 10^3$$

$$= 10 \text{ volts}$$

Step 7.

$$V_C = IX_C$$

$$= 10^{-3} \times 5 \times 10^3$$

$$= 5 \text{ volts}$$

Step 8.   To check, use Kirchhoff's voltage law:

$$V_{gen} \overset{?}{=} \sqrt{V_R^2 + (V_L - V_C)^2}$$

$$13 \overset{?}{=} \sqrt{12^2 + (10 - 5)^2}$$

$$= \sqrt{12^2 + 5^2}$$

$$= 13 \quad \checkmark$$

More complicated circuits involving sinusoidal waveforms can also be analyzed using the extended forms of Ohm's law and Kirchhoff's voltage and current laws.

Summary

1. A capacitor consists of conductors separated by a dielectric. Since the dielectric is an insulator no current can flow through a capacitor.
2. A capacitor stores charge if a voltage is applied. The farad is the unit of capacitance.
3. Capacitance is determined by geometry and the dielectric material used.
4. A capacitor blocks DC. Current can flow in a capacitive circuit only while voltage is changing.
5. The concept of displacement current allows us to retain the principle of a complete circuit as a requirement for current flow.
6. An inductor stores energy in a magnetic field as long as current flows. The henry is the unit of inductance.
7. There will be a voltage across an inductor only when the current through the inductor varies.
8. In RL and RC circuits there is a transient period prior to reaching steady-state conditions. The duration of the transient depends on the values of R, L, and C.
9. In a series RC situation the current is a maximum at $t = 0$ and decreases with time. The steady-state condition is no current.
10. In a series RL situation the current is zero at $t = 0$ and increases with time. The steady-state condition is maximum current.
11. Inductive reactance depends on frequency and inductance. Inductive reactance increases as frequency increases.
12. Capacitive reactance depends on frequency and capacitance. Capacitive reactance decreases as frequency increases.
13. Ohm's law can be extended to cover sinusoidal waveforms in L and C circuits by using reactance. In the case of RL, RC, and RLC circuits impedance must be considered.
14. Kirchhoff's voltage law may be extended to RL, RC, and RLC circuits by adding voltages geometrically instead of algebraically.

Questions

1. Discuss why current cannot flow through a capacitor.
2. What is the charge relationship in a series capacitor circuit? How does this compare with current in a series resistor circuit?
3. What is the charge relationship in a parallel capacitor circuit? How does this compare with current in a parallel resistor circuit?
4. Compare the results of combining capacitors in series and parallel with resistors in series and parallel.
5. Describe why current cannot flow in a capacitive circuit if the source voltage is DC.
6. Describe why current can flow in a capacitive circuit if the source voltage varies.
7. How can a negative current flow in a capacitive circuit while the source voltage remains positive?
8. How can a positive current flow in a capacitive circuit while the source voltage remains negative?
9. What is meant by displacement current?

10. Describe the term inductor.
11. Compare inductors and capacitors on the basis of ability to store energy.
12. Compare the results of connecting
    (a) A capacitor to a DC source
    (b) An inductor to a DC source
13. Compare the results of connecting inductors in series and parallel with resistors in series and parallel.
14. Describe how electrical power may be transferred without a wire connection.
15. What is meant by a circuit time constant?
16. What is the difference between transient and steady-state conditions?
17. Show how the difference between capacitors and inductors leads to different transient situations.
18. What is the difference between resistance and reactance?
19. What is the difference between inductive reactance and capacitive reactance?
20. Explain why no power is dissipated in ideal inductors and capacitors.
21. What is the difference between impedance and resistance?

Problems

1. Determine the capacitance if 0.01 coulomb is stored on the plates of a capacitor when the applied voltage is 200 volts.
2. What is the stored charge on a 0.2-μF capacitor when the applied voltage is
   (a) 50 volts
   (b) 100 volts
3. A parallel plate capacitor has a plate area of 2 cm² and a dielectric which is 0.5×10^{-3} cm thick. Find the capacitance if the dielectric is
   (a) Paper
   (b) Mica
   (c) Teflon
4. There are a 100-volt battery, a 3-μF capacitor, and a 6-μF capacitor. Determine the charge and voltage for each capacitor if
   (a) The capacitors are in series
   (b) The capacitors are in parallel
5. Verify Eq. 7.4.
6. A 0.01-μF capacitor is connected to a generator with a voltage waveform as shown in Fig. 7.27.
   (a) Plot current versus time.
   (b) What would be the current if the voltage is doubled?
7. The voltage waveform shown in Fig. 7.28 is connected across a 0.2-μF capacitor. Plot current versus time.
8. The capacitor is the same as in Problem 7. The waveform has the same shape except that the time scale is doubled (i.e., 1 msec becomes 2 msec, etc.). Plot current versus time.
9. Figure 7.29 shows voltage (top waveform) and current (bottom waveform) relationship for a capacitor. Find the value of capacitance.

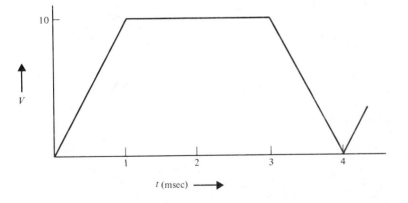

7.27 Waveform for Problem 6.

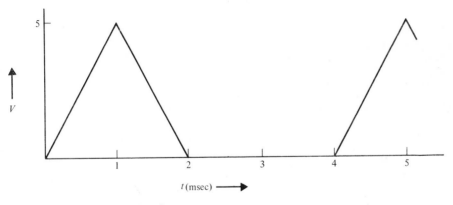

7.28 Waveform for Problem 7.

10. The current waveform shown in Fig. 7.30 is connected to a 100-mH inductor. Plot voltage versus time.
11. A 100-turn inductor is 0.2 cm in diameter and 2 cm long. Find the inductance if the core is
    (a) Air
    (b) Iron
12. There is a 100-mH inductor and a 300-mH inductor. Neglecting the effect of mutual inductance, find the total inductance if they are connected in
    (a) Series
    (b) Parallel
13. Verify Eq. 7.8a.
14. A 50-mH inductor and a 30-mH inductor are connected in series so that the fluxes add. If the total inductance is 100 mH, what is the mutual inductance?

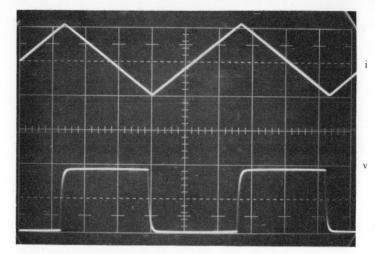

7.29   Oscilloscope photograph for Problem 9.

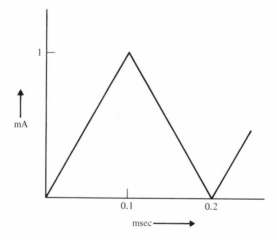

7.30   Waveform for Problem 10.

15. A step-down transformer which has 500 turns on the input winding is connected to a 20-volt source. If the required output voltage is 5 volts, how many turns must the output winding have?

16. For the transformer in Problem 16, find the output current if the input current is 1 amp.

17. A 1-μF capacitor is charged through a 1-kΩ resistor from a 10-volt DC source. Find the voltage across the capacitor at
   (a) $t = 0$
   (b) $t = 1\,RC$
   (c) $t = 5\,RC$

18. Approximately how long will it take for a 1-μF capacitor charged to 20,000 volts to discharge through a 1-MΩ resistor?

19. For the circuit in Problem 18, find the current at
   (a) $t = 0$
   (b) $t = 5\,RC$

20. A 1-mH inductor is connected in series with a 1-kΩ resistor to a 50-volt DC source. Find the voltage across the inductor at
   (a) $t = 0$
   (b) $t = 1$ time constant
   (c) $t = 5$ time constant

21. Verify that R/L is a pure number by showing that it has the dimension $1/t$.

22. Determine the reactance of a 1-H inductor at
   (a) 0 Hz
   (b) 100 Hz
   (c) 1000 Hz
   (d) Plot X_L versus frequency

23. Determine the reactance of a 1-μF capacitor at
   (a) 0 Hz
   (b) 100 Hz
   (c) 1000 Hz
   (d) Plot X_C versus frequency.

24. At what frequency will the current through a 100-mH inductor be 1 mA. if $V_L = 5$ volts?

25. At what frequency will the current through a 0.5-μF capacitor be 1 mA. if $V_C = 5$ volts?

26. A series RLC circuit is connected to a 20-V_{rms} generator. If $V_L = 25\ V_{rms}$ and $V_C = 9\ V_{rms}$, find V_R.

PART II ELECTRONICS

Chapter 8 Diodes and Power Supplies

8.1   Introduction

Previously described semiconductor principles are used to explain the formation of a rectifying contact. This discussion is extended to describe filtered power supplies for electronic applications.

8.2   *pn* Junctions

In Chapter 1 the doping of intrinsic material was described. We saw that it was possible to dope silicon and germanium with either Valence III or Valence V atoms. Both *p*-doped and *n*-doped semiconductors can be manufactured.

Figure 8.1 shows what happens when a piece of *p*-type material is connected to a piece of *n*-type material. (This formation must actually occur within the same crystal, but the principle is correct.)

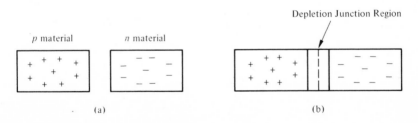

8.1   Formation of a *pn* junction. (a) Before. (b) After.

Before the *p*-type and *n*-type materials are brought together they are both electrically neutral. That is, despite the fact that the *n*-type material has more electrons than normal silicon or germanium, this excess of electrons is balanced by more protons; each atom in the semiconductor has the same number of electrons as protons, and there is no excess of either. In the same way, *p*-type material is also electrically neutral—it has the same number of electrons as protons, although it has fewer of these than regular silicon or germanium. As long as the *p*-type and *n*-type materials are kept apart from each other, if we examined any particular region within the materials, no matter where, we would always find the same number of protons as electrons.

But as soon as the *p*-type material is connected to the *n*-type material, a striking change occurs. The protons, which lie inside the cores of the individual atoms, still stay in the same relative positions within each material. But the electrons move into new positions and upset the electrical balance. Before we put the two materials together, we have the condition shown in Fig. 8.1 (a).

After they are together we have the condition shown in Fig. 8.1 (b). The area where the *p* and *n* materials meet is called the **junction.** In the vicinity of the junction between the two materials there is a small area where the holes from the *p*-type material have been filled with electrons from the *n*-type material, caused by some of the electrons flowing left from the *n*-type material to the *p*-type material. This small region around the junction is called the **depletion region,** because it has neither holes nor electrons.

If this process continued we would achieve a really startling result— electrical current without a battery causing it. In practice, though, there is another result of this flow which soon causes it to slow down and stop. If we look carefully into the depletion region, we see something like that shown in Fig. 8.2. The *p*-type material has many acceptor atoms. Their holes have

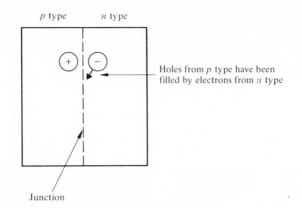

Holes from *p* type have been
filled by electrons from *n* type

Junction

8.2   Enlarged view of depletion region.

been filled by electrons from the *n*-type material. These acceptor atoms now have more electrons than protons, and this region is now negatively charged.

The *n*-type material has many donor atoms. One electron from many of these donors has gone to the *p*-type material. These donor atoms now have more protons than electrons, and this region is now positively charged.

As a result, within the depletion region, that part of the depletion region within the *p*-type material is negatively charged, while the part within the *n*-type region is positively charged. This causes an electrical field which eventually becomes so large that it stops further current flow. A **barrier**

potential has been created at the *pn* interface and such a *pn* junction is called a **diode.**

As shown in Fig. 8.3, there are two ways to connect a battery across a diode. In Fig. 8.3 (a) the positive side of the battery is connected to the *p* side of the diode and the negative side of the battery is connected to the *n* side of the diode. For this connection holes in the *p* material will be repelled from

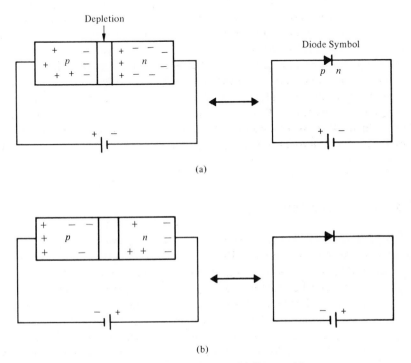

(a)

(b)

8.3   Diode biasing conditions. (a) Forward bias. (b) Reverse bias.

the positive battery terminal and drift toward the depletion region. Also, electrons in the *n* material will be repelled from the negative battery terminal and drift toward the depletion region. However, the polarity of the barrier potential opposes both holes and electrons from crossing.

If the external battery voltage is increased to a value greater than the barrier voltage, both holes and electrons acquire sufficient energy to cross the barrier and a large current flows. Attaching the *p* side of the diode to the positive battery terminal and the negative side of the diode to the negative battery terminal permits current to flow if the battery voltage is large enough to overcome the barrier potential. This type of connection is called positive or **forward bias.**

In Fig. 8.3 (b) the battery connections are reversed; the negative battery terminal is connected to the p side and the positive battery terminal is connected to the n side of the diode. For this connection holes in the p side of the diode are attracted to the negative battery terminal and electrons in the n side are connected to the positive battery terminal. Since the majority current carriers are attracted toward the battery terminals, away from the junction, the depletion region widens and the barrier potential actually increases. This means that there should be no current flow since the diode is now **reverse biased.** However, this reverse-bias connection (positive battery terminal to n side of diode and vice versa) is actually forward biased as far as minority carriers are concerned.

The very terms forward and reverse bias refer to the action of the majority carriers in each material. Thus the forward-bias condition is actually the reverse-bias condition as far as minority carriers are concerned. In most diode material the ratio of majority to minority carriers is at least 1000 to 1. Thus, **when a diode is forward biased a large positive current flows, and when a diode is reverse biased a small negative current flows.**

8.3   Diode Characteristics

We have just seen that the current-voltage relationship of a diode is quite different from that of a resistor. In a resistor, reversing the battery changes the current polarity. However, the magnitude of the current will be the same. This is a consequence of Ohm's law. For example, if a 10-volt battery is connected across a 100-Ω resistor the current will be 0.1 Amp. If the battery is reversed we shall have -10 volts and the current will be -0.1 Amp.

For a diode the situation is not so simple. A forward-biased diode (positive battery terminal to p side of diode) results in a large positive current. A reverse-biased diode (positive battery terminal to n side of diode) results in a small negative current.

Figure 8.4 shows the current-voltage relationship of two components. One is a resistor and the other is a diode. The relationship between current and voltage in a resistor is a straight line; that is, there is a linear current-voltage relationship, regardless of whether the voltage is positive or negative.

The situation for the diode is completely different. In the positive voltage region the current-voltage relationship is nonlinear, and there does not even appear to be a current in the negative voltage region. Actually there is a small negative current with negative bias. The reason that we cannot see the negative diode current in Fig. 8.4 is simply that it is very small. Minority current is much less than majority current.

We can determine the value of the resistor whose I–V characteristic is shown in Fig. 8.4.

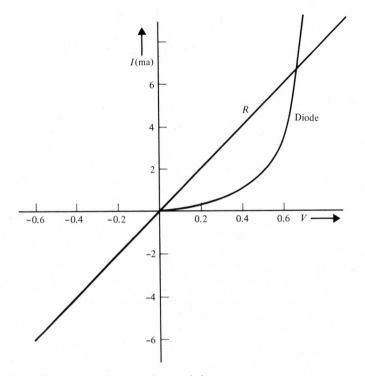

8.4   Comparing diode and resistor characteristics.

Example 8.1

Find the value of the resistor shown in Fig. 8.4.

Solution Step 1.   From the scale data given in Fig. 8.4, the vertical scale is 2 mA/cm and the horizontal scale is 0.2 V/cm.

Step 2.   Thus at, say, 0.2 volts we have

$$R = \frac{V}{I}$$

$$= \frac{0.2 \text{ volts}}{2 \times 10^{-3} \text{ Amp.}}$$

$$= 100 \, \Omega$$

Of course, since the resistor is a linear device we would get this same ratio at any other voltage level.

The situation for the diode is completely different, as illustrated in Example 8.2.

Example 8.2

Find the resistance of the diode shown in Fig. 8.4 at 0.4 volts and at 0.6 volts.

Solution Step 1.   Using the given scale data we find that at 0.4 volts the current is 0.5 mA and that at 0.6 volts the current is 3.0 mA.

Step 2.   Therefore, at 0.4 volts,

$$R = \frac{V}{I}$$

$$= \frac{0.4 \text{ volt}}{0.0005 \text{ Amp}}$$

$$= 800 \, \Omega$$

Step 3.   Similarly, at 0.6 volts,

$$R = \frac{V}{I}$$

$$= \frac{0.6 \text{ volt}}{0.003 \text{ Amp.}}$$

$$= 200 \, \Omega$$

Although the diode curve in Fig. 8.4 shows clearly that Ohm's law does not apply to a diode, it is quite legitimate to use Ohm's law at individual voltage levels. The justification is that at an individual level a linear resistor based on Ohm's law could replace the diode. However, over a voltage range, **Ohm's law does not apply to a diode because its resistance is not constant.**

Notice that for the particular diode shown in Fig. 8.5, the current rises sharply above about 0.25 volts. This diode is a germanium diode and the barrier potential for a germanium diode is approximately 0.25 volts at room temperature. Below 0.25 volts the current is small because very few current carriers have sufficient energy to surpass the barrier potential. Above 0.25 volts the external battery exceeds this barrier potential. Thus a much larger current flows when the barrier potential is exceeded. The barrier potential for a silicon diode is approximately 0.6 volts at room temperature.

If we want to observe the negative current-voltage characteristic of a diode we must expand the current scale for negative values. This is shown in Fig. 8.5. Between 0 and −50 millivolts the current becomes more negative as the voltage becomes more negative, but beyond −50 the current remains relatively constant even though the voltage gets more negative. The reason for this behavior is the comparatively small number of minority current carriers. That is, at relatively low negative bias (50 mV in this case) all the minority carriers have acquired sufficient energy to constitute current. Thus, **further increase of negative bias cannot result in a further increase in current since no additional minority carriers are available.**

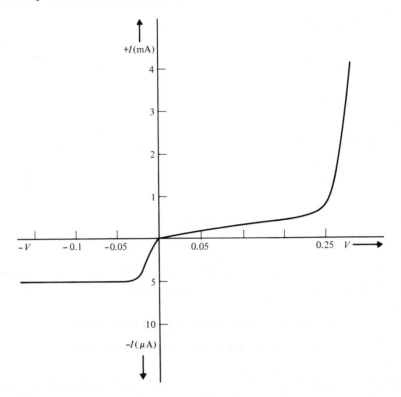

8.5   Diode *I-V* characteristics (negative current range expanded).

Example 8.3

For the diode *I-V* characteristic shown in Fig. 8.5, find the diode resistance at
$-25\,\text{mV}$, $-100\,\text{mV}$, and -1.0 volts.

Solution Step 1.   From Fig. 8.5,

$$-25\,\text{mV} \qquad I = -2.5\,\mu\text{A}$$
$$-100\,\text{mV} \qquad I = -5.0\,\mu\text{A}$$
$$-1.0\,\text{volt} \qquad I = -5.0\,\mu\text{A}$$

Step 2.   At $-25\,\text{mV}$,

$$R = \frac{V}{I}$$

$$= \frac{-25 \times 10^{-3}\,\text{volt}}{-2.5 \times 10^{-6}\,\text{Amp.}}$$

$$= 10\,\text{k}\Omega$$

Step 3. At −100 mV,

$$R = \frac{V}{I}$$

$$= \frac{-100 \times 10^{-3}}{-5 \times 10^{-6}}$$

$$= 20\, k\Omega$$

Step 4. At −1.0 volt

$$R = \frac{V}{I}$$

$$= \frac{-1.0}{5 \times 10^{-6}}$$

$$= 200\, k\Omega$$

By comparing the results of Example 8.2 for a forward-biased diode and Example 8.3 for a reverse-biased diode we see that

A forward-biased diode has a very low resistance;

a reverse-biased diode has a very high resistance.

The current value at which the *I-V* characteristic for a reverse-biased diode levels off is called the reverse **saturation current** (I_s). Typically, silicon diodes have lower reverse saturation currents than germanium diodes. Therefore reverse-biased silicon diodes have even higher resistances.

It has been found that the equation for the *I-V* characteristic of a diode can be described in terms of saturation current:

$$I = I_s(\varepsilon^{qV/KT} - 1) \tag{8.1a}$$

where

ε = base of natural logarithms $\simeq 2.72$
q = electron charge = 1.6×10^{-19} coulomb
V = voltage
K = Boltzmann's constant = 1.38×10^{-23} joule/°K
T = Temperature in degrees Kelvin (room temperature $\simeq 300°$K)

Using these values the diode current at room temperature is given by

$$I = I_s(\varepsilon^{39V} - 1) \tag{8.1b}$$

Example 8.4

Find the resistance at $+200\,mV$ and $-200\,mV$ for a diode that has $I_s = 1\,\mu A$ (assume room temperature).

Solution Step 1.   The required data are $V = 0.2$ volts and $I_s = 10^{-6}$ Amp.

Step 2.

$$I = I_s(\varepsilon^{39V} - 1)$$
$$= 10^{-6}(\varepsilon^{7.8} - 1) = 10^{-6}(2450 - 1) \simeq 10^{-6} \times 2450$$
$$\simeq 2.45 \times 10^{-3}\,\text{Amp.}$$

Step 3.

$$R = \frac{V}{I}$$
$$= \frac{2 \times 10^{-1}}{2.45 \times 10^{-3}}$$
$$= 81.5\,\Omega$$

Step 4.   For the negative bias situation $V = -0.2$ volts and $I_s = 10^{-6}$ Amp.

Step 5.

$$I = I_s(\varepsilon^{39V} - 1)$$
$$= 10^{-6}(\varepsilon^{-7.8} - 1)$$
$$\simeq 10^{-6}(0.00042 - 1)$$
$$\simeq -10^{-6}\,\text{Amp.}$$

Step 6.

$$R = \frac{V}{I}$$
$$= \frac{-2 \times 10^{-1}}{-10^{-6}}$$
$$= 200\,\text{k}\Omega$$

Again we see that there is a tremendous difference between the resistances of a forward-biased and a reverse-biased diode ($81.5\,\Omega$ at 0.2 volt versus $200\,\text{k}\Omega$ at -0.2 volt). For this reason the diode is referred to as a **unilateral** (one-sided) device as compared to a resistor, which passes current equally in both directions. Thus a resistor is a **bilateral** (two-sided) device.

The diode current equation (Eq. 8.1a) indicates that it is possible to use the diode as an electronic thermometer. That is, if we select a particular diode and connect a constant source voltage the only factor which can change the diode current is temperature. Thus if an ammeter is connected to a diode as shown in Fig. 8.6, the ammeter can be calibrated to read directly in degrees of

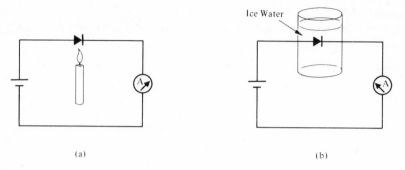

8.6 Diode as an electronic thermometer. (a) High temperature results in much current. (b) Low temperature results in little current.

temperature. On the other hand, if we require a circuit which operates well over a large temperature range, the temperature dependence of a diode presents problems.

8.4   Rectification

Figure 8.7 consists of a battery, reversing switch, diode, and load resistor (R_L). The reversing switch permits us alternately to reverse and forward bias the diode. When the switch is thrown to the left, the negative terminal of the power supply is connected to the p side of the diode [Fig. 8.7 (b)]. Thus,

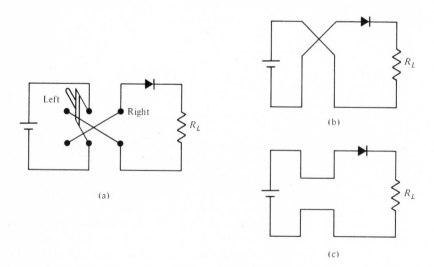

8.7 Diode circuit with reversing switch. (a) Schematic. (b) Switch to left. (c) Switch to right.

with the switch to the left the diode is reverse biased. When the switch is thrown to the right the positive terminal of the power supply is connected to the p side of the diode [Fig. 8.7 (c)]. Thus, with the switch to the right the diode is forward biased.

Regardless of which position the switch is in, Kirchhoff's voltage law may be applied to this circuit:

$$V_{\text{battery}} = V_D + V_{R_L} \qquad \text{(8.2a)}$$

When the diode is reverse biased the diode resistance is very high, so most of the battery voltage will be across the diode and very little voltage will be across the load resistor.

$$\text{reverse bias} \quad \begin{matrix} V_{\text{battery}} \simeq V_D \\ V_{R_L} \simeq 0 \end{matrix} \qquad \text{(8.2b)}$$

When the diode is forward biased the diode resistance is very low, so most of the battery voltage will be across the load resistor and very little voltage (a little more than the barrier potential) will be across the diode:

$$\text{forward bias} \quad \begin{matrix} V_{\text{battery}} \simeq V_{R_L} \\ V_D \simeq 0 \end{matrix} \qquad \text{(8.2c)}$$

If we work the switch continuously from left to right we shall generate a series of pulses as shown in Fig. 8.8. This graph assumes that no current flows when the diode is reverse biased. While this is not quite the case, our previous diode discussion has shown that very little current (I_s) flows through a reverse-biased diode. If we want to generate negative pulses instead of positive

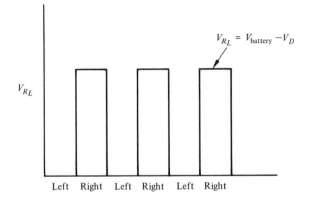

8.8   Reversing switch generates pulses.

pulses, all we need do is reverse the diode connection. In this way the diode will be reverse biased when the switch is to the right and forward biased when the switch is to the left.

In either case, when the diode is forward biased the voltage across the load resistor will be equal to the battery voltage minus the drop across the forward-biased diode, as shown in Fig. 8.8. In effect we use the low resistance of a forward-biased diode and the high resistance of a reverse-biased diode to generate pulses which have only one polarity. The diode acts as a polarity-sensitive switch. An ideal diode would have zero resistance when forward biased and infinite resistance when reverse biased. An actual diode, as we have seen, has low resistance when forward biased and high resistance when reverse biased. Figure 8.9 compares real and ideal diode I-V characteristics. The characteristics are not exactly the same, but are quite similar.

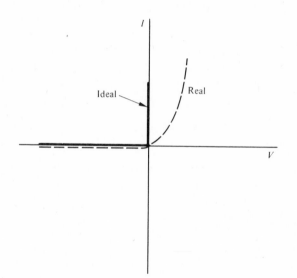

8.9   Comparison of diode characteristics.

We have used a battery and a reversing switch to achieve a voltage which varies in amplitude; that is, by mechanically operating the reversing switch we have achieved an input voltage which fluctuates. A much simpler method would be to start with AC from a generator as shown in Fig. 8.10. In this case, during the time when the side of the generator which is connected to the p side of the diode is positive the diode is forward biased. During the alternate half-cycle, the p side of the diode will be connected to negative voltage and the diode will be reverse biased. Frequently, the term **cathode** is used for the n side of a diode and the term **anode** is used for the p side of a diode. Figure

8.10   Diode circuit connected to a generator.

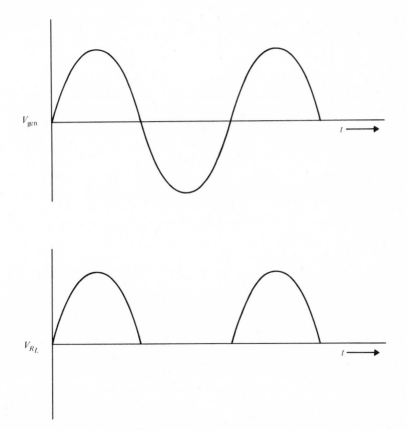

8.11 compares the generator and load voltages for this circuit. **The polarity-sensitive resistance properties of a diode have been used to change AC into pulsating DC.**

8.11   Waveforms for Fig. 8.10.

Power companies generate and deliver AC because transformers can be used to provide appropriate voltage levels, and as has already been indicated, transformers do not work on DC. However, most electronic equipment (radio, TV, oscilloscope, computers, etc.) must operate on DC. Thus it is necessary to transform the AC from the line into battery-type DC. The diode is used to perform the first step in this process. The diode changes AC into pulsating DC. Changing AC to pulsating DC is called **rectification.** The diode is used as a rectifier. The circuit shown in Fig. 8.10 is a **half-wave rectifier,** because only half of the sine wave is used.

Example 8.5

For the half-wave rectifier shown in Fig. 8.10, $V_{gen} = 20 \text{ V}_{p-p}$, the diode is silicon, and the load resistor is 1 kΩ. Estimate the maximum and minimum load current.

Solution Step 1.   For the circuit shown in Fig. 8.10,

$$V_{gen} = V_D + V_{R_L}$$

Step 2.   The barrier voltage for silicon diodes is 0.6 volts. The maximum current occurs when the generator has its maximum positive value:

$$10 = 0.6 + V_{R_L(max)}$$

$$V_{R_L(max)} = 9.4 \text{ volts}$$

Step 3.   Therefore

$$I_{R_L(max)} = \frac{V_{R_L(max)}}{R}$$

$$= \frac{9.4 \text{ volts}}{10^3 \, \Omega}$$

$$= 9.4 \text{ mA}$$

Step 4.   The minimum current flows when the diode is reverse biased. Therefore

$$I_{min} = I_s = 1 \text{ microampere or less}$$

From Example 8.5 we can see that very little accuracy is lost in neglecting the drop across the forward biased diode (the barrier voltage) if the maximum generator voltage is much higher than this value. Also, since only micro-amperes flow during the time that the diode is reverse biased the drop across the load will be in the millivolt range. Thus we may say that **the load voltage is essentially zero when the diode is reverse biased.**

When the diode is reverse biased, almost the entire negative voltage from the generator appears across the diode. Thus the diode must be able to withstand the most negative voltage which the generator produces without destroying itself. This is an important figure of merit and is called the **peak inverse voltage (PIV)** rating of the diode. Diodes which can withstand higher negative voltages (higher PIV's) are generally more expensive than diodes which can withstand only lower negative voltages (lower PIV's).

Another important diode parameter is the maximum forward current (I_f) which the diode can carry without destroying itself. Generally, diodes with higher I_f ratings cost more than diodes with lower I_f ratings.

8.5   Types of Rectifiers

As a practical matter there are very few electronic devices which operate precisely at line voltage. Typically, semiconductor circuits operate below line voltage and vacuum-tube circuits operate above line voltage. In both cases a transformer is required to obtain proper voltage prior to rectification. Figure 8.12 shows a half-wave rectifier operating from a step-down transformer.

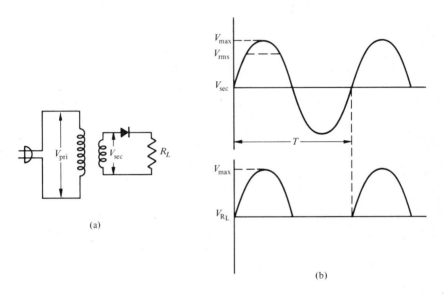

8.12   Half-wave rectifier operated from a transformer. (a) Schematic. (b) Waveforms.

For the loop consisting of the transformer secondary, diode, and load resistor, Kirchhoff's voltage law is

$$V_{\text{sec}} = V_D + V_{R_L} \tag{8.3}$$

Transformer voltages are specified in terms of root-mean-square values. In the case of rectifiers we are interested in maximum load voltage and maximum load current. Thus it is necessary to convert from V_{rms} to V_{max}.

Example 8.6

The transformer shown in Fig. 8.12 has a 25-V_{rms} secondary and the diode is silicon. Find the maximum load voltage.

Solution Step 1.   Convert from V_{rms} to V_{max}:

$$V_{max} = \sqrt{2} \times V_{rms}$$
$$= \sqrt{2} \times 25$$
$$= 35 \text{ volts}$$

Step 2.   For a silicon diode the barrier voltage is 0.6 volts:

$$V_{max} = V_D + V_{R_L}$$
$$35 = 0.6 + V_{R_L}$$
$$V_{R_L} = 34.4 \text{ volts}$$

If we compare the input and load voltage waveforms shown in Fig. 8.12 (b) we see that although they are dissimilar, both have the same period. That is, the time required for a complete excursion of the input sine wave is the same as the time required to go from the start of a rectified half-wave to the beginning of the next rectified half-wave.

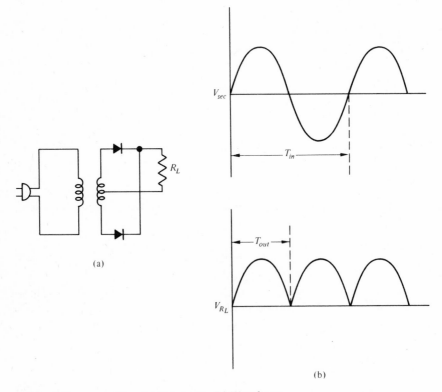

8.13   Full-wave rectifier. (a) Schematic. (b) Waveforms.

As already indicated, PIV is an important parameter in selecting a particular diode. In a half-wave rectifier, when the diode is reverse biased it must
withstand the most negative voltage. The most negative voltage has the same
magnitude as V_{max}. It is customary to give only the magnitude of the PIV
since it must be negative. Thus we say that the PIV of a half-wave rectifier is
V_{max}. For example, in the half-wave rectifier of Example 8.6 the PIV is
35 volts.

A transformer which has a lead attached to the center of the secondary is
called a **center-tapped transformer.** By using a center-tapped transformer, it is
possible to construct a circuit which rectifies both halves of the sine wave.
The schematic and waveforms of such a **full-wave rectifier** are shown in
Fig. 8.13.

The action of a full-wave rectifier can be understood by considering two
situations:

1. The top of the transformer secondary is positive and the bottom is
   negative.
2. The alternate half-cycle, when the top of the transformer is negative
   and the bottom is positive.

These conditions are illustrated in Fig. 8.14. In Fig. 8.14 (a) diode D_1 is
forward biased and D_2 is reverse biased. Consider the reverse-biased diode
to be ideal (an open circuit). We can see that for this situation current flows
through R_L from top to bottom. During the alternate half-cycle [Fig. 8.14 (b)]

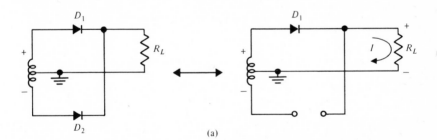

(a)

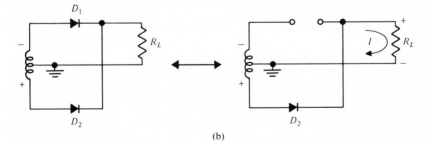

(b)

8.14   Full-wave rectifier conditions. (a) D_1 forward biased, D_2 reverse biased. (b) D_2
forward biased, D_1 reverse biased.

D_2 is forward biased and D_1 is reverse biased. Notice that for this situation the current still flows in the same direction through R_L. Both halves of the sine wave have been rectified.

The symbol along the middle line represents **"ground."** Strictly speaking the circuit is rarely connected to the ground or earth. Most of the time the chassis itself is used as a reference point and the ground symbol is usually incorrect in this sense. If the circuit is to be truly grounded the chassis should be connected to a water pipe or some other rod that actually goes into the ground.

Assume that the center-tapped transformer has the same secondary voltage as the transformer which was used in the half-wave rectifier. For this situation the maximum load voltage from the full-wave rectifier will be only half that for the half-wave rectifier. This is because only half of the secondary (from one end to the center tap) is being used during each half-cycle. This may be seen by referring to Fig. 8.14. Regardless of which diode is reverse biased, the only path for current is from one end of the transformer through the forward-biased diode, the load resistor, and the center tap of the transformer.

Example 8.7

A 25-V_{rms} secondary has a center tap. Find the maximum load voltage if silicon diodes are used in the full-wave rectifier.

Solution Step 1.   As in Example 8.6,

$$V_{sec(max)} = 35 \text{ volts}$$

Step 2.   Since only half of the transformer is used on each half-cycle we have

$$\frac{V_{max}}{2} = \frac{35}{2} = 17.5 \text{ volts}$$

as the source voltage available for rectification.

Step 3.   Applying Kirchhoff's voltage law,

$$V_{source} = V_D + V_{R_L}$$

Since the diodes are silicon $V_D = 0.6$ volts for forward bias:

$$17.5 = 0.6 + V_{R_L}$$

$$V_{R_L(max)} = 16.9 \text{ volts}$$

Notice that in a full-wave rectifier the input and load voltage waveforms [Fig. 8.13 (b)] do not have the same period. In fact the period of the input sine wave is exactly twice as long as the period of the load voltage. Another way to say the same thing is that the frequency of the load voltage is double the input frequency for a full-wave rectifier.

Each diode in this full-wave rectifier must have the same PIV as the single diode in the half-wave rectifier because the reverse-biased diode in the full-wave rectifier must withstand the entire voltage across the transformer secondary, and not just the voltage from one end to the center tap. Although a full-wave rectifier with center tap provides only half the maximum load voltage of a half-wave rectifier the PIV must be the same in both cases.

Another type of full-wave rectifier is shown in Fig. 8.15. This circuit is called a **bridge rectifier.** Notice that the diodes in the opposite arms of the

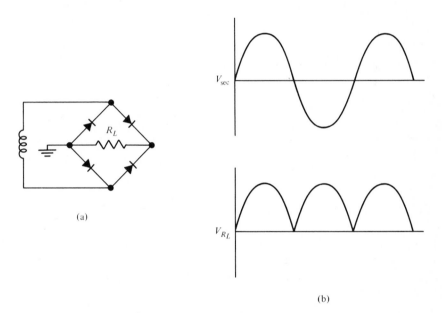

(a)

(b)

8.15   Bridge rectifier. (a) Schematic. (b) Waveforms.

bridge face in the same direction. The action of a bridge rectifier can be understood by considering alternate half-cycles as shown in Fig. 8.16.

In Fig. 8.16 (a) the top of the transformer is positive and the bottom is negative. For this situation D_2 and D_4 are forward biased and D_1 and D_3 are reverse biased. Again, if we consider reverse-biased diodes as open circuits, the only way for current to flow through R_L is from right to left. During the alternate half-cycle [Fig. 8.15 (b)] conditions are reversed; that is, D_1 and D_3 are forward biased and D_2 and D_4 are reverse biased. Notice that current flows in the same direction through the load resistor during both halves of the cycle.

Although a bridge rectifier requires twice as many diodes as a full-wave rectifier with a center tap, the load voltage is twice as great for the bridge as for

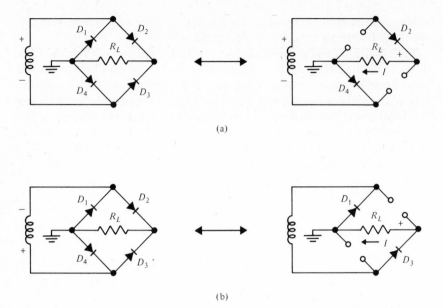

(a)

(b)

8.16 Bridge rectifier conditions. (a) D_2 and D_4 forward biased. (b) D_1 and D_3 forward biased.

the center-tap situation, because the entire transformer secondary is being used in the bridge rectifier while only half of the secondary is used at any given time in the center-tapped rectifier.

Example 8.8
A bridge rectifier is constructed using the same transformer as in Example 8.6. If silicon diodes are used, determine the maximum load voltage.

Solution Step 1. Since the transformer secondary is 25 V_{rms}:

$$V_{max} = 35 \text{ volts}$$

Step 2. Applying Kirchhoff's voltage law to the forward-biased loop of a bridge rectifier:

$$V_{max} = V_D + V_{R_L} + V_D$$
$$V_{max} = 2V_D + V_{R_L}$$

Step 3. For silicon diodes the barrier voltage is 0.6 volt:

$$35 = 2 \times 0.6 + V_{R_L}$$
$$= 1.2 + V_{R_L}$$
$$V_{R_L} = 33.8 \text{ volts}$$

Comparing Examples 8.6, 8.7, and 8.8 we see that for the same transformer secondary voltage the half-wave and full-wave bridge rectifiers both give about twice as much voltage ax the full-wave rectifier with center tap.

Both the full-wave, center-tapped and the full bridge rectifiers have load frequencies which are double the input frequency. The PIV in a bridge rectifier is the same as is required for a center tap, because in a bridge both of the reverse-biased diodes withstand the entire transformer secondary voltage. Table 8.1 compares $V_{L(max)}$, PIV, and load frequency for these rectifiers, assuming the same secondary voltage in all cases.

Table 8.1   Rectifier Characteristics

Rectifier	$V_{L(max)}$	PIV	f_{load}
Half-wave	$V_{sec(max)} - V_D$	V_{max}	f_{input}
Center-tap	$\frac{1}{2}V_{sec(max)} - V_D$	V_{max}	$2 \times f_{input}$
Bridge	$V_{sec(max)} - 2V_D$	V_{max}	$2 \times f_{input}$

8.6   Filters

All the rectifiers which have been discussed convert AC to pulsating DC. The next step is to smooth out the pulsating DC to a waveform which looks like battery-type DC.

If the load resistor in a rectifier is replaced with a capacitor there will still be rectification, but the load voltage will have a completely different waveform. Consider the half-wave rectifier shown in Fig. 8.17. During the time that the voltage at the top of the transformer is increasing to V_{max}, the diode is forward biased. The capacitor will charge up in accordance with Kirchhoff's voltage law to the maximum transformer voltage minus the drop across the diode. When the transformer voltage drops below V_{max}, the diode is reverse biased; that is, the n side of the diode is at V_{max} while the p side of the diode is at a lower voltage.

For example, if the maximum voltage across the transformer secondary is 20 volts, the capacitor will charge to approximately 20 volts. When the transformer voltage drops below 20 volts, to say 18 volts, the p side of the diode is at 18 volts and the n side of the diode is still at 20 volts. Thus the diode is reverse biased and **the capacitor cannot discharge through the diode.** The effect of this is that for a capacitor load, the capacitor charges up to V_{max} and remains at V_{max}. This has achieved the objective. A constant voltage across a capacitor is battery-type DC. **Pulsating DC has been converted to steady DC.**

As a practical matter, the voltage across the capacitor will drop somewhat even though the capacitor cannot discharge through the diode. Any real

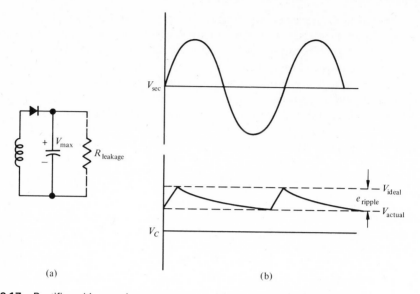

8.17   Rectifier with capacitor across output. (a) Schematic. (b) Waveforms.

capacitor has leakage resistance since there is no perfect dielectric. Thus the capacitor will begin to discharge through its own leakage resistance even though it cannot discharge through the diode. Then, on the next positive-going cycle the capacitor will again charge to V_{max}. The diode will conduct when the diode becomes forward biased. In this way the capacitor discharge is compensated for. The voltage across the capacitor consists of a steady DC value with a **"ripple"** superimposed. The ripple is the result of the alternate discharge and recharge of the capacitor.

If a load resistor is connected across the capacitor the discharge will be greater (the ripple voltage will increase). Since we are interested in obtaining steady DC our object is to make the ripple as small as possible. Capacitor discharge through a resistor is a time-constant situation, as discussed in Chapter 7. In this case we can **decrease the ripple by increasing the RC time constant**; that is, if we have larger time constants the voltage will not drop as much during the time that the diode is reverse biased. On the next positive-going cycle the slight discharge will be replenished.

Using larger capacitors increases the time constant. It is usually not possible to increase R to reduce the ripple since R is really the load resistance, which is a specified quantity. Circuits which reduce ripple are called **filters**. A practical filter circuit is shown in Fig. 8.18. Regardless of the type of rectifier C_1 will charge to V_{max} during the time that the transformer voltage is increasing. During the remaining portion of the cycle the capacitor will partially discharge. Since the capacitor cannot discharge through the diode, it must discharge through the inductor. The discharge is a ripple. A ripple is, of

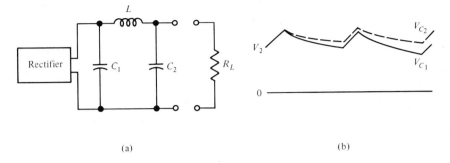

8.18 *LC* Filter. (a) Circuit. (b) Waveforms.

course, a voltage that varies with time. In Section 7.6 we saw that inductive reactance is determined by frequency. As frequency increases so does ωL. This means that **inductors tend to block waveforms that vary.**

Capacitor C_2 also reduces the ripple across the load resistor. An ideal inductor has no resistance, so the DC voltage across C_2 is approximately the same as across C_1. However, the ripple across C_2 is much smaller, as shown in Fig. 8.18 (b). Filtering modifies the PIV requirements for a filtered half-wave rectifier. We require 2 V_{max} and for a filtered bridge we require V_{max}.

The filter of Fig. 8.18 is called a pi-type (because of its resemblance to the Greek letter π) *LC* filter. It is possible to derive a formula to predict ripple which is based on writing loop equations, making some approximations, and a little higher mathematics. The result is

$$e_r \simeq \frac{\sqrt{2} I_{DC}}{\omega C_1 \times \omega C_2 \times \omega L} \qquad (8.4a)$$

where

$$e_r = \text{the ripple voltage}$$
$$I_L = \text{the DC load current}$$
$$\omega = \text{the lowest radian frequency component}$$

Generally C_1 and C_2 will be equal, so Eq. 8.4a becomes

$$e_r \simeq \frac{\sqrt{2} I_{DC}}{(\omega C)^2 \omega L} \qquad (8.4b)$$

It is possible to reduce the ripple voltage by adding additional pi sections. A two-section *LC* filter is shown in Fig. 8.19. A two-section *LC* filter has three capacitors and two inductors. Equation 8.4b must be modified : Since there are three capacitors ωC will be to the third power. Since there are two inductors ωL will be to the second power. That is, the power to which ω is

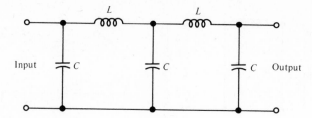

8.19 Two-section *LC* filter.

raised is equal to the number of capacitors in the filter and the power to which
ωL is raised is equal to the number of inductors:

$$e_r \simeq \frac{\sqrt{2}I_{DC}}{(\omega C)^{n_C}(\omega L)^{n_L}} \qquad (8.4c)$$

Since the ω which appears in Eq. 8.4 is the lowest frequency component of
the rectified voltage, we can see that a full-wave rectifier will have a lower
ripple voltage than a half-wave rectifier. As summarized in Table 8.1, the
lowest frequency component of a half-wave rectifier is the input frequency,
while the lowest frequency component of a full-wave rectifier is twice the
input frequency. Therefore the denominator of Eq. 8.4c will be larger for a
full-wave rectifier and the ripple voltage will be smaller.

Example 8.9

A pi-section *LC* filter connected to a rectifier (as shown in Fig. 8.18) delivers 50 mA
to a load. 20-μF capacitors are used with a 5-H inductor. Determine the ripple voltage
if (a) a half-wave rectifier is used; (b) a full-wave rectifier is used.

Solution Part (a) Step 1. A single-section *LC* filter has two capacitors and one
inductor. $I_L = 50$ mA. Therefore for this problem Eq. 8.4c becomes

$$e_r \simeq \frac{\sqrt{2} \times 50 \times 10^{-3}}{(\omega \times 20 \times 10^{-6})^2 (\omega \times 5)^1}$$

$$= \frac{70.7 \times 10^{-3}}{\omega^3 4 \times 10^{-10} \times 5}$$

$$= \frac{3.54 \times 10^7}{\omega^3}$$

Step 2. The powerline frequency is 60 Hz. Thus for a half-wave rectifier the minimum
frequency component is 60 Hz:

$$\omega = 2\pi f$$

$$= 2\pi \times 60$$

$$\simeq 377 \text{ rad/sec}$$

Step 3.   Using this value of ω we obtain

$$e_r = \frac{3.54 \times 10^7}{(3.77 \times 10^2)^3}$$

$$= \frac{3.54 \times 10^7}{53.5 \times 10^6}$$

$$\simeq 0.652 \text{ volts} = 652 \text{ mV}$$

as the power-supply ripple voltage.

Part (b) Step 1.   The values of capacitor, inductor, and load current are the same. Therefore

$$e_r \simeq \frac{3.54 \times 10^7}{\omega^3}$$

Step 2.   For a full-wave rectifier the minimum frequency component is twice the input frequency. Therefore

$$\omega = 2\pi f$$

$$= 2\pi \times 120$$

$$\simeq 754 \text{ rad/sec}$$

Step 3.   Using this value of ω we obtain

$$e_r \simeq \frac{3.5 \times 10^7}{(7.54 \times 10^2)^3}$$

$$= \frac{3.5 \times 10^7}{426 \times 10^6}$$

$$\simeq 0.082 \text{ volts} = 82 \text{ mV}$$

Using a full-wave rectifier has reduced the ripple voltage by a factor of 8.

8.7   *RC* Filtering

In the case of *LC* filtering the capacitors are used to store DC voltage while passing the ripple component to ground. The inductors are used to reduce the ripple in the current which flows through the load. It is possible to use *RC* filtering instead of *LC* filtering. A single-section *RC* filter is shown in Fig. 8.20.

The capacitors in an *RC* filter perform the same function as in an *LC* filter. The resistors in an *RC* filter perform the same function as the inductors in a series circuit, but the resistors are not as efficient as inductors. An ideal

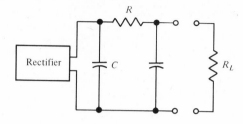

8.20 Single-section *RC* filter.

inductor has no effect on DC, but as frequency increases inductors become better and better "opposers" of AC ($X_L = \omega L$). For this reason inductors are often referred to as **chokes.** Resistors, on the other hand, perform identically with both AC and DC. Thus while a resistor opposes AC, it opposes DC equally well.

The function of *RC* filters is the same as that of *LC* filters. They convert pulsating DC to steady-state DC with a ripple. The equations for ripple voltages are quite similar. For an *RC* filter,

$$e_r \simeq \frac{\sqrt{2}I_{DC}}{(\omega C)^{n_C} R^{n_R}} \tag{8.5}$$

where R is the value of resistance and n_R is the number of resistors. Notice that the numerator and most of the denominator is exactly the same as for an *LC* filter. The only difference is that the R^{n_R} term replaces the $(\omega L)^{n_L}$ term.

Resistors do not depend on ω. Therefore ω will appear to a lower power in the ripple equation for *RC* than for *LC* filtering. This means that for equal-value capacitors additional sections of *RC* filtering will be required to obtain the same ripple as with *LC* filtering. Also, there will be a DC voltage drop across the resistors in an *RC* filter while we ignore the DC resistance of an inductor. This means that we shall have to start with a higher-voltage transformer with *RC* filtering to obtain the same voltage at the load. Since there are DC voltage drops across the filter resistors power is being wasted; that is, it costs more to operate an *RC* filter than an *LC* filter. However, resistors are less expensive and a good deal smaller than inductors, so *RC* filters are smaller and less expensive to build than *LC* filters. The final design of a power supply filter must be a compromise between such conflicting situations.

In the case of an *LC* filter, calculating the transformer secondary voltage is a straightforward process. We ignore the DC voltage drop across the inductors. Thus the voltage across the first capacitor is approximately the same as across the load. Depending on the type of rectifier, we account for the voltage drops across one or two forward-biased diodes and arrive at a transformer secondary voltage.

The situation is more complicated for *RC* filtering since there is a voltage drop across the filter resistors. How much voltage should we "waste" across the filter resistors? Again a compromise must be struck. From an efficiency standpoint we do not want to waste any voltage which is used only to heat filter resistors. From a ripple-reduction standpoint Eq. 8.5 shows that larger resistors result in smaller ripple voltage.

One reason that we are interested in low ripple voltage is that **amplifiers, for example, can amplify power-supply ripple as well as signals.** Thus the lowest level of the signal which can be amplified will be affected by the value of the power-supply ripple. Also, lower ripple will result in less distortion of the signal being amplified. Example 8.10 illustrates the procedure involved in designing a DC power supply using *RC* filtering:

Example 8.10

As shown in Fig. 8.21, use a bridge rectifier and two sections of *RC* filtering to design a power supply. The load is 1 KΩ and requires 10 V_{DC} with a 3 mV ripple.

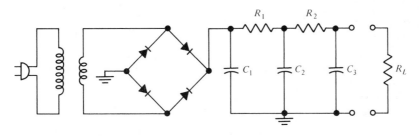

8.21   Complete DC power supply schematic.

Solution Step 1.   At first glance Fig. 8.21 may seem to be a completely new configuration. This is not the case at all. A bridge rectifier is connected to a two-section *RC* filter which is in turn connected to the load. Notice that one side of the bridge and the filter are both connected to ground. The entire filter and load actually fit "inside" the bridge, as in Fig. 8.15 for example. Drawing the filter "outside" the rectifier is just a drafting convenience.

Step 2.   The load current is the load voltage divided by the load resistance:

$$I_L = \frac{V_L}{R_L}$$

$$= \frac{10}{10^3}$$

$$= 10 \text{ mA.}$$

Step 3.   Since there is a DC voltage drop across the filter resistor we must start with a higher voltage for this loss. Start with a transformer with a 25 V_{rms} secondary. As in Table 8.1, V_{C_1} will be $V_{max} - 2V_D$:

$$V_{C_1} = \sqrt{2}V_{rms} - 2 \times 0.6$$
$$= \sqrt{2} \times 25 - 1.2$$
$$= 34 \text{ volts}$$

Step 4.   Regarding DC considerations, we can consider C_1 as a 34-volt battery and neglect C_2 and C_3 (temporarily) since capacitors do not pass DC. This is shown in Fig. 8.22. Using Kirchhoff's voltage law,

$$V_{C_1} = V_{R_1} + V_{R_2} + V_{R_L}$$
$$34 = V_{R_1} + V_{R_2} + 10$$
$$V_{R_1} + V_{R_2} = 24 \text{ volts}$$

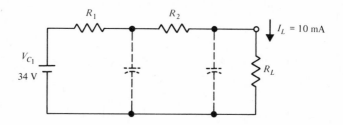

8.22   DC equivalent of *RC* filter.

Step 5.   The voltage drop across the two filter resistors is 24 volts. Using equal filter resistors there will be a 12-volt drop across each filter resistor:

$$V_{R_1} = V_{R_2} = 12 \text{ volts}$$

Step 6.   Since the DC equivalent of the filter circuit is a series circuit as shown in Fig. 8.22, $I_L = I_{filter}$. Therefore

$$I_{filter} = 10 \text{ mA.}$$
$$R_1 = \frac{V_{R_1}}{I_{filter}}$$
$$= \frac{12}{10 \times 10^{-3}}$$
$$= R_2 = 1.2 \text{ k}\Omega$$

Step 7.   We can now determine the value of the capacitors necessary to obtain a
3-mV ripple:

$$e_r \simeq \frac{\sqrt{2}I_{DC}}{(\omega C)^3 R^2}$$

$$C^3 = \frac{\sqrt{2}I_{DC}}{\omega^3 R^2 e_r}$$

$$= \frac{\sqrt{2} \times 10 \times 10^{-3}}{(7.54 \times 10^2)^3 (1.2 \times 10^3)^2 \times 3 \times 10^{-3}}$$

$$= 0.766 \times 10^{-14} = 7.66 \times 10^{-15}$$

$$C = (7.66 \times 10^{-15})^{1/3}$$

$$= 1.97 \times 10^{-5} = 19.7 \times 10^{-6}$$

$$\simeq 20 \,\mu F$$

Step 8.   We have determined the values of the transformer and the components in
the filter design. Strictly speaking we should determine I_f and PIV ratings for the
diodes, power ratings for the filter resistors, and voltage ratings for the capacitors.

Realistic values of filter capacitors are generally in tens of microfarads.
The only capacitors which can provide such large capacitance in reasonable
volume are **electrolytic.** Such capacitors are chemical in nature and therefore
have polarized terminals. The higher voltage level must be connected to the
positive capacitor terminal and the lower voltage level to the negative
capacitor terminal. Failure to observe proper polarity will result in an
explosion of the capacitor. As shown in Fig. 8.21, the negative capacitor
terminal is indicated by a curved rather than a straight line.

In Example 8.10 we started with 34 V_{DC} to end up with 10 V_{DC}. A partial
compensation for this "wasted" voltage is that several DC voltages are
available from a single power supply. That is, the voltage across C_1 is 34 volts
and the voltage across C_2 is 22 volts $(34 - 12)$. From this power supply we
have three different DC voltages (with different ripples). To obtain three
different voltages with *LC* filtering would require three different power
supplies. Moreover, if we use unequal filter resistors and filter capacitors we
can adjust both the voltage across C_2 and also the ripple levels.

8.8   Regulated Power Supplies

We know from experience that line voltage does not remain constant.
Depending on the season and time of day lamps will be brighter, indicating
voltage above 115 V_{rms}, or dimmer, indicating lower voltage. Similar
experiences occur with toasters, TV sets, and so on. Variation in line voltage

means that the load voltage for the power supplies which we have been discussing will also fluctuate, because a variation in line voltage results in a variation in transformer secondary voltage (Eq. 7.9c). A variation in transformer secondary voltage results in a variation in load voltage for both LC and RC filtered power supplies.

Typically, line voltage may vary between 105 V_{rms} and 130 V_{rms}. In extreme cases the variation may be even greater. Example 8.11 illustrates the effect of line-voltage variation on power-supply load voltage.

Example 8.11

Assuming that the nominal 115-volt line voltage varies between 105 and 125 V_{rms}, determine the minimum and maximum load voltages for the power supply of Example 8.10.

Solution Step 1.   Using Eq. 7.9c, calculate the transformer turns ratio:

$$\frac{V_1}{V_2} = \frac{N_1}{N_2}$$

$$\frac{115}{25} = \frac{N_1}{N_2}$$

$$\frac{N_1}{N_2} = 4.6:1$$

Step 2.   Calculate the transformer secondary voltage when the line voltage drops to 105 V_{rms}:

$$\frac{V_1}{V_2} = \frac{N_1}{N_2}$$

$$\frac{105}{V_2} = \frac{4.6}{1}$$

$$V_2 = 22.8 \text{ volts}$$

Step 3.   When the transformer secondary voltage drops to 22.8 volts the voltage across C_1 will drop to

$$V_{C_1} = \sqrt{2}V_{rms} - 2V_D$$
$$= \sqrt{2} \times 22.8 - 1.2 = 32.2 - 1.2$$
$$V_{C_1} = 31.0 \text{ volts}$$

Step 4.   The components of the power supply are constant even though the line voltage fluctuates; that is, $R_L = 1 \text{ k}\Omega$ and $R_{filter(T)} = 2.4 \text{ k}\Omega$. Therefore

$$V_{L(\text{min})} = V_{C_1} \frac{R_L}{R_{\text{filter}(T)} + R_L}$$

$$= 31 \frac{10^3}{2.4 \times 10^3 + 10^3}$$

$$= 9.1 \text{ volts}$$

Step 5. In a similar manner, when the line voltage rises to 125 V_{rms} the secondary voltage will be

$$\frac{125}{V_2} = \frac{4.6}{1}$$

$$V_2 = 27.2$$

Step 6.

$$V_{C_1(\text{max})} = \sqrt{2} V_{\text{rms}} - 2V_D$$

$$= \sqrt{2} \times 27.2 - 1.2 = 38.5 - 1.2 = 37.3$$

$$= 37.3 \text{ volts}$$

Step 7.

$$V_{L(\text{max})} = V_{C_1} \frac{R_L}{R_{\text{filter}(T)} + R_L}$$

$$= 37.3 \frac{10^3}{3.4 \times 10^3}$$

$$= 10.95 \text{ volts}$$

Example 8.11 shows that with a typical line-voltage variation the voltage from a nominal 10 volt power supply will range from a low of 9.1 volts to a high of 10.95 volts. Under certain conditions this will not matter, although for precision applications power-supply variation will be a disaster.

Therefore we are interested in maintaining a constant load voltage even though line voltage fluctuates; that is, we require a **regulated power supply.** It may seem like a contradiction of Ohm's law to maintain a constant load voltage even though the source voltage varies. In fact, what we require is a device which does not obey Ohm's law. Fortunately a component which maintains constant voltage, even though the current through it varies, does exist.

Figure 8.23 shows a diode *I-V* characteristic curve with more of the negative voltage region than is shown in Fig. 8.4. In this particular case, at -10 volts the voltage remains constant even though there can be almost any current value. The reason for this effect is quite interesting. When a diode is

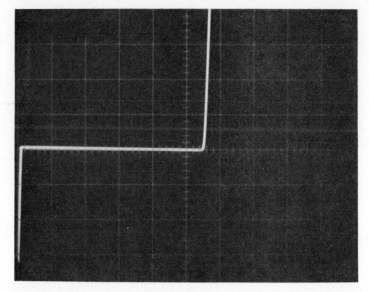

8.23 Zener diode *I-V* characteristics. Vertical scale = 2 mA/cm; horizontal scale = 2 v/cm.

reverse biased only minority carrier current flows. As the reverse bias is increased no additional carriers are available so that the increase in energy goes into accelerating the already existing minority carriers. Ultimately the accelerated minority carriers acquire sufficient energy to dislodge additional charges from the parent atoms. When this occurs, the result is **an increase in current without any increase in voltage.** The increase in current with constant voltage is called the **avalanche** effect. Depending on the doping ratios in the *p* and *n* regions, diodes can be made to avalanche from very low voltages up to hundreds of volts. Diodes are available with almost any avalanche voltage which may be needed. Such diodes are called **Zener diodes** in honor of Clarence Zener, an American who first investigated this effect.

We can use a Zener diode to construct a regulated power supply. A schematic of a regulated supply is shown in Fig. 8.24. The symbol for a Zener diode has "tails" on the *n* side of the diode. Notice that the *p* side of the Zener is connected to the negative side of the load and that the *n* side of the Zener is connected to the positive side of the load. This is because the constant voltage characteristic occurs in the negative voltage portion of the diode characteristic, so that **the Zener diode must be reverse biased to obtain regulation.**

If the Zener can be maintained in avalanche the load voltage will remain constant; because the load is in parallel with the Zener. We must ensure that the Zener is in avalanche when the line voltage is at its minimum value. In this way any increase in line voltage will only drive the Zener deeper into avalanche and the load voltage will remain constant. At minimum line voltage

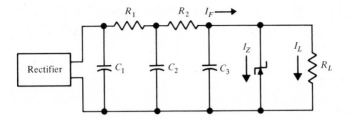

8.24 Regulated power supply.

the Zener must be biased past the "knee" of the avalanche region. The rule of thumb for assuring proper Zener operation is

$$I_{z(min)} = 5\text{mA or } 10\% \text{ of } I_L, \text{ whichever is greater} \qquad (8.6)$$

This means that the filter circuit must be recalculated since the filter current has to be increased even though the load current is constant. That is, the current which leaves the filter is now the sum of the Zener and load current. This is a consequence of Kirchoff's current law:

$$I_{\text{filter}} = I_Z + I_L \qquad (8.7)$$

Example 8.12

For a line voltage range of 105–130 V_{rms}, determine the proper component values for a regulated supply which has the same load requirements as in Example 8.10.

Solution Step 1. The requirements of Example 8.10 are 10 mA. into a 1 kΩ load. Select a 10-V Zener.

Step 2. Ten percent of I_L, which is 10 mA., is only 1.0 mA. Five mA. is greater so this is the minimum Zener current.

Step 3. Therefore the minimum load current is

$$I_{\text{filter(min)}} = I_{2(min)} + I_L$$
$$= 5 + 10 \text{ mA.}$$
$$= 15 \text{ mA.}$$

Step 4. Minimum filter current will occur when the line voltage is minimum. From Example 8.11 we saw that this results in a V_{C_1} of 30.8 volts.

Step 5. Since the load voltage will still be 10 volts due to the Zener,

$$V_{C_1} = V_{R_1} + V_{R_2} + V_L$$
$$30.8 = V_{R_1} + V_{R_2} + 10$$
$$V_{R_1} + V_{R_2} = 20.8 \text{ volts}$$

Step 6.   As in Examples 8.10 and 8.11 we are using equal filter resistors:

$$V_{R_1} = V_{R_2} = \frac{20.8}{2} = 10.4 \text{ volts}$$

Step 7.   Therefore

$$R_1 = R_2 = \frac{10.4}{I_{\text{filter}}}$$

$$= \frac{10.4}{15 \times 10^{-3}}$$

$$= 680 \,\Omega$$

compared with 1.2 kΩ for the unregulated supply of Example 8.10.

Step 8.   We need to determine a suitable power rating for the Zener. Zener current will be a maximum when line voltage is maximum. From Example 8.11,

$$V_{C_1(\text{max})} = 37 \text{ volts}$$

Step 9.   Since the Zener is holding the load voltage constant at 10 volts the maximum voltage across the filter is

$$V_{C_1(\text{max})} = V_{\text{filter(max)}} + V_L$$

$$37 = V_{\text{filter(max)}} + 10$$

$$V_{\text{filter(max)}} = 27 \text{ volts}$$

Step 10.   The load resistors cannot change value. Therefore

$$I_{\text{filter(max)}} = \frac{V_{\text{filter(max)}}}{R_{\text{filter}}}$$

$$= \frac{27}{680 + 680}$$

$$= 19.8 \text{ mA.}$$

Step 11.   Therefore

$$I_{\text{filter(max)}} = I_{Z(\text{max})} + I_L$$

and I_L is constant at 10 mA.

$$19.8 \text{ mA.} \quad = I_{Z(\text{max})} + 10 \text{ mA.}$$

$$I_{Z(\text{max})} = 9.8 \text{ mA.}$$

Step 12.   Since power dissipation is voltage × current,

$$P_{Z(\text{max})} = I_{Z(\text{max})}V_Z$$
$$= 9.8 \times 10^{-3} \times 10$$
$$= 98 \text{ mW}$$

Zener diodes generally will also help in reducing ripple, depending on the particular Zener selected.

8.9   Vacuum Diodes

It is possible to build rectifiers and power supplies of the types which have been discussed using vacuum diodes instead of semiconductor diodes. The principle of vacuum conduction was introduced in Chapter 1. As shown in Fig. 8.25, a heated filament injects electrons into an evacuated jar. The electrons are attracted to the other element in the jar, the plate, only when the plate has a positive potential, because electrons are negatively charged. Thus if an alternating voltage is applied between the plate and the filament a half-wave rectifier results.

Electrons are injected into the vacuum during the entire cycle. However, during the half-cycle that the AC is negative, electrons are repelled by the plate. Current flows only during the positive half-cycles of the AC waveform. Figure 8.26 shows a vacuum diode *I-V* characteristic curve. Although it is quite similar in form to the semiconductor characteristic of Fig. 8.4, the principle of operation is quite different.

The reason that the vacuum diode *I-V* curve increases slowly at low voltage is that the filament has a slight positive charge; the electrons which are emitted from the filament are negatively charged so the filament acquires a positive charge. Therefore at low plate voltage the emitted electrons are just as likely to "fall back" to the filament as to be attracted to the plate. When the plate is made increasingly positive the slight positive charge on the filament is overcome and the current begins to rise sharply.

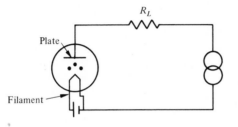

8.25   Vacuum diode half-wave rectifier.

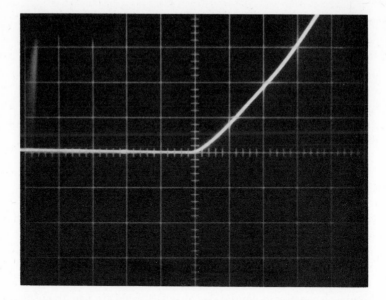

8.26 Vacuum diode *I-V* characteristics. Vertical scale = 10 mA/cm; horizontal scale = 2 v/cm.

When the vacuum diode is reverse biased there is no current flow. There are no minority carriers in vacuum conduction, only electrons. Therefore there is no equivalent of the reverse saturation current which exists in a semiconductor diode.

A vacuum diode requires electrical power to heat the filament. In a semiconductor diode there is no filament so less power is required to operate semiconductor diodes. A diode filament eventually must burn out just as the filament of a light bulb burns out. Therefore a properly operated semiconductor diode will outlast a vacuum diode. Also, semiconductor diodes are physically much smaller than a vacuum diode with corresponding characteristics.

Summary

1. A semiconductor is formed by joining *p*-type and *n*-type material.
2. When a diode is forward biased there is a large positive current. When a semiconductor diode is reverse biased there is a small negative current.
3. There is a large difference between the resistance of a forward- and a reverse-biased diode. A forward-biased diode has low resistance and a reverse-biased diode has high resistance.
4. The diode is a nonlinear unilateral device and the resistor is linear and bilateral.

5. The unilateral properties of a diode can be used to change AC into pulsating DC. This process is called rectification.

6. Rectification is the first part of changing AC to battery-type DC. This is necessary since most electronics equipment operate on DC only, while power companies deliver AC.

7. Half-wave and full-wave rectifiers change AC to pulsating DC but have different characteristics as to amplitude, frequency, and PIV.

8. Attaching an LC filter to a rectifier changes pulsating DC into steady DC with a ripple component. Ripple can be reduced by using large values of L and C, full-wave instead of half-wave, and several sections of filtering.

9. RC filtering can be used instead of LC filtering. RC filtering requires that a higher-voltage transformer be used.

10. Power is dissipated in the resistors of RC filters, but several different DC voltages are available simultaneously.

11. Many electronic circuits require a constant load voltage despite line-voltage variations. A properly biased Zener diode can be operated as a constant voltage element.

12. Placing the appropriate Zener diode across the load maintains constant load voltage since parallel components have equal voltages.

13. Vacuum diodes can also be used as rectifiers. Although semiconductor and vacuum diodes have similar I-V curves the mechanism of conduction is different.

Questions

1. How is the depletion region formed?
2. Why do forward- and reverse-biased diodes have different current-voltage characteristics?
3. Discuss the differences between the resistance of a forward- and a reverse-biased diode.
4. What is diode reverse saturation current?
5. Under what circumstances can Ohm's law be used for a nonlinear device?
6 What is the difference between nonlinear and unilateral?
7. What is rectification?
8. Why is rectification necessary?
9. Compare the characteristics of half-wave and full-wave rectifiers.
10. What is the function of a filter in a DC power supply?
11. Why is the ripple from a full-wave rectifier less than that from a half-wave rectifier even if the same filter is used?
12. Why must a higher-voltage transformer be used with RC filtering?
13. Compare the advantages and disadvantages of LC and RC filtering.
14. Describe some factors which determine the required level of ripple voltage.
15. What is meant by the avalanche effect in diodes?
16. How is a Zener diode used to make a regulated voltage supply?
17. How does a vacuum diode operate?
18. Compare vacuum and semiconductor diode characteristics.

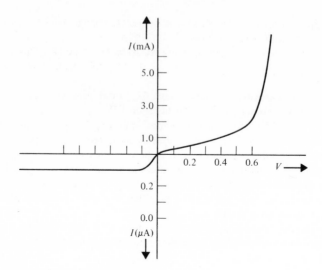

8.27   *I-V* characteristic for Problem 1.

Problems

1. For the silicon diode *I-V* characteristic in Fig. 8.27, find the diode resistance at 0.1 and 0.6 volts.
2. Repeat Problem 1 except find the diode resistance at -0.1 and -0.6 volts.
3. A certain diode has a reverse saturation current of 2 μA. Find the diode resistance (assuming room temperature) at 24 mV and 250 mV.
4. For what value of positive bias will neglecting the -1 term in the diode current equation cause less than a 5% error?
5. Use the same diode as in Problem 3 and find the diode resistance at -25 mV and -250 mV.
6. For what negative bias will neglecting the $\varepsilon^{39\,V}$ term in the diode current equation cause less than a 5% error?
7. A half-wave rectifier is built using a germanium diode with $I_s = 10\ \mu$A. The generator voltage is 20 V_{p-p} and the load resistance is 1 kΩ. Find the actual values of
   (a) $I_{L(max)}$ and $V_{R_L(max)}$
   (b) $I_{L(min)}$ and $V_{R_L(min)}$
8. Repeat Problem 7 for a silicon diode with a 1-μA saturation current.
9. For a half-wave rectifier using a germanium diode, at what value of generator voltage can the barrier voltage be neglected (less than a 5% error)?
10. Repeat Problem 9 for a silicon diode.
11. A half-wave rectifier is attached to a transformer with a 12.6-V_{rms} secondary. The load is a 100-Ω resistor.
    (a) Determine $I_{L(max)}$
    (b) Specify a PIV rating
12. Repeat Problem 11 for a full-wave, center-tap rectifier.

13. Repeat Problem 11 for a bridge rectifier.

14. A single-section LC filter connected to a bridge rectifier furnished 20 V_{DC} to a 1-kΩ load. If 40-μF capacitors are used, what value of inductance is necessary to keep the ripple voltage at 5 mV?

15. Determine the secondary voltage of the transformer necessary in Problem 14.

16. A power-supply filter delivers 50 mA to a load using 25-μF capacitors and 10-H inductors. If a full-wave rectifier is used, determine the ripple voltage if the following are used:
   (a) A single-section LC filter
   (b) A two-section LC filter.

17. The design requirements are the same as for Example 8.10, but a 12-V_{rms} transformer is to be used. Determine the filter capacitor and filter resistor values.

18. Using a transformer with a 48-V_{rms} secondary, design a power supply which delivers 35 mA to a 1-kΩ load with a 1-mV ripple. Two sections of RC filtering and a bridge rectifier are to be used.

19. The power supply of Problem 18 must be regulated; the line fluctuates between 100 and 130 V_{rms}. Determine
   (a) The proper values of filter resistors
   (b) The Zener voltage
   (c) Maximum Zener power dissipation

Chapter 9 Transistors

9.1   Introduction

In this chapter we shall extend the action of a *pn* junction to cover the transistor which can amplify power. Various methods of using transistors to optimize performance are investigated.

9.2   Diodes Back to Back

In Chapter 8 the *pn* junction was introduced. Diode action was discussed and diodes were used as rectifiers. Figure 9.1 shows an "unusual" diode circuit. D_1 is forward biased by V_1 and D_2 is reverse biased by V_2. If this circuit is actually constructed the "leakage" current as shown will be very large and nothing useful will happen. However the principle is important.

Assume for the time being that the leakage current does not exist. If this is the case, all current which flows through the forward-biased diode must also flow through the reverse-biased diode. This is a consequence of Kirchhoff's current law, which states that the current entering a junction is equal to the current which leaves the junction:

$$I_f = I_{\text{leakage}} + I_r \tag{9.1a}$$

If, however,

$$I_{\text{leakage}} = 0$$

$$I_f = I_r \tag{9.1b}$$

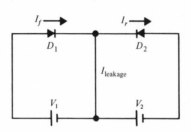

9.1   Diodes back to back.

We can calculate the power dissipation in the forward- and reverse-biased diodes in terms of diode current and diode resistance:

$$\text{for } D_1 \qquad P_1 = I_f^2 R_{\text{fwd}} \qquad\qquad (9.1c)$$

$$\text{for } D_2 \qquad P_2 = I_r^2 R_{\text{rev}} \qquad\qquad (9.1d)$$

where R_{fwd} and R_{rev} refer to the diode forward- and reverse-bias resistance. If we divide P_2 by P_1 we obtain

$$\frac{P_2}{P_1} = \frac{I_r^2 R_{\text{rev}}}{I_f^2 R_{\text{fwd}}} \qquad\qquad (9.2a)$$

However, if the circuit shown in Fig. 9.1 can actually be realized, I_r is equal to I_f (Eq. 9.1b) since no current flows through the component with the question mark. Therefore

$$\frac{P_2}{P_1} = \frac{I_r^2 R_{\text{rev}}}{I_f^2 R_{\text{fwd}}} = \frac{R_{\text{rev}}}{R_{\text{fwd}}} \gg 1 \qquad\qquad (9.2b)$$

From our discussion of diode resistance in Chapter 8 we know that the reverse-bias resistance of a diode is much greater than the forward-bias resistance of a diode. Thus the ratio P_2/P_1 is much greater than unity. If the reverse-biased diode is used as an output resistor and the forward-biased diode is used as an input resistor, the **output power is greater than the input power** due to the resistance ratio $R_{\text{rev}}/R_{\text{fwd}}$. Such a device *trans*fers power from a low to a high res*istor* (*trans + istor = transistor*).

Example 9.1

Compute the P_2/P_1 ratio for a diode with an $R_{\text{rev}} = 200\text{ k}\Omega$ and an $R_{\text{fwd}} = 20\ \Omega$ if
(a) All the forward-biased diode current flows in the reverse-biased diode
(b) Only 90% of the forward-biased current reaches the reverse-biased diode

Solution Part (a) Step 1. Since $I_f = I_r$, Eq. 9.2b is directly applicable.

Step 2. Thus

$$\frac{P_2}{P_1} = \frac{2 \times 10^5}{2 \times 10^1} = 10,000$$

Part (b) Step 1. In this case $I_r = 0.9\, I_f$; that is, 10% of the forward-biased diode current "leaks" out.

Step 2. Therefore

$$\frac{P_2}{P_1} = \frac{I_r^2 R_{\text{rev}}}{I_f^2 R_{\text{fwd}}} = \frac{(0.9 I_f)^2 \times 2 \times 10^5}{I_f^2 \times 2 \times 10^1} = 8100$$

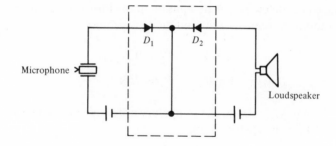

9.2 Power amplification by transistor action.

Example 9.1 shows that even if a substantial portion of the forward-biased diode current does not reach the reverse-biased diode it is still possible for the output power to be much greater than the input power; that is, **a transistor can amplify power.**

A circuit which amplifies signal power by transistor action is shown in Fig. 9.2. The microphone signal is superimposed on the forward-biased diode current. The output signal is superimposed on the reverse-biased diode current. Since the loudspeaker is in series with the reverse-biased diode they have the same current. Thus amplified signal power drives the loudspeaker. The output power (loudspeaker) is greater than the input power (microphone) due to the resistance ratio of the forward- and reverse-biased diodes. This is what permits transistors to act as power amplifiers.

We are using a transistor to amplify signal power, but this does not mean that we are getting something for nothing. Conservation of energy is not being violated. The amplified signal power is obtained as a result of the battery power which is being used to forward bias the input diode and reverse bias the output diode. Thus what we are doing is exchanging one form of power for another. **Battery power is being traded to achieve an increase in signal power.**

Even under ideal conditions not all of the power calculated in Example 9.1 is available. One reason for this is the maximum power transfer theorem which was discussed in Chapter 3. Thus if we were to match resistances perfectly at both the input and output the best we could do would be one fourth of the power calculated in Example 9.1. This is because we would lose one half of the microphone power in the forward-biased diode and one half of the power in the transistor output resistance. However, even one fourth of the values obtained in Example 9.1 are very respectable power amplification ratios.

When the transformer was discussed in Chapter 7 we saw that the transformer could amplify voltage (step-up transformer). The transformer can also amplify current (step-down transformer). However, the transformer cannot amplify voltage and current simultaneously. Thus the transformer cannot amplify power. The transistor, however, is a true power amplifying device.

9.3   Practical Transistors

The principle of using diodes back to back to achieve transistor action is correct, but a transistor cannot be constructed by using two separate diodes. Practical transistors, however, do exist.

In Fig. 9.3 (a) there are two diodes back to back. Notice that the sides of the two diodes which are connected together are both *n* doped. That is, a transistor as shown in Fig. 9.3 (b) consists of a "sandwich" of *n*-doped material between two layers of *p*-doped material. If the center *n* section shown in Fig. 9.3 (b) is made very thin and the entire structure exists within a single crystal we can achieve the desired result. Holes from the forward-biased *p* region are injected into the very thin *n* region. Since the *n* region is very thin, very little hole-electron recombination will occur. Also, since the *n* region is thin very few holes will leak out. Therefore most of the holes emitted by the forward-biased *p* region will arrive at the reverse-biased *n* region. These holes will be attracted by the negative bias and transistor action will be achieved. This structure must be created within a single crystal.

In an actual transistor **we forward bias one *pn* junction and reverse bias the other *pn* junction.** This is exactly the same as in our initial discussion. The *pnp* sandwich in a single crystal is an actual transistor.

The concept and development of a practical transistor was accomplished by three Americans. John Bardeen, Walter Brattain, and William Schockley were awarded the Nobel price in physics for this tremendous achievement in 1948. It is the transistor which necessitated the discussion of doping in Chapter 1. A *PNP* configuration must be doped into a single crystal of

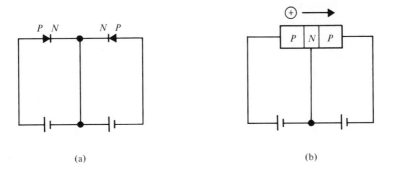

(a)   (b)

9.3   Transistor junctions. (a) Principle. (b) Actual configuration.

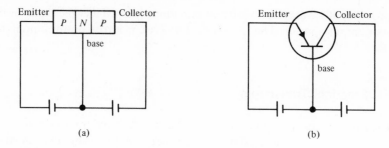

9.4 *PNP* transistor biasing. (a) Configuration. (b) Schematic.

either germanium or silicon; if not, current from the forward-biased diode will not enter the reverse-biased diode and transistor action will not have been accomplished.

Figure 9.4 shows the terminology used to describe transistors. The *p* region which is forward biased and emits holes is called the **emitter.** The *p* region which is reverse-biased and collects the holes is called the **collector.** The *n* region between the emitter and the collector is called the **base.**

An actual transistor does consist of two diodes back to back, with the important condition that the diodes are within a single crystal. Using transistor terminology the proper biasing requirements to achieve transistor action are

1. Forward bias the emitter-base diode (junction)
2. Reverse bias the collector-base diode (junction).

In terms of diodes back to back it is the *n* region which is common to both diodes in a *PNP* transistor. It is also possible to connect diodes back to back by having the *p* region common as shown in Fig. 9.5. It is just as necessary to forward bias the emitter-base junction and reverse bias the collector-base junction in an *NPN* transistor as in a *PNP* transistor. However, since the materials are reversed the biasing batteries must also be reversed.

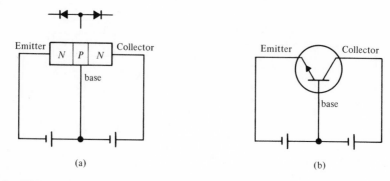

9.5 *NPN* transistor biasing. (a) Configuration. (b) Schematic.

If we compare the schematic of the *PNP* transistor in Fig. 9.4 (b) with the *NPN* schematic in Fig. 9.5 (b) we see that they are almost identical. In both types the base and collector are exactly the same. In both types the emitters are indicated by arrowheads.

The only difference between a *PNP* and an *NPN* transistor schematic is that in a *PNP* type the emitter points towards the base and in an *NPN* type the emitter points away from the base.

Notice that in both *PNP* and *NPN* transistors the emitter and collector are made of the same material. However, the requirements for a good emitter are not the same as for a good collector. Thus the resistivity and geometry of emitters and collectors will be different despite the fact that they are made of the same material. The importance of this is that it may be possible to use the emitter as a collector and vice versa. However, due to the structural differences between emitter and collector transistor action will not be as efficient in the **inverted mode.**

We have already seen (in Chapter 8) that while there is a relationship between current and voltage in a diode (Eq. 8.1), diodes do not obey Ohm's law. Since transistors are based on diode action, transistors will not obey Ohm's law. All devices, however, must obey Kirchhoff's current and voltage laws. In the case of a transistor the current which enters is the emitter current (I_e). The currents which leave the transistor are the collector current (I_c) and the base current (I_b). Therefore Kirchhoff's current law for transistors is

$$I_e = I_b + I_c \tag{9.3}$$

Although the preferred direction of current in a transistor is from emitter to collector, a certain amount of current will "leak" out through the base as shown in Fig. 9.6. (Incidentally, is the transistor in Fig. 9.6 *NPN* or *PNP*?) The ratio of collector current to emitter current is α:

$$\alpha = \frac{I_c}{I_e} \tag{9.4}$$

If no current flowed out of the base α would be unity. The ratio current/current has no dimensions so α is dimensionless.

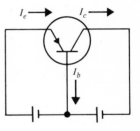

9.6   Transistor current flow.

Example 9.2

For a certain properly biased transistor the collector current is 1 mA. If the transistor has an α of 0.98 find the emitter and base currents.

Solution Step 1.

$$\alpha = 0.98 = \frac{I_c}{I_e}$$

Step 2. Since $I_c = 1$ mA.

$$0.98 = \frac{10^{-3}}{I_e}$$

$$I_e = \frac{10^{-3}}{0.98}$$

$$\simeq 1.02 \text{ mA.}$$

Step 3. $I_e = I_b + I_c$ and I_e and I_c are now both known.

$$1.02 \text{ mA} = I_b + 1 \text{ mA.}$$

$$I_b = 0.02 \text{ mA} = 20 \text{ } \mu\text{A.}$$

9.4   Transistor Equivalent Circuits

The transistor has the capability of amplifying power. We now under-stand the transistor in terms of transferring current from a forward-biased diode to a reverse-biased diode. This concept is correct but we must also understand the transistor as a component with specific values.

If we inject some input signal, what are the best values of load and generator resistance to obtain maximum power transfer? What if instead we switch to achieve minimum loading and yet require amplification? What are the best values? What is the appropriate transistor? To answer such questions we need a model of the transistor, a "black box". We can determine a transistor equivalent circuit using the black-box techniques which were introduced in Chapter 5, but since transistors are generally used to amplify AC signals, we shall use AC voltages and currents to measure the black-box parameters.

The black-box approach for transistors is somewhat different than for black boxes which consist of resistors, capacitors, and inductors. In the case of R, L, C components we can immediately attach signal sources and make appropriate input and output measurements. But a **transistor does not function unless it is first properly biased.** Thus in the case of a transistor **we must first DC bias the junctions and then superimpose the AC signals.**

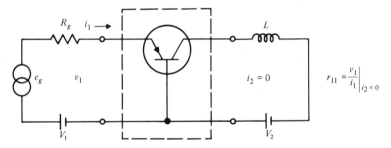

9.7   Determining r_{11} for a transistor.

This will lead us to a signal equivalent model of the transistor which is excactly what we require.

A method of measuring the value of r_{11} for a transistor is shown in Fig. 9.7. We are interested in the AC equivalent of Eq. 5.2a; that is, we want the ratio of input signal voltage (v_1) to input signal current (i_1) when there is no output signal ($i_2 = 0$). However, we must still maintain the collector junction reverse biased although there is no output signal current. As shown in Fig. 9.7 this is accomplished with the aid of an inductor. In Chapter 7 we saw that the inductive reactance was ωL. In the DC case $\omega = 0$. Therefore an inductor passes DC while it blocks AC. The inductor is in the output loop. Thus it has no effect on the DC current needed to reverse bias the collector-base junction. This is accomplished by V_2. However, the inductor does oppose the output signal current which is an AC quantity. Thus with a large enough value of inductance we can essentially reduce the output signal current (i_2) to zero while proper bias is maintained. Similarly, we can strategically use the properties of an inductor to determine the values of r_{12}, r_{21}, and r_{22} for the transistor.

Once we obtain the r values for the transistor a tee equivalent circuit for the transistor can be constructed. This is shown in Fig. 9.8. Notice that the tee equivalent for a transistor is somewhat different from a purely resistive tee. Both have three resistors. In the transistor tee we use r_e (the emitter resistance), r_b (the base resistance), and r_c (the collector resistance).

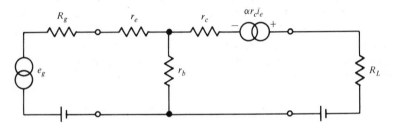

9.8   Transistor tee equivalent circuit.

The difference between a resistor tee and a transistor tee is the component marked $\alpha r_c i_e$.

We have already seen that α is dimensionless and $r_c i_e$ is the product of collector resistance and emitter current. This has the dimension of voltage (Ohm's law). Thus the component is **a voltage generator which depends on the value of emitter current.** The value will vary for different transistors since different transistors will have different values of α. A generator (such as $\alpha r_c i_e$) whose value depends on some other quantity in a circuit is called a **controlled source.**

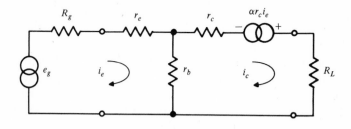

9.9   Signal analysis equivalent circuit.

Thus the tee equivalent of the transistor is seen to be consistent with Kirchhoff's voltage law since the r values are based on input and output black-box measurements. Just as important is the fact that this tee equivalent is consistent with transistor action. Suppose the input current, which is the emitter current in this case, increases. Then the controlled voltage source ($\alpha r_c i_e$) will increase since it is controlled by i_e. Similarly, a decrease in the input current to the emitter will result in a decrease in the value of the controlled voltage source. This is in accordance with the principle of transistor action. The current from the forward-biased diode junction is controlling the current in the reverse-biased diode junction.

This is what the black box approach is all about. In the signal analysis we neglect the biasing batteries, as shown in Fig. 9.9. This circuit is a two-loop, two-generator configuration. This type of circuit has already been investigated in Chapter 3. The only difference is that here we are dealing with one independent (the signal generator) and one controlled source. In Chapter 3 we had two independent sources (two batteries). The circuit of Fig. 9.9 can be used to determine transistor design equations. First we write the loop equations:

$$\text{input loop} \qquad e_g = i_e(R_g + r_b + r_e) - i_c r_b$$

$$\text{output loop} \qquad \alpha r_c i_e = -i_e r_b + i_c(r_b + r_c + R_L) \qquad \textbf{(9.6)}$$

Equations 9.5 and 9.6 provide the basis for analyzing transistor performance. If we wish to determine the **voltage amplification** of this circuit,

$$A_v = \frac{e_{out}}{e_{in}} = \frac{i_c R_L}{e_g} \tag{9.7}$$

we need only manipulate Eqs. 9.5 and 9.6 as follows: The equation for the
input loop (Eq. 9.5) contains the i_c and e_g terms needed in gain equation 9.7.
However, an i_e term also appears in Eq. 9.5. We can eliminate this i_e term
by solving for i_e in Eq. 9.6:

$$i_e = i_c \frac{r_b + r_c + R_L}{\alpha r_c + r_b} \tag{9.8}$$

and substituting this expression in Eq. 9.5:

$$e_g = i_c \frac{(r_b + r_c + R_L)(R_g + r_b + r_e)}{\alpha r_c + r_b} - i_c r_b \tag{9.9a}$$

If we now solve Eq. 9.9 for i_c:

$$i_c = e_g \frac{\alpha r_c + r_b}{(r_b + r_c + R_L)(R_g + r_b + r_e) - r_b(\alpha r_c + R_L)} \tag{9.9b}$$

Now multiply both sides of Eq. 9.9b by R_L and divide by e_g to obtain the
voltage gain:

$$A_v = \frac{i_c R_L}{e_g} = \frac{R_L}{\cancel{e_g}}\cancel{e_g}\frac{\alpha r_c + r_b}{(r_b + r_c + R_L)(R_g + r_b + r_e) - r_b(\alpha r_c + R_L)} \tag{9.10}$$

We have used the transistor equivalent circuit together with loop analysis
to determine transistor voltage gain (Eq. 9.10).

Example 9.3

A certain transistor has $\alpha = 0.99$, $r_e = 20\,\Omega$, $r_b = 200\,\Omega$, and $r_c = 900\,k\Omega$. This
transistor is connected to a voltage generator with a 5-mV open-circuit voltage and a
50-Ω internal resistance. What value of load resistance will give a 15-mV load voltage?

Solution Step 1. Find the voltage gain:

$$A_v = \frac{e_{out}}{e_{in}}$$

$$= \frac{15 \times 10^{-3}}{5 \times 10^{-3}}$$

$$= 3$$

Step 2. Using this value of A_v, all the data needed to use Eq. 9.10 is available:

$$A_v = \frac{R_L(\alpha r_c + r_b)}{(r_b + r_c + R_L)(R_g + r_b + r_e) - r_b(\alpha r_c + R_L)}$$

$$3 = \frac{R_L(0.99 \times 9 \times 10^5 + 200)}{(200 + 9 \times 10^5 + R_L)(50 + 200 + 20) - 200(0.99 \times 9 \times 10^5 + R_L)}$$

$$R_L \simeq \frac{186 \times 10^7}{8.9 \times 10^5}$$

$$= 208 \, \Omega$$

9.5   Transistor Performance

The method of determining transistor performance described in Section 9.4 is straightforward although the algebraic manipulations may obscure what is happening:

1. A transistor equivalent circuit is generated which fits the principle of transistor action. This results in a tee equivalent with a controlled voltage source.
2. Using the equivalent circuit we write the loop equations. These equations are then solved for the quantity of interest, for example voltage amplification.

In addition to voltage amplification we shall be interested in other performance parameters: current amplification (A_i), power amplification (A_p), input resistance (r_{in}) and output resistance (r_{out}). These five factors are performance characteristics.

$$A_v = \frac{e_{out}}{e_{in}} \tag{9.11a}$$

$$A_i = \frac{i_{out}}{i_{in}} \tag{9.11b}$$

$$A_p = A_i A_v \tag{9.11c}$$

$$r_{in} = \frac{e_{in}}{i_{in}} \tag{9.11d}$$

$$r_{out} = \frac{e_{out}}{i_{out}} \tag{9.11e}$$

The first three quantities (Eqs. 9.11a, b, c) are important because they specify amplification properties; that is, they indicate how much "gain" we achieve by using a transistor. Frequently the terms **voltage gain, current gain,** and **power gain** are used to indicate how much a signal has been amplified.

The last two performance characteristics (Eqs. 9.11d, e) are resistances. The input resistance is important because it determines what should be connected to the transistor input to achieve maximum power transfer. In other cases we may intentionally want to mismatch so that we draw minimum current from the source. In either case we must know what the transistor input resistance is. For similar reasons we shall be interested in the value of transistor output resistance. This tells us the value of load resistance which will achieve maximum power transfer.

The voltage gain equation (Eq. 9.10) although correct is unwieldy. It is not readily apparent which factors should be made large and which factors should be made small to achieve large voltage gains. All that we can really see from Eq. 9.10 is that voltage gain depends on two external parameters (R_L and R_g) and on four internal transistor parameters (α, r_b, r_c, and r_e).

Fortunately, the relative values of these parameters allows some simplifications to be made. Typically collector resistance is of the order of 1 million ohms. Base resistance is several hundred ohms and emitter resistance is in tens of ohms. Keeping these values in mind, Eq. 9.10 reduces to

$$A_v \simeq \frac{\alpha R_L}{r_e + (1 - \alpha)r_b + R_g} \tag{9.12}$$

This approximate formula for voltage amplification shows more readily what to do to enhance voltage amplification: use large values of load resistance. This will make the numerator of Eq. 9.12 large. Also we should use small values of generator resistance to make the denominator small. Notice also that the voltage gain is not affected by collector resistance.

Example 9.4

A transistor with $\alpha = 0.98$, $r_b = 200\,\Omega$, and $r_e = 20\,\Omega$ is connected to a generator with $50\,\Omega$ internal resistance. What value of load resistance will give a voltage gain of (a) 2; (b) 10.

Solution Step 1. For $A_v = 2$,

$$A_v = \frac{\alpha R_L}{r_e + (1 - \alpha)r_b + R_g}$$

$$2 = \frac{0.98 R_L}{20 + (1 - 0.98)200 + 50}$$

$$R_L \simeq 151\,\Omega$$

Step 2. Similarly, for $A_v = 10$,

$$10 = \frac{0.98R_L}{20 + 4 + 50}$$

$$R_L = 755\,\Omega$$

We cannot continue to increase R_L without limit to increase voltage gain. Equation 9.12 was based on certain approximations. Once we violate these approximations (e.g., using too large an R_L) Eq. 9.12 can no longer be used and we must go back to the exact form (Eq. 9.10). Using this exact form we shall see that increasing R_L beyond a certain point will actually result in a decrease in output signal.

The generator resistance and load resistance are factors which are external to the transistor. However, it may not always be possible to select either R_g or R_L at will. For example, the generator may be a microphone. A practical microphone resistance might be about 500 Ω. Similarly, the load resistance may be a loudspeaker. Practical values of loudspeaker resistance range from about 3 Ω up to 16 Ω. We must always keep in mind the practical considerations and not adhere rigidly to formulas.

We have discussed voltage gain. We might also be concerned with current gain (Eq. 9.11b). Current gain will be high when the load resistance is small, in accordance with Ohm's law. High current requires low values of resistance. This means that the requirements for voltage gain (high R_L) and current gain (low R_L) conflict. In fact if we are concerned with power gain (Eq. 9.11c) we really appear to have conflicting requirements.

There is really not much of a conflict here. Referring to Fig. 9.8, we see that the output current is the collector current and the input current is the emitter current. The ratio of these two currents is the current gain (Eq. 9.11b):

$$A_i = \frac{i_{\text{out}}}{i_{\text{in}}} = \frac{i_c}{i_e} = \alpha \tag{9.13}$$

Equation 9.13 shows that we cannot achieve current gain (at least not by using a transistor this way) since α must be less than unity; that is, collector current must be less than emitter current since there is base current. This conclusion can also be reached by using the circuit loop equation. We start with Eq. 9.6:

$$\alpha r_c i_e = -i_e r_b + i_c(r_b + r_c + R_L)$$

or

$$i_e(\alpha r_c + r_b) = i_c(r_b + r_c + R_L)$$

We have already discussed the relative values of these parameters. Thus

$$\alpha r_c + r_b \simeq \alpha r_c \qquad\qquad \text{(9.14a)}$$

and

$$r_b + r_c + R_L \simeq r_c \qquad\qquad \text{(9.14b)}$$

In this case we have

$$i_e \alpha r_c \simeq i_c r_c \qquad\qquad \text{(9.15)}$$

or

$$\frac{i_c}{i_e} = A_i = \alpha$$

Again we reach the same conclusion: No current gain is possible by using a transistor as shown. By combining the voltage gain equation (Eq. 9.12) with the current gain equation (Eq. 9.1a) we obtain power gain (Eq. 9.11c):

$$A_p = A_i A_v \simeq \frac{\alpha^2 R_L}{r_e + (1 - \alpha)r_b + R_g} \qquad\qquad \text{(9.16)}$$

Example 9.5

Determine the power gain for the values used in Example 9.4.

Solution Step 1. For $R_L = 151\ \Omega$,

$$A_p = \frac{\alpha^2 R_L}{R_e + (1 - \alpha)r_b + R_g}$$

$$= \frac{(0.98)^2 151}{20 + 4 + 50}$$

$$= 1.96$$

Step 2. For $R_L = 755\ \Omega$,

$$A_p = \frac{(0.98)^2 755}{20 + 4 + 50}$$

$$= 9.8$$

Example 9.5 shows that although it is not possible to achieve current gain it is possible to achieve power gain as long as there is voltage gain.

A schematic and tee equivalent of the transistor amplifier being discussed is shown in Fig. 9.10. Emitter current is the input current and collector current is the output current. Under such conditions the base is common to both the input and output loops. For this reason the circuit in Fig. 9.10 is called a common-base amplifier.

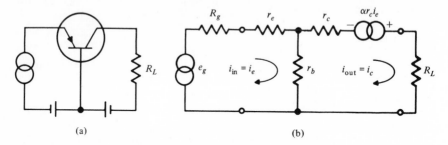

(a)   (b)

9.10   Common-base amplifier. (a) Schematic. (b) Tee equivalent.

Thus the equations which we have developed for voltage current and power gain are specifically for the **common-base (CB) configuration.** Starting with the same loop equations which were used to determine the various gains (Eqs. 9.11a, b, c), we could also determine the input and output resistance. Using the same type of approximations, we get

$$r_{in(CB)} \simeq r_e + (1 - \alpha)r_b \qquad\qquad \textbf{(9.17a)}$$

$$r_{out(CB)} \simeq r_c\left(1 - \frac{\alpha r_b}{r_b + r_e + R_g}\right) \qquad\qquad \textbf{(9.17b)}$$

Example 9.6

For the same conditions as in Examples 9.4 and 9.5 determine the input and output resistances.

Solution Step 1. The values used were $\alpha = 0.98$, $r_b = 200\,\Omega$, $r_c = 900\,\text{k}\Omega$, $r_e = 20\,\Omega$, $R_g = 50\,\Omega$, and $R_L = 755\,\Omega$.

Step 2. Thus the input resistance is

$$\begin{aligned}
r_{in(CB)} &= r_e + (1 - \alpha)r_b \\
&= 20 + (1 - 0.98)200 \\
&= 24\,\Omega
\end{aligned}$$

Step 3. Similarly, to find the output resistance,

$$r_{\text{out(CB)}} \simeq r_c\left(1 - \frac{\alpha r_b}{r_b + r_e + R_g}\right)$$

$$= 9 \times 10^5\left(1 - \frac{0.98 \times 200}{200 + 20 + 50}\right)$$

$$\simeq 248\ \text{k}\Omega$$

Example 9.6 shows that the CB configuration has low input resistance and high output resistance. Generally, this is the exact reverse of the characteristics which we require.

At the input we may not want to match the generator resistance to obtain maximum power transfer. Instead we may want to affect the generator as little as possible. The previous discussion about microphone resistance indicates that we are seeking transistor input resistances of several hundred to several hundred thousand ohms. We conclude that the input resistance of the common base configuration (24 Ω in this example) is often not useful.

At the output of our amplifier we shall either intentionally want to match or intentionally want to avoid loading whatever our amplifier is connected to. Both situations will generally require a low output resistance. Typically we are seeking output resistances of the order of tens to hundreds of ohms. We conclude that the output resistance of the common base is not useful (248 kΩ in this example).

9.6 Other Transistor Configurations

Our analysis of the CB configuration shows that some voltage and power gain is available although no current gain is possible. However, the chief obstacles to using a CB amplifier are the values of input and output resistance which are the opposite of what most applications require.

Fortunately there are other methods of connecting transistors to furnish gain. In Fig. 9.11 we have a circuit in which the transistor is connected so that the **emitter is common to both the input and output loops.** Thus this configuration is called the **common emitter (CE).**

At first glance it appears that the difference between CE and CB configuration is insignificant. This is not true. **In the CE configuration the input current is base current,** rather than the emitter current in the CB configuration. Base current was originally discussed in terms of current "leaking" out of the transistor. In terms of the CB amplifier this concept is correct. However, in the CE amplifier defeat is converted into victory.

As we already know, base current is much smaller than either collector or emitter current. Thus in the case of the CE configuration we have **a very**

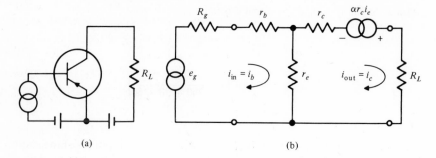

9.11   Common-emitter amplifier. (a) Schematic. (b) Tee equivalent.

small input current (base current) **controlling a much larger output current** (collector current). Inherently the common emitter should provide a good deal of current gain:

$$A_{i(CE)} = \frac{i_{out}}{i_{in}} = \frac{i_c}{i_b} \qquad (9.18a)$$

Using Kirchhoff's current law (Eq. 9.3) for transistors we can eliminate i_b from Eq. 9.18a:

$$A_{i(CE)} = \frac{i_c}{i_e - i_c} \qquad (9.18b)$$

Dividing through by i_c,

$$A_{i(CE)} = \frac{i_c/i_c}{i_e/i_c - i_e/i_e} = \frac{1}{1/\alpha - 1} = \frac{\alpha}{1 - \alpha} \qquad (9.18c)$$

Example 9.7

A transistor has an $\alpha = 0.98$. Find the current gain if the transistor is used in (a) CB, (b) CE configuration.

Solution Step 1. For the common base configuration (Eq. 9.15),

$$A_{i(CB)} = \alpha = 0.98$$

Step 2. For the common emitter configuration,

$$A_{i(CE)} = \frac{\alpha}{1 - \alpha} = \frac{0.98}{1 - 0.98} = 49$$

Example 9.7 is the first indication that even though the same transistor is used, the configuration is most important. In this case we see that we go from current loss (CB) to a current gain of almost 50 if we switch to the CE configuration. This same conclusion could also have been obtained by writing loop equations for the CE configuration circuit [Fig. 9.11(b)] and solving for current gain. The factor $\alpha/1 - \alpha$ is important enough to have its own symbol:

$$A_{i(CE)} = \frac{\alpha}{1 - \alpha} = \beta \qquad (9.18d)$$

Thus we can speak of a transistor which has an α of 0.98 as having a β of 49, or a transistor with an α of 0.99 as having a β of 99. That is, very small changes in α result in very large changes in β.

We could also determine the common emitter current gain by writing and analyzing the loop equations for Fig. 9.11(b). The other figures of merit are also obtained by this method:

$$A_{v(CE)} \simeq \frac{\beta R_L}{r_b + (\beta + 1)r_e + R_g} \qquad (9.19a)$$

$$A_{p(CE)} = A_{i(CE)}A_{v(CE)} \qquad (9.19b)$$

$$r_{in(CE)} \simeq r_b + (\beta + 1)r_e \qquad (9.19c)$$

$$r_{out(CE)} \simeq r_c(1 - \alpha)\left(1 + \frac{\beta r_e}{r_b + r_e + R_g}\right) \qquad (9.19d)$$

Example 9.8

A transistor with $\alpha = 0.98$, $r_b = 200\ \Omega$, $r_e = 20\ \Omega$, and $r_c = 900\ k\Omega$ is connected to a 600-Ω generator. Compute the five performance characteristics if a common emitter configuration is used and the load resistor is 1 kΩ.

Solution Step 1. To find the current gain:

$$A_{i(CE)} = \beta = \frac{\alpha}{1 - \alpha} = \frac{0.98}{1 - 0.98}$$

$$= 49$$

Step 2. To find the voltage gain:

$$A_{v(CE)} \simeq \frac{\beta R_L}{r_b + (\beta + 1)r_e + R_g}$$

$$= \frac{49 \times 1 \times 10^3}{200 + (49 + 1)20 + 600}$$

$$= 27.2$$

Step 3. To find the power gain:

$$A_{p(CE)} = A_{i(CE)}A_{v(CE)}$$
$$= 49 \times 27.2$$
$$= 1330$$

Step 4. To find the input resistance:

$$r_{in(CE)} \simeq r_b + (\beta + 1)r_e$$
$$= 200 + (49 + 1)20$$
$$= 1200\,\Omega$$

Step 5. To find the output resistance:

$$r_{out(CE)} \simeq r_c(1 - \alpha)\left(1 + \frac{\beta r_e}{r_b + r_e + R_g}\right)$$
$$= 9 \times 10^5(1 - 0.98)\left(1 + \frac{49 \times 20}{200 + 20 + 600}\right)$$
$$\simeq 39.5\,\text{k}\Omega$$

The transistor used in Example 9.8 is the same as the CB examples. Although different (and more realistic) generator and load resistances were used we can see that the CE configuration is superior to the CB. The CE has higher A_i, A_v, A_p and higher r_{in} as well as lower r_{out} than does the CB.

Another useful transistor configuration is shown in Fig. 9.12. In this case **the input current is the base current and the ouput current is the emitter current.** Since the collector is in both the input and output loops this configuration is called the **common collector (CC).** Since the emitter leg in the common collector circuit follows the input signal, the CC is sometimes referred to as an **emitter follower.**

As in the two other configurations (CB and CE) the CC performance characteristics are determined by writing loop equations and solving for the appropriate terms. After making practical approximations we get:

$$A_{i(CC)} \simeq \beta + 1 \qquad\qquad\qquad\qquad \textbf{(9.20a)}$$

$$A_{v(CC)} \simeq 1 \qquad\qquad\qquad\qquad\qquad \textbf{(9.20b)}$$

$$A_{p(CC)} = A_{i(CC)}A_{v(CC)} \qquad\qquad \textbf{(9.20c)}$$

$$r_{in(CC)} \simeq (\beta + 1)(R_L + r_e) \qquad \textbf{(9.20d)}$$

$$r_{out(CC)} \simeq r_e + \frac{R_g + r_b}{\beta + 1} \qquad\qquad \textbf{(9.20e)}$$

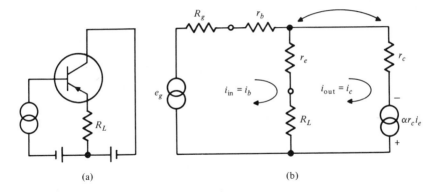

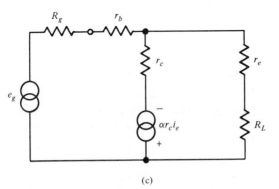

9.12   Common-collector amplifier. (a) Schematic. (b) Tee equivalent. (c) Tee redrawn.

Example 9.9

Using the same transistor and conditions as in Example 9.8, determine the performance in the CC configuration:

Solution Step 1. To find current gain:

$$A_{i(CC)} \simeq \beta + 1$$
$$= 49 + 1$$
$$= 50$$

Step 2. To find voltage gain:

$$A_{v(CC)} \simeq 1$$

Step 3. To find power gain:

$$A_{p(CC)} = A_{i(CC)} A_{v(CC)}$$
$$= 50 \times 1$$
$$= 50$$

Step 4. To find input resistance:

$$r_{\text{in(CC)}} \simeq (\beta + 1)(R_L + r_e)$$
$$= (49 + 1)(1000 + 20)$$
$$= 51 \text{ k}\Omega$$

Step 5. To find output resistance:

$$r_{\text{out(CC)}} \simeq r_e + \frac{R_g + r_b}{\beta + 1}$$
$$= 20 + \frac{600 + 200}{49 + 1}$$
$$\simeq 36 \, \Omega$$

By comparing the result of Example 9.8 (CE) with Example 9.9 (CC) we see the relative advantages of each configuration. The common emitter has much better voltage and power gain while the common collector has slightly better current gain. **The chief advantage of the common collector is the higher input resistance and lower output resistance.** These are exactly the characteristics which were required for connecting transistors without loading at either end.

Table 9.1 compares the figures of merit for the three configurations. The numbers in the brackets beneath each equation are for a "typical" transistor

Table 9.1   Transistor Performance

	CB	CE	CC
A_i	α [0.98]	β [49]	$\beta + 1$ [50]
A_v	$\dfrac{\alpha R_L}{r_e + (1 - \alpha)r_b + R_g}$ [3.1]	$\dfrac{\beta R_L}{r_b + (\beta + 1)r_e + R_g}$ [47]	$\simeq 1$ [$\simeq 1$]
A_p	$A_i A_v$ [3]	$A_i A_v$ [2300]	$A_i A_v$ [50]
r_{in}	$r_e + (1 - \alpha)r_b$ [29 Ω]	$r_b + (\beta + 1)r_e$ [1450 Ω]	$(\beta + 1)(R_L + r_e)$ [101 kΩ]
r_{out}	$r_c\left(1 - \dfrac{\alpha r_b}{r_b + r_e + R_g}\right)$ [762 kΩ]	$r_c(1 - \alpha)\left(1 + \dfrac{\beta r_e}{r_b + r_e + R_g}\right)$ [50 kΩ]	$r_e + \dfrac{R_g + r_b}{\beta + 1}$ [36 Ω]

($\alpha = 0.98$, $r_e = 25\,\Omega$, $r_b = 200\,\Omega$, $r_c = 10^6\,\Omega$) with "typical" generator and
load resistance ($R_g = 600\,\Omega$, $R_L = 2\,\text{k}\Omega$).

Not only does Table 9.1 summarize and compare the performance
characteristics of the three configurations, but it shows at a glance which
parameters to vary for desired results. For example, in cases where it is
desirable to increase r_{in}, doubling the value of R_L will approximately double
the value of r_{in} in the CC configuration. Similarly, doubling the value of R_L
will double the voltage gain in the CE configuration, and so on.

9.7 Practical Transistor Biasing

Regardless of which transistor configuration is used, it will be necessary
to forward bias the base-emitter junction and to reverse bias the collector-
base junction. To this extent the biasing circuits which have been shown are
correct in principle. However, they are not practical.

In all the circuits which have been described thus far, the signal generator
(or the input device) is shown directly in series with the base-emitter DC
power supply. This means that DC bias current flows through the signal
generator and AC signal current flows through the battery. Neither of these
conditions is realistic. DC current through the signal source hampers or
destroys the signal source in many applications. In addition it would be
advantageous if a single power supply could be used to properly bias both
transistor junctions.

A CE circuit which uses only a single power supply and properly separates
bias and signal current at the input is shown in Fig. 9.13. The capacitor at
the input prevents DC current from flowing into the generator. However,
it is still possible for DC bias current to enter the base. The method of
obtaining proper biasing of both transistor junctions can be understood by

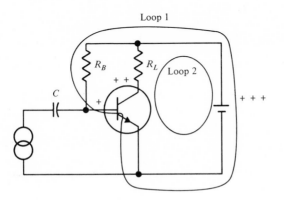

9.13 Practical CE amplifier.

considering loops 1 and 2 of Fig. 9.13. Recall that Kirchhoff's voltage law is correct regardless of how a loop is situated. Thus for loop 1 we have

$$V_{\text{battery}} = V_{R_B} + V_{be} \tag{9.21a}$$

where V_{be} is the base-emitter voltage. If the value of R_B (biasing resistor) is chosen correctly, sufficient current will flow through the base-emitter junction to create forward bias.

Now consider loop 2. In this case Kirchhoff's voltage law yields

$$V_{\text{battery}} = V_{R_L} + V_{ce} \tag{9.21b}$$

where V_{ce} is the collector-emitter base. If the proper value of R_L is chosen, the voltage between the collector and emitter (V_{ce}) will be greater than the base-emitter voltage (V_{be}). In this case **the voltage at the collector is greater** (more positive) **than the voltage at the base.** This means that the collector base junction is reverse biased. Therefore the circuit shown in Fig. 9.13

1. Has a forward-biased base-emitter junction
2. Has a reverse-biased collector-base junction
3. Uses a single power supply

Such a biasing procedure is called **fixed bias.**

Example 9.10

The fixed-bias circuit shown in Fig. 9.13 uses a germanium transistor with $\beta = 50$. Base current should be $25\,\mu A$ and the battery is 5 V. If V_{ce} must be 2.5 V, determine R_B and R_L.

Solution Step 1. For a germanium diode $V_{be} = 0.25$ V. Therefore for loop 1 of Fig. 9.13,

$$V_{\text{battery}} = V_{R_B} + V_{be}$$
$$5 = V_{R_B} + 0.25$$
$$V_{R_B} = 4.75\,\text{volts}$$

Step 2. The current through R_B flows through the base-emitter junction. It is given that $I_b = 25\,\mu a$. Since both V_{R_B} and I_b are known, Ohm's law can be used to find R_B:

$$R_B = \frac{V_{R_B}}{I_b}$$
$$= \frac{4.75}{25 \times 10^{-6}}$$
$$= 190\,\text{k}\Omega$$

Step 3. The current in loop 2 of Fig. 9.13 is the collector current. Since β and I_b are known we can find I_c:

$$\beta = \frac{I_c}{I_b}$$

$$50 = \frac{I_c}{25 \times 10^{-6}}$$

$$I_c = 1.25 \text{ mA}.$$

Step 4. Since the battery and the collector-emitter voltage are known, V_{R_L} can be determined using loop 2:

$$V_{\text{battery}} = V_{R_L} + V_{ce}$$

$$5 = V_{R_L} + 2.5$$

$$V_{R_L} = 2.5 \text{ volts}$$

Step 5. Since the collector current flows through R_L and V_{R_L} is now known, Ohm's law is used to determine R_L:

$$R_L = \frac{V_{R_L}}{I_c}$$

$$= \frac{2.5}{1.25 \times 10^{-3}}$$

$$2 \text{ k}\Omega$$

In this case we have selected values so that V_{be} has the proper value and V_{ce} is greater than V_{be} (0.25 versus 2.5 volts). Thus, as required, the base-emitter junction is forward biased and the collector-base junction is reverse biased.

Also observe that the collector-to-emitter voltage is half of the supply voltage (2.5 V versus 5.0 V). This is typical. If V_{ce} is half of the power supply voltage, the output signal can swing approximately equal amounts above and below the bias voltage. That is, the output voltage will be symmetrical before **distortion** occurs at either extreme.

Two types of distortion are possible due to extremely large output signals:
1. **Cutoff.** In this case the output tries to exceed the level of the power supply voltage. This cannot be so the upper portion of the signal is cut off as shown in Fig. 9.14 (a).
2. **Saturation.** In this case the collector current is so great that the voltage across the load resistor becomes too large. There is not enough voltage across the collector-base junction to keep it reverse biased. This is shown in Fig. 9.14 (b).

Thus, in addition to establishing proper DC bias, the signal levels must also be considered. **Gain and bias affect each other.**

(a)   (b)

9.14   Distorted amplifier outputs. (a) Cutoff. (b) Saturation.

9.8   Bias Stabilization

We saw in Section 8.2 that saturation current (I_s) flows when a diode is reverse biased. The saturation current was seen to be the result of minority carrier current. A properly biased base-collector junction is also a reverse-biased diode. Thus minority carrier current will flow in a properly biased base-collector junction even if the emitter is open circuited. This is shown in Fig. 9.15.

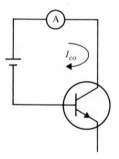

9.15   Collector leakage current

For a transistor we use the term **collector leakage current** (I_{co}) instead of saturation current. Thus we see that in a properly biased transistor the total collector current is the sum of two currents:
1. Current due to transistor action (αI_e)
2. Collector leakage current (I_{co}).
Therefore

$$I_c = \alpha I_e + I_{co} \qquad\qquad \textbf{(9.22a)}$$

Using Kirchhoff's current law we can substitute for I_e:

$$I_c = \alpha(I_c + I_b) + I_{co} \qquad\qquad \textbf{(9.22b)}$$

Rearranging terms we obtain

$$I_c(1 - \alpha) = \alpha I_b + I_{co} \qquad\qquad (9.22c)$$

or

$$I_c = \frac{\alpha}{1 - \alpha}I_b + \frac{1}{1 - \alpha}I_{co} \qquad\qquad (9.22d)$$

Thus

$$I_c = \beta I_b + (\beta + 1)I_{co} \qquad\qquad (9.22e)$$

Equation 9.22e shows that **the CE transistor does a slightly better job of amplifying collector leakage current than signal current.** This in itself is not serious. Typically I_{co} is of the order of microamperes. Thus if the value of I_{co} were known it could be included in the biasing considerations and all is well.

This is not the case. The difficulty is not I_{co} itself but the temperature dependence of I_{co}:

1. I_{co} doubles every 8°C (14.4°F) in germanium transistors
2. I_{co} doubles every 10°C (18°F) in silicon transistors

Under normal summer-to-winter driving conditions car temperatures may range between 130°F and −20°F. Thus there are several doublings of I_{co} at summer temperatures while there are several halvings of I_{co} at winter temperatures. It is quite possible that the increase in temperature could saturate the transistors in a car radio while the decrease could cut the transistor off.

The trouble with the fixed-bias scheme discussed in the previous section is that the bias does remain fixed. Fixed bias is practical provided that some external means such as air conditioning is used to stabilize temperature. That is, under fixed bias the base current stays constant despite either increase or decrease in temperature.

What is needed is a method of compensation. **An increase in temperature results in an increase in collector current. This should be compensated for by a decrease in base current,** since base current controls collector current. Similarly, a decrease in temperature which results in a decrease in collector current should be compensated for by an increase in base current.

A circuit which achieves these objectives is shown in Fig. 9.16. This type of circuit adjusts itself automatically to temperature changes. Compare this bias-stabilization schematic with the fixed-bias schematic shown in Fig. 9.13. The only difference is the addition of the external emitter resistor (R_E). This is a most significant difference although it amounts only to a single resistor.

Loop 1

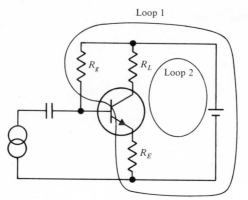

9.16   Bias-stabilization circuit.

The effect of R_E may be understood by considering the situation which arises when temperature increases:

1. An increase in temperature results in an increase in I_{co}. This causes an increase in collector current (Eq. 9.22e).
2. An increase in collector current (which is the current in loop 2 of Fig. 9.16) results in an increase in the voltage across R_E. This is in accordance with Ohm's law.
3. An increase (↑) in the voltage across R_E results in a decrease (↓) in the voltage across R_B. This can be seen by writing Kirchhoff's voltage law for loop 1 of Fig. 9.16:

$$V_{\text{battery}} = \overset{\downarrow}{V_{R_B}} + V_{be} + \overset{\uparrow}{V_{R_E}}$$

Since V_{battery} and V_{be} are constant an increase in V_{R_E} must result in a decrease in V_{R_B}.

4. A decrease in the voltage across R_B means a decrease in the current through R_B. This is a consequence of Ohm's law.
5. But the current through R_B is the base current I_B. Thus **an increase in collector current results in a decrease in base current.** Since collector current is controlled by base current, **the addition of R_E has made the circuit self-compensating.**

In a similar manner a decrease in collector current is compensated by an increase in base current. The addition of R_E does not offer perfect temperature compensation. But the compensation is in the correct direction, and thus large temperature variations will result only in minor shifts in collector current.

The ratio of the change in collector current to the change in collector leakage current is call the **stability factor** (S).

$$S = \frac{\Delta I_c}{\Delta I_{co}}$$

(9.24a)

where Δ means a small variation. That is, the stability factor shows how much a change in collector leakage current affects the collector current. For germanium transistors the maximum value of S should be about 6 and for silicon the maximum value of S should be about 10. By writing the appropriate loop equations in terms of I_c and I_{co} it is possible to relate the stability factor to circuit components:

$$S \simeq 1 + \frac{R_B}{R_E} \qquad\qquad \text{(9.24b)}$$

Since very little current (I_b) flows through the base resistor, R_B must be quite large (several hundred kilohms). Thus for realistic values of R_E (several kilohms) the stability factor will be much too large. There are at least two practical methods of reducing S. In Fig. 9.17 (a) we go back to two separate batteries. In this way a lower voltage battery can be used with the base resistor and thus R_B can be reduced.

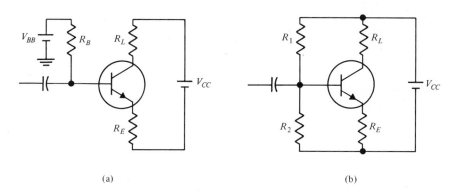

(a)   (b)

9.17   Circuits which reduce S. (a) Two batteries. (b) One battery.

In Fig. 9.17 (b) the base resistor is split into two resistors, R_1 and R_2. This permits low values of S and still uses only a single battery. In terms of the stability factor equation (Eq. 9.24 b) the parallel combination of R_1 and R_2 replaces R_B:

$$R_B = \frac{R_1 R_2}{R_1 + R_2} \qquad\qquad \text{(9.24c)}$$

In addition to compensating for changes in collector leakage current with temperature, the addition of R_E also helps to reduce variations which occur due to components changing with age.

Summary

1. A transistor operates by transferring power from a forward-biased diode to a reverse-biased diode.
2. Transistors are capable of amplifying power.
3. Real transistors must be fabricated within a single crystal. This is the method by which most of the emitter current becomes collector current.
4. Both *PNP* and *NPN* transistors are manufactured. For both types proper biasing consists of forward bias of the emitter-base junction and reverse bias of the collector-base junction.
5. Black-box techniques can be used to determine an equivalent transistor circuit for analysis. The black-box equivalent of a transistor contains a controlled source.
6. The tee equivalent circuit can be used to predict how well a transistor amplifies and what its input and output resistances are. The common-base configuration yields no current gain, some voltage gain, and some power gain. Input resistance is low and output resistance is high.
7. In the common-emitter configuration the base current is the input and the collector current is the output. This yields current gain. The common emitter has higher A_V and A_P than the common base. Also the common emitter has higher r_{in} and lower r_{out} than the common base.
8. In the common collector, the base is the input current and the emitter is the output. The common collector has the highest current gain. Also the common collector has the highest r_{in} and lowest r_{out}.
9. Practical biasing methods require separation of signal and biasing circuits. In addition it is generally desirable to use a single bias source.
10. Failure to establish a proper bias will result in distortion of the output due to saturation and/or cutoff.
11. Transistor bias circuits must be stabilized for temperature variation. A chief effect of temperature variation is the change in I_{co} which causes a change in I_c.
12. Changes caused by temperature variation can be compensated for (at least partially) by placing a resistor in the emitter circuit.

Questions

1. Describe the principle of transistor action.
2. What is the origin of the word transistor?
3. Describe why a practical transistor must be fabricated within a single crystal.
4. What are the biasing requirements to achieve transistor action?
5. Describe how an *NPN* transistor operates in terms of electrons and holes.
6. What is the difference between making black-box measurements on resistive black boxes and transistor black boxes?
7. What is meant by a controlled source?
8. How is the transistor tee equivalent circuit used?
9. What is meant by common-base configuration?
10. Why are the input and output resistances of the common base configuration not too useful?

11. What is the difference in input current between the CB and CE configuration? Why is this difference important?
12. Why can the CC furnish slightly greater current gain than the CE?
13. Why are r_{in} and r_{out} important performance characteristics?
14. Why should bias and signal circuits be separated?
15. What causes a transistor to saturate?
16. What causes a transistor to cut off?
17. What causes I_{co}?
18. Why do changes in I_{co} affect the biasing conditions?
19. How does the addition of R_E stabilize the circuit against temperature variations?

Problems

1. Compute the ratio P_2/P_1 for two diodes in which $R_{fwd} = 25\,\Omega$ and $R_{rev} = 100\,k\Omega$.
2. Repeat Problem 1 if 5% of the forward-biased diode current leaks out.
3. A transistor with an α of 0.98 draws 1 mA of emitter current. Find I_c and I_b.
4. A transistor with an $\alpha = 0.99$ has 10 μA of base current. Find I_e and I_c.
5. Draw a schematic of a circuit which reads α directly for the condition that $I_e = 1$ mA. Use either NPN or PNP but proper bias must be maintained.
6. A transistor with $\alpha = 0.98$, $r_e = 25\,\Omega$, $r_b = 250\,\Omega$, and $r_c = 1\,M\Omega$ is connected to a 600-Ω generator. What will be the gain if $R_L = 2\,k\Omega$.
7. Repeat Problem 6 for $R_L = 3\,k\Omega$.
8. Repeat Problem 6 using the approximate formula (Eq. 9.12) for voltage gain.
9. Repeat Problem 7 using the same approximate formula.
10. Determine the power gain for Problem 8.
11. Determine the power gain for Problem 9.
12. Determine the input and output resistance for the conditions of Problem 6.
13. Repeat Problem 12 for the conditions of Problem 7.
14. Show that the current gain of the CC configuration is $\beta + 1$.
15. A transistor is connected to a 600-Ω generator and load resistance is 1 kΩ. The transistor characteristics are $\alpha = 0.99$, $r_e = 25\,\Omega$, $r_b = 200\,\Omega$, and $r_c = 1\,M\Omega$. Find the current gain in all three configurations.
16. Find the voltage gain for all three configurations of Problem 15.
17. Find the power gain for all three configurations of Problem 15.
18. Find the input resistance for all three configurations of Problem 15.
19. Find the output resistance for all three configurations of Problem 15.
20. What happens to r_{in} and r_{out} of the CC configuration if R_L is made 2 kΩ instead of 1 kΩ?
21. Use fixed bias to operate a silicon transistor with $\beta = 100$. The requirements are $I_b = 20\,\mu$A, $I_e = 1$ mA, $V_{ce} = 2.4$ V, $R_E = 1\,k\Omega$, $V_{CC} = 5$ V and $S = 5$, determine R_B and R_L, and sketch a schematic.
22. The situation is the same as in Problem 21 except $\beta = 50$.
23. The transistor shown in Fig. 9.17 (a) is a silicon transistor. If the requirements are $I_b = 20\,\mu$A, $I_e = 1$ mA., $V_{ce} = 2.4$ V, $R_E = 1\,k\Omega$, $V_{CC} = 5$ V and $S = 5$, determine R_L, R_B, and V_{BB}.
24. The conditions are the same as in Problem 23 except that the single-battery circuit of Fig. 9.17 (b) is used. Determine R_1 and R_2.

Chapter 10 Amplifiers

10.1 Introduction

In this chapter the principles of amplification are extended to include multistage high-gain amplifiers. Various techniques and problems associated with amplifiers are discussed.

10.2 Practical Common-Emitter Stages

In Chapter 9 the effect of adding an emitter resistor was covered and an amplifier stage using R_E was evolved. This amplifier was drawn as a CE stage. However, since R_E is added the emitter is not common to anything. R_E was added to stabilize the amplifier against temperature variation; that is, R_E was added for stable DC bias conditions. But signal current will also flow through R_E and this means that the voltage across R_E will fluctuate as the signal fluctuates.

The problem is that while R_E is necessary to maintain stable bias, signal current through R_E causes the bias to fluctuate. The solution is to separate the signal and bias circuits as shown in Fig. 10.1. A capacitor C_E has been

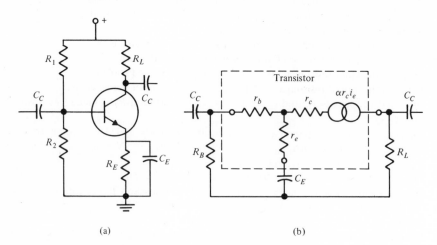

(a)   (b)

10.1   Practical CE amplifier. (a) Schematic. (b) Equivalent circuit.

connected in parallel with the emitter resistor R_E. If the reactance of the capacitor is much less than the resistance of R_E, most of the signal current will flow through C_E. In this way a constant bias level is maintained across R_E while most of the signal current flows through C_E. When used in this manner a capacitor is referred to as a **bypass capacitor**. As a rule of thumb the reactance of the capacitor should be about $\frac{1}{10}$ of the resistance of R_E.

Example 10.1

The emitter resistor in Fig. 10.1 is 1 kΩ. Determine the value of C_E if the amplifier is meant to operate at 1 kHz.

Solution Step 1. $R_E = 1 \,\text{k}\Omega$. Since $X_{C_E} = \frac{1}{10}R_E$,

$$X_{C_E} = \frac{10^3}{10} = 100 \,\Omega$$

Step 2.

$$X_c = \frac{1}{2\pi f C}$$

$$100 = \frac{1}{2\pi \times 10^3 C}$$

$$C = 1.59 \,\mu\text{F}$$

Since a 1.59-μF (actually the closest commercial value is 2.0 μF) capacitor represents 100 Ω compared to an R_E of 1000 Ω, we can see that most of the signal current is bypassed around R_E rather than through R_E. **Capacitor C_E creates** (from a signal standpoint) **what is essentially a short circuit to ground.** Thus it is legitimate to consider the circuit shown in Fig. 10.1 as a CE configuration. Recall that originally, CE, CB, and CC were discussed in terms of the signal properties and did not take into account DC bias considerations.

The actual gain equations in Chapter 9 should be modified by adding X_{C_E} wherever r_e appears. This will decrease the gain somewhat but it will also make the gain more uniform with respect to transistor β variation. Typically transistors of the same type will have a β variation of at least 3:1; that is, for a transistor type with a nominal β of 50, the minimum value of β may be 25 and the maximum may be 75.

Thus although the addition of C_E has reduced the overall gain it has also reduced the variation in gain so that performance is now more uniform. Recall also that the reasons for such large variations in β for a given type are due to the difficulties inherent in controlling doping and other manufacturing processes.

10.3   Frequency Response

We have seen that C_E provides a bypass for signal current. Since the reactance of a capacitor varies with frequency, the efficiency of bypass will vary
with frequency. As frequency increases C_E will become a better bypass.
But as frequency decreases the reactance of C_E will increase. For example,
the 1.59 μF capacitor of Example 10.1 has a reactance of 10,000 Ω at 10 Hz.
Under this condition hardly any signal current flows through C_E since R_E
is 1000 Ω. Thus, **the effectiveness of the emitter bypass capacitor depends on
frequency.**

There are other capacitors to be considered. The coupling capacitor C_C
is such a case. Typically, for the circuit shown in Fig. 10.1 (b), R_B is much
greater than r_b. Also the reactance of the emitter leg is much less than r_c.
Thus, from a signal standpoint C_C and C_E are approximately in series. The
equivalent capacitance of C_C will be less than the smaller value of C_C and C_E.
Coupling capacitors and emitter bypass capacitors are obvious capacitors.
We have intentionally placed them in the amplifier circuit.

There are other capacitors which, although not as obvious, must also be
considered. As shown in Fig. 10.2, there is capacitance between transistor
junctions. Since there is voltage across the charge-free region of each transistor element, there are actual charged capacitors at each transistor junction. In addition there is capacitance between any two wires, since a pair of
wires is effectively two conductors separated by an insulator (i.e., a capacitor).
This type of capacitance is called **stray capacitance.** Both transistor and stray
capacitance represent capacitance which is in parallel with the transistor
while coupling capacitance is connected in series.

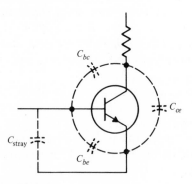

10.2   Additional circuit capacitors.

We already know that circuits which have resistance and capacitance
respond differently to different frequencies. Since a transistor stage contains
resistance and capacitance, such a circuit is sensitive to the frequency of the

signal to be amplified. **An amplifier does not amplify all frequencies equally
well.**

One method of representing the input to a transistor amplifier is shown in
Fig. 10.3. C_c' represents approximately the series combination of C_C and C_E.

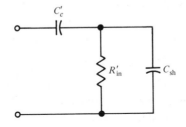

10.3   Equivalent transistor input circuit.

Typically C_c' will be in the microfarad range. Capacitance C_{sh} is the shunt
capacitance due to transistor and stray capacitance. Typically C_{sh} will be in
the tens of picofarads range (1 pF = 10^{-12} F). Resistance R_{in}' represents the
parallel combination of the transistor input resistance r_{in} and the bias
resistor(s) R_B. Typically R_{in}' will be about 1 kΩ. It is necessary to investigate
the circuit shown in Fig. 10.3 in some detail. This will permit us to determine
how an amplifier will perform over a range of frequencies.

One approach would be to consider Fig. 10.3 as a series parallel circuit.
While such an approach is correct, it is tedious and the mathematical
manipulations tend to obscure what is happening. A more useful method is
to recognize the value of the components and make appropriate approximations.

Example 10.2

For the input circuit shown in Fig. 10.3 $C_c' = 10\,\mu\text{F}$, $C_{sh} = 10\,\text{pF}$, and $R_{in}' = 1\,\text{k}\Omega$.
Determine X_c at 20 Hz, 20 kHz, and 20 MHz.

Solution Step 1.   Capacitive reactance is

$$X_C = \frac{1}{\omega C} = \frac{1}{2\pi f C}$$

Step 2.   Inserting the appropriate values we obtain

	20 Hz	20 kHz	20 MHz
$X_{C_c'}$	800 Ω	0.8 Ω	0.0008 Ω
$X_{C_{sh}}$	800 MΩ	800 kΩ	800 Ω

The computations involved in Example 10.2 are straightforward, but the results are extremely significant. Consider the shunt reactance $X_{c_{sh}}$. At low and middle frequencies $X_{c_{sh}}$ is much larger than the 1 kΩ value of R'_{in} with which it is in parallel. Thus we need only be concerned with shunt capacitance at high frequencies. For the series capacitance the reverse is true: C_c is in series with R'_{in}. At low frequencies X'_{c_c} is comparable to R'_{in}, while at middle and higher frequencies the series combination of R'_{in} and C'_c is essentially equal to R'_{in} alone. That is, we may think in terms of **three frequency ranges:**

1. Low frequency—only C'_c and R'_{in} in series need be considered.
2. Middle frequency—only R'_{in} need be considered.
3. High frequency—only C_{sh} and R'_{in} in parallel need be considered.

The middle-frequency range will have the greatest amount of signal since no capacitance exists to reduce the signal. At low frequency the signal is reduced by the series capacitance. At high frequency the signal is reduced by shunt capacitance. It is useful to determine the frequencies at which the signal drops to $1/\sqrt{2}$ of the middle frequency. At the low-frequency end the frequency at which the signal is reduced to $1/\sqrt{2}$ of the middle frequency is given by

$$f_l = \frac{1}{2\pi R'_{in} C'_c} \qquad A_l = \frac{1}{\sqrt{2}} A_{mid} \qquad \text{(10.1a)}$$

where

$$f_l = \text{the frequency at which this occurs.}$$

$$A_l = \text{the gain at this frequency}$$

$$A_{mid} = \text{the gain at the middle frequency}$$

At high frequencies the frequency at which the signal is reduced to $1/\sqrt{2}$ of the middle frequency is given by

$$f_h = \frac{1}{2\pi R'_{in} C_{sh}} \qquad A_h = \frac{1}{\sqrt{2}} A_{mid} \qquad \text{(10.1b)}$$

The value of the middle frequency can be determined if the low and high frequencies are known:

$$f_{mid} = \sqrt{f_l f_h} \qquad \text{(10.1c)}$$

Example 10.3

A certain transistor amplifier has an equivalent coupling capacitance of 5 μF, an equivalent input resistance of 1500 Ω, and a total shunt capacitance of 100 pF. Determine $f_l, f_h,$ and f_{mid}.

Solution Step 1.   From the given data, $C'_c = 5\ \mu F$, $R'_{in} = 1.5\ k\Omega$, and $C_{sh} = 100\ pF$.

Step 2.   Therefore, to find the lower frequency

$$f_l = \frac{1}{2\pi R'_{in} C'_c}$$

$$= \frac{1}{2\pi \times 1.5 \times 10^3 \times 5 \times 10^{-6}}$$

$$= 21.2 \text{ Hz}$$

Step 3.   Similarly, to find the higher frequency,

$$f_h = \frac{1}{2\pi R'_{in} C_{sh}}$$

$$= \frac{1}{2\pi \times 1.5 \times 10^3 \times 100 \times 10^{-12}}$$

$$= 1.06 \text{ MHz}$$

Step 4.   Since both f_l and f_h are known,

$$f_{mid} = \sqrt{f_l f_h}$$

$$= \sqrt{21.2 \times 1.06 \times 10^6}$$

$$= 4700 \text{ Hz}$$

The highest gain occurs at the middle frequency since only resistors are involved. The gain equations which were developed in Chapter 9 are based on a purely resistive model. Thus the gain equations give the middle-frequency gain. Once this is known we are in a position to determine the gain at the upper and lower frequencies.

Example 10.4

The middle-frequency voltage gain for the condition of Example 10.3 is 10. Determine the gain at the lower and higher frequency.

Solution Step 1.   At both the lower and higher frequency the gain is reduced to $1/\sqrt{2}$ of the middle frequency gain.

Step 2.   Therefore

$$A_l = A_h = \frac{A_{mid}}{\sqrt{2}}$$

$$= \frac{10}{\sqrt{2}}$$

$$= 7.07$$

10.4   Frequency Range

We are now in a position to plot a graph of gain versus frequency. There will be a middle range of frequencies over which all the capacitors may be neglected. This is the region of maximum gain. At lower frequencies coupling and bypass capacitors will reduce the gain and we know how to determine the frequency at which the gain is reduced by $1/\sqrt{2}$ or 0.707. At higher frequencies shunt capacitance will reduce the gain and we also know how to determine the upper frequency at which the gain is 0.707 of the maximum value. Thus a plot of gain versus frequency will appear as shown in Fig. 10.4.

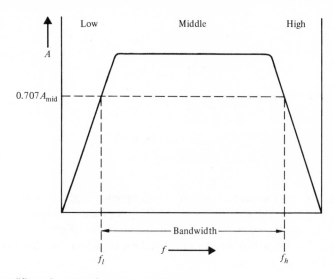

10.4   Amplifier gain versus frequency characteristic.

The frequency difference between the two frequencies at which the gain falls to $1/\sqrt{2}$ of maximum gain is called the **bandwidth** of the amplifier. For example, an audio amplifier may be specified as having a bandwidth of 20–20,000 Hz. This means that at both 20 and 20,000 Hz the gain is down to 0.707 of the maximum gain.

We have seen that at both f_l and f_h the voltage (or current) gain is reduced to $1/\sqrt{2}$ of the maximum value. Recall that power is proportional to voltage (or current) squared. Since $(1/\sqrt{2})^2$ is equal to $1/2$, f_l and f_h are called the **half-power frequencies.**

The significance of half-power relates to sensitivity of the human ear and eye. Experiments have shown that the intensity of sound or light must change by at least a factor of 2 before most people can detect a change in level. Thus the half-power frequencies are those at which we begin to detect a change in volume relative to the midband frequencies. For example, if an amplifier is putting out 1 watt a reasonably good ear would detect a change in intensity when the volume either fell to $\frac{1}{2}$ watt or increased to 2 watts.

Thus in comparing levels in intensity it is more useful to discuss the ratio of power level rather than the actual levels. In particular it is convenient to think in terms of the logarithm of the power ratio. This unit is called a **Bel**.

$$\text{bel} = \log \frac{P_{\text{out}}}{P_{\text{in}}} \tag{10.2a}$$

in honor of Alexander Graham Bell. As in the case of the farad the Bel is too large for most applications. Instead we use the **decibel** (dB), which is equal to one tenth of a Bel ($\frac{1}{10}$ dB):

$$\frac{1}{10} \, dB = \log \frac{P_{\text{out}}}{P_{\text{in}}}$$

$$\tag{10.2b}$$

$$dB = 10 \log \frac{P_{\text{out}}}{P_{\text{in}}}$$

Example 10.5

An audio amplifier puts out 10 watts when the input is 0.1 watt. What is the gain in dB?

Solution Step 1. Since

$$dB = 10 \log \frac{P_{\text{out}}}{P_{\text{in}}}$$

we have

$$dB = 10 \log \frac{10}{0.1}$$

$$= 10 \log 100$$

Step 2. Since $\log 100 = 2$ we have

$$dB = 10 \times 2 = 20 \, dB$$

If we use Eq. 10.2b to compute decibels for a power ratio of 2 (or $\frac{1}{2}$) we see that a factor of 2 in power is equal to 3 dB. Thus the half-power frequencies are often referred to as the frequencies at which the **power is down 3 dB.**

10.5 Phase Shift

In addition to the variation of gain with frequency (called the **frequency response** of an amplifier) we are also interested in the phase shift between amplifier input and output. Consider the *CE* amplifier shown in Fig. 10.5.

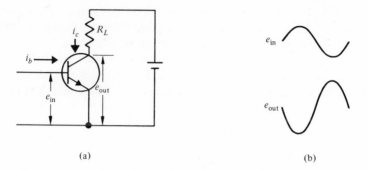

(a)   (b)

10.5   A CE stage. (a) Configuration. (b) Waveforms.

An increase in input signal current (base current) results in an increase in collector current, which results in a larger voltage across R_L. When V_{R_L} increases V_{ce} must decrease. This is a consequence of Kirchhoff's voltage law applied to the output loop of Fig. 10.5 (a).

The output of a *CE* stage is taken across the collector to the emitter and we have seen that this voltage decreases as the base voltage increases. This does not mean that the output signal is decreased. It means that **in a CE stage the input and output are 180° out of phase,** as shown in Fig. 10.5 (b).

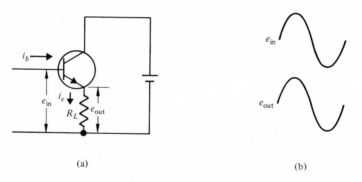

(a)   (b)

10.6   A CC stage. (a) Configuration. (b) Waveforms.

A CC amplifier is shown in Fig. 10.6. In this case the situation is different. An increase in base current results in an increase in emitter current. Since in the CC configuration the output is directly across the emitter resistor, the **input** and **output signals are in phase in the CC stage.**

The phase-shift situation is affected by the same series and shunt capacitances which affect amplifier gain. Thus the preceding remarks concerning CE and CC phase shift apply only to the midband range and must be modified for higher and lower frequencies.

Whether or not we need be concerned with amplifier phase shift depends on the application. Most tests seem to indicate that the ear cannot detect a change in phase. Thus phase shift is not a primary concern in an audio amplifier. However, if the phase of the video signal in a TV set were to change by 180° we would see the negative of the picture instead of the actual picture.

10.6   Multistage Amplifiers

The amplifiers which have been described so far have gains which range from about 1 to 80. In many applications such gain is not enough. An ordinary radio, for example, sequires several volts to drive a loudspeaker. Yet the antenna typically receives microvolts (millionths of a volt).

Example 10.6
A certain radio needs 1 V to drive a loudspeaker. If the signal at the antenna is 10 μV, what gain must the radio furnish?

Solution Step 1.   We have already seen that voltage gain is the ratio of output voltage to input voltage:

$$A_v = \frac{e_{out}}{e_{in}}$$

Step 2.   Thus the gain required of the radio will be

$$A_v = \frac{1}{10 \times 10^{-6}}$$

$$= 100,000$$

Clearly a single stage of amplification will not be able to supply such gain.

The way to increase gain is to construct a **multistage amplifier**; that is, the output of one stage is connected to the input of the next stage. This is called **cascading**. Figure 10.7 shows a two-stage CE amplifier. Transistor Q_1 amplifies the signal from the source. This amplified signal (e_{out_1}) is the input to the next stage (Q_2). Thus Q_2 takes the output of the first stage and further amplifies the signal. In effect the output of Q_1 is the signal source for Q_2 so **the total gain will be the product of the individual stage gains**:

$$A_T = A_1 A_2 \cdots$$

Example 10.7
A multistage amplifier consists of three stages with identical gain. If the total gain of the amplifier is 125,000 what is the gain of each stage?

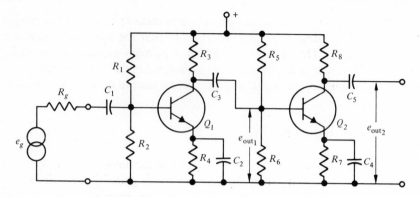

10.7 Two-stage CE amplifier.

Solution Step 1. The total gain is the product of the individual gains:

$$A_T = A_1 A_2 A_3 \qquad\qquad (10.3)$$

Step 2. Since the stages have identical gain,

$$A_1 = A_2 = A_3$$

Therefore

$$A_T = (A_1)^3 = 125,000$$
$$A_1 = (125,000)^{1/3}$$
$$A_1 = A_2 = A_3 = 50$$

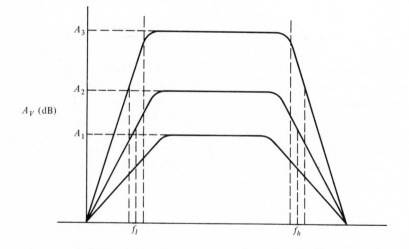

10.8 Cascading stages of amplification.

A frequency-response plot of Example 10.7 might look something like Fig. 10.8. We see that cascading stages does indeed increase the gain. However, **cascading stages decreases the bandwidth.** The decrease in bandwidth is due to the increased capacitance. Additional stages of amplification require additional coupling and bypass capacitors. This has the effect of lowering the series capacitance and results in an increased value of lower half-power frequency.

Similarly, increasing the number of stages increases the shunt capacitance since capacitors in parallel add. Thus the increase in shunt capacitance results in a lower value of upper half-power frequency. The overall result is that to achieve a given overall bandwidth each individual stage must have a larger bandwidth.

Notice in Fig. 10.8 that voltage gain is plotted in decibels. This allows wide gain (50–125,000) to be shown with reasonable detail. Otherwise the scale would be too compressed for the ranges of interest. To plot voltage gain in decibels we start with the basic definition of decibel (Eq. 10.2b):

$$dB = 10 \log \frac{P_{out}}{P_{in}}$$

Since one form of the power equation (Eq. 2.9) is

$$P = \frac{V^2}{R}$$

we can substitute in the decibel equation to get

$$dB = 10 \log \frac{V^2_{out}/R_{out}}{V^2_{in}/R_{in}} \tag{10.4a}$$

or

$$= 10 \log \frac{V^2_{out}}{V^2_{in}} \tag{10.4b}$$

$$= 20 \log \frac{V_{out}}{V_{in}}$$

Strictly speaking, the step from Eq. 10.4a to Eq. 10.4b is not correct. This is because R_{in} and R_{out} are generally quite different. We have already seen that an amplifier generally requires a high input resistance and a low output resistance. Nevertheless Eq. 10.4b is used almost universally and we shall continue this convention.

Example 10.8

Determine the voltage gain in decibels for each stage in Example 10.7 (this is actually determining the values of A_1, A_2, and A_3 in Fig. 10.8).

Solution Step 1.   The gain of $A_1 = 50$. Therefore

$$dB = 20 \log \frac{V_{out}}{V_{in}}$$

$$= 20 \log \frac{50}{1}$$

$$= 20 \times 1.7$$

$$dB_1 = 34 \, dB$$

Step 2.   At the output of A_2 the gain is

$$A = A_1 A_2 = 50 \times 50 = 2500$$

$$dB = 20 \log \frac{V_{out}}{V_{in}}$$

$$= 20 \log \frac{2500}{1}$$

$$= 20 \times 3.4$$

$$dB_2 = 68 \, dB$$

Step 3.   The total gain (A_1, A_2, A_3) is 125,000. Then

$$dB = 20 \log \frac{V_{out}}{V_{in}}$$

$$= 20 \log \frac{125,000}{1}$$

$$= 20 \times 5.096$$

$$dB_T = 102 \, dB$$

Our calculations of gain have not yet included the phase shift. We have seen that at midband the phase shift of a CE amplifier is 180°. Thus we should have used a gain of -50 rather than $+50$ for the two previous problems. The minus sign accounts for the 180° shift. Keeping this in mind we can see that an amplifier which consists of an odd number of stages $(1, 3, 5, \ldots)$ of CE amplifiers will have a negative gain (180° phase shift). Similarly, an even number of CE stages $(2, 4, 6, \ldots)$ will result in positive gain (0° phase shift).

If we use an amplifier which contains both CE and CC stages we need only count the number of CE stages since CC stages have 0° phase shift. As a practical matter a good many amplifiers will have CC stages at both the input and output because the CC configuration has high input and low output resistance. However, the CC configuration does not furnish voltage gain (although current gain is high). Thus an amplifier designed primarily for voltage gain would have CC input and output stages; the intervening stages would be CE stages.

10.7   Power Amplifiers

Amplifiers which have been discussed were cascaded by using resistors and capacitors. This type of connection is called **RC coupling.** Generally RC coupling is used when the primary objective is to obtain either current or voltage gain.

Frequently an amplifier is required to drive a load which requires large amounts of power. For example loudspeakers, motors, and so on require large amounts of power and power efficiency is an important factor. High-power loads such as speakers and motors have relatively low resistances. In this way the heat dissipation is kept down.

To achieve maximum power transfer we have seen that the resistance of the load must be equal to the resistance of the generator (i.e., maximum power transfer theorem). In this case the generator resistance is the output resistance of the amplifier and the load is the speaker or motor. The problem is that the output resistance of the amplifier is generally greater than the load resistance so that maximum power transfer is a problem. Also optimum frequency response goes along with maximum power transfer. Thus efficiency and fidelity are both affected if generator and load do not match.

Fortunately the use of a transformer as a coupling element between amplifiers makes it possible to match unlike resistances. Transformer coupling is illustrated in Fig. 10.9. In Chapter 7 we saw that transformer voltages were related to their turns ratio by

$$\frac{V_1}{V_2} = \frac{N_1}{N_2}$$

or   (10.5a)

$$V_1 = V_2 \frac{N_1}{N_2}$$

In an ideal transformer the product of the input ampere turns equals the product of the output ampere turns:

$$I_1 N_1 = I_2 N_2$$

or   (10.5b)

$$I_2 = I_1 \frac{N_1}{N_2}$$

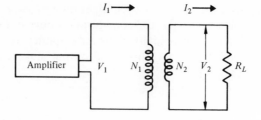

10.9 Transformer coupling to a load.

But from Ohm's law we can also say that

$$I_2 = \frac{V_2}{R_L}$$

Thus

$$\frac{V_2}{R_L} = I_1 \frac{N_1}{N_2} \tag{10.5c}$$

or

$$I_1 = \frac{V_2}{R_L} \frac{N_2}{N_1}$$

In Chapter 9 the input resistance of the transistor was discussed. From a signal standpoint we saw that the input resistance was the ratio of input voltage to input current. Similarly we can determine the input resistance of a transformer from a signal (rather than a DC) standpoint:

$$r_{in} = \frac{v_{in}}{i_{in}} \tag{10.5d}$$

Using the results of Eq. 10.5a for V_{in} and Eq. 10.5c for i_{in} we obtain

$$r_{in} = V_2 \frac{N_1}{N_2} \frac{R_L N_1}{V_2 N_2}$$

or   (10.6)

$$r_{in} = \left(\frac{N_1}{N_2}\right)^2 R_L$$

Equation 10.6 shows that the input resistance of a transformer is determined by the load resistance and the turns ratio squared. Thus if the output resistance of an amplifier (input resistance of the transformer) and load resistance are known, a transformer with the proper turns ratio can be selected to match the load to the amplifier.

Example 10.9

A certain audio amplifier has a 100-Ω output resistance. It is to be connected to an 8-Ω loudspeaker. Determine the required turns ratio for a matching transformer.

Solution Step 1.   From the given data, $r_{in} = 100\,\Omega$ and $R_L = 8\,\Omega$.

Step 2.   Thus

$$r_{in} = \left(\frac{N_1}{N_2}\right)^2 R_L$$

$$8 = \left(\frac{N_1}{N_2}\right)^2 100$$

$$\left(\frac{N_1}{N_2}\right)^2 = 12.5$$

$$\frac{N_1}{N_2} = 3.25$$

Thus a transformer with 3.25 as many turns on the primary as on the secondary will match the amplifier and speaker. Figure 10.10 shows an output stage which uses transformer coupling to the load.

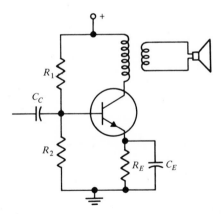

10.10   Transformer-coupled output stage.

The resistors R_1, R_2, and R_E intentionally bias the transistor so that it conducts even when no signal is present. This is exactly the same situation as described for *RC*-coupled amplifiers. Since we are now considering power amplifiers it may not be desirable to use the same bias approach; that is, a good deal of power is being wasted just because current flows when no signal exists.

A circuit in which no current flows unless a signal is present is shown in Fig. 10.11 (a). When no input signal is present no base current flows in either transistor since neither base-emitter junction is forward biased. There is no collector current since there is no base current.

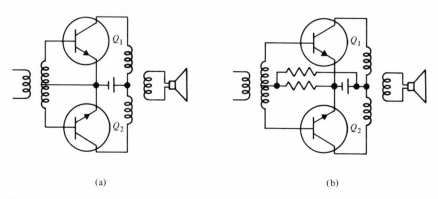

(a)   (b)

10.11   Power-amplifiers. (a) Signal bias. (b) Push-pull.

Any input signal will forward bias transistor Q_1 and reverse bias Q_2 (or vice versa). When Q_1 is forward biased it conducts and Q_2 does not. During the opposite half-cycle Q_2 conducts and Q_1 does not. In the configuration shown in Fig. 10.11 (a), it is the signal which furnishes its own bias. Since no current flows unless a signal is present this circuit is much more efficient than the single-ended configuration. However, there must be distortion. Thus if the prime consideration is efficiency, the circuit shown in Fig. 10.11 (a) is superior. If the prime consideration is superior fidelity, the single-ended circuit is superior.

In another version, shown in Fig. 10.11 (b), base bias is provided by the power supply. This configuration is called a push-pull power amplifier; when an input signal is applied one transistor will conduct more than the other on alternate halves of the cycle. The outputs of the two transistors are combined in the transformer. Push-pull circuits have good efficiency and good fidelity. Typically push-pull amplifiers are used in "hi-fi" amplifier output stages.

10.8   Direct Current Amplifiers

There are many applications where signals to be amplified change very slowly. Electrocardiogram pulses, for example, occur about once a second.

Signal levels from thermocouples, strain gauges, and so on change even more slowly in many cases. It is unrealistic to use RC coupling in such slowly changing conditions.

Example 10.10

An amplifier with a 1-kΩ input resistance must amplify a 0.5-Hz signal. What value coupling capacitor should be used at the input?

Solution Step 1.   As in the case of the emitter bypass capacitor, X_C should be about $\frac{1}{10}$ or less of the resistance. Therefore

$$X_C = \frac{1000}{10}$$

$$= 100 \, \Omega$$

Step 2.   Since $X_C = 100 \, \Omega$ and $f = 0.5$ Hz, we can find C:

$$X_C = \frac{1}{2\pi f C}$$

$$C = \frac{1}{2\pi f X_C}$$

$$= \frac{1}{2\pi \times 0.5 \times 10^2}$$

$$= 3200 \, \mu F$$

While this is a correct mathematical solution, capacitors of such value are unrealistic both from a size and a quality standpoint. Inductors (i.e., transformers) are also unrealistic at such extremely low frequencies. Thus, **the solution to amplifying low frequency is to eliminate capacitors and transformers and to couple stages directly.** Such amplifiers are called **DC amplifiers.** Two possible DC amplifiers are shown in Fig. 10.12.

In Fig. 10.12 (a) two transistors of the same type (*NPN* in this case) are used. Notice that R_1 serves two functions: It is the load resistor of Q_1 and the base resistor of Q_2. Since the collector of Q_1 and the base of Q_2 are at the same voltage, the power-supply voltage will have to be increased if many stages of amplification are required. A possible solution is the use of **complementary transistors.** Complementary transistors have similar characteristics but are of opposite type. One is *NPN* and the other is *PNP*. Thus by reversing alternate stages as shown in Fig. 10.12 (b) lower supply voltages can be used. Notice that to maintain proper bias polarity, emitter and collector connections must be reversed.

At first glance it may seem that DC amplifiers are to be preferred over *RC*-coupled amplifiers. No coupling capacitors are required which reduces cost and extends the low-frequency response. Also the biasing is simplified

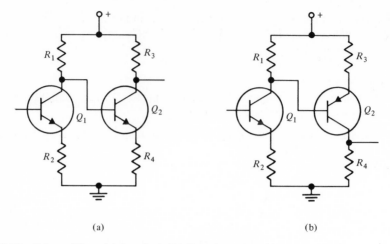

(a)   (b)

10.12   DC amplifiers. (a) Standard. (b) Complementary.

since fewer resistors are required. Unfortunately, practical problems create more difficult problems for DC amplifiers.

We have observed that temperature changes will shift the bias conditions. Since temperature changes are a slowly varying effect (essentially DC) capacitors in an *RC*-coupled amplifier will block temperature changes from the next stage. But there are no capacitors in a DC amplifier. Thus a change in bias due to temperature cannot be distinguished from a change in signal level. Also, power-supply ripple which may be outside the frequency range of an *RC*-coupled amplifier will appear at the output of a DC amplifier. Thus elimination of capacitors and some of the biasing resistors is at best a mixed blessing.

The apparent advantages associated with DC amplifiers have vanished. We need techniques to make practical DC amplifiers when they are required. One method is to convert the DC signal into an AC signal. This method is called **chopping.** In Fig. 10.13 we have an electromechanical switch which alternately opens and shorts the input. In this way the slowly varying input signal is converted into an AC signal. This AC signal is then fed into an AC

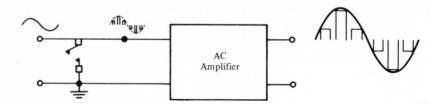

10.13   Chopper-type amplifier.

amplifier. The amplified output contains the amplified input signal as well as the chopping frequency. In most cases it will be necessary to remove the chopping frequency from the output. Thus the chopping frequency must be much higher than the highest frequency component of the signal. In addition to electromechanical choppers there are also electronic choppers which have no moving parts.

Another technique for amplifying DC is shown in Fig. 10.14. **The input is applied between the bases** of Q_1 and Q_2 **instead of between a base and ground.** The output is taken between the two collectors rather than between

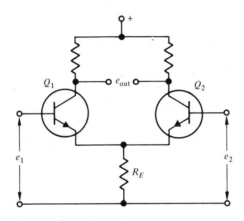

10.14   Differential amplifier stage.

a collector and ground. The advantage of this method is that any shift in operating point due to temperature, power-supply ripple, and so on will occur to both stages simultaneously. **Since we are looking at the difference between the two transistors there will be no shift due to any signal that is common to both.**

For example, an increase in temperature will increase the collector current through both Q_1 and Q_2. However, the output is taken between the collectors of Q_1 and Q_2. Since it is the difference between the two outputs that is the signal, whatever is common to both transistors will not affect the output. The only time a **differential amplifier** will have an output is when the signals at the two bases are different and this is a true input signal.

Another advantage of the differential amplifier is its relative immunity to 60-Hz **pick-up**. High-gain amplifiers are so sensitive that they pick up 60 Hz which is being carried on power lines, instrument leads, and so on. In many practical situations this 60-Hz "noise" can obliterate the low-level signals which we desire to amplify. The differential amplifier greatly reduces the effect of 60-Hz pick-up:

$$e_1 = V_{be_1} + V_{R_E} \qquad\qquad\qquad \text{(10.7a)}$$

and

$$e_2 = V_{be_2} + V_{R_E} \qquad\qquad\qquad \text{(10.7b)}$$

However, the input is the difference between

$$e_{\text{in}} = e_1 - e_2$$
$$= V_{be_1} - V_{be_2} \qquad\qquad\qquad \text{(10.7c)}$$

Notice that the voltage across R_E is not part of the input signal although it is part of the signal between input and ground. By making R_E very large we do not affect a true input signal but we greatly reduce any 60-Hz signal which exists between the base and ground.

Differential amplifiers require matched components and more transistors than single-ended amplifiers. However, when the situation requires, these penalties are well worth the improvement in performance.

10.9   Vacuum Triodes

In Chapter 1 the notion of conduction in vacuum was presented and in Chapter 8 the vacuum diode was introduced. By adding a third element to a vacuum diode it is possible to amplify. In a similar manner we can think of a transistor as the addition of a third element to a semiconductor diode.

In the case of a vacuum tube the third element is called a **grid.** The grid is a metallic screen which is placed between the filament and the plate. The grid is physically much closer to the filament than to the plate. Figure 10.15 shows the symbol of such a tube, which is called a **triode.**

If no voltage exists on the grid and the plate is made positive with respect to the filament, current will flow provided that the filament is heated to

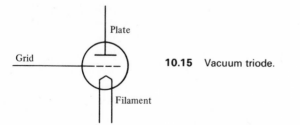

10.15   Vacuum triode.

emit electrons. This is vacuum diode action. Now if the grid is made negative with respect to the filament the current flowing from the filament to the plate will be reduced, because the negative voltage on the grid will repel the electrons being emitted from the filament.

If the grid is made more negative even less current will flow. Finally, if the grid is made too negative no current will reach the plate and the triode will be cut off. If the grid is made positive with respect to the filament plate current will flow but grid current will also flow; generally this is undesirable.

The principle of triode amplification is illustrated in Fig. 10.16. The filament battery (V_A) heats the filament to a temperature which is hot enough to emit electrons into the vacuum. Battery (V_B) biases the plate

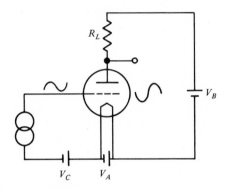

10.16 Principle of triode amplification.

positive with respect to the filament. Battery (V_C) biases the grid slightly negative with respect to the filament. Under these conditions plate current flows through the load resistor. This situation is similar to that of biasing a transistor without an input signal. Just as in a transistor, a triode must be properly biased before amplification is possible.

Now assume that a signal is superimposed on the negative bias. When the signal is increasing, the resultant voltage between the grid and filament is less negative. This results in an increase in plate current. When the input signal is decreasing, the grid-to-filament voltage is more negative and so plate current is decreasing. These variations in plate current appear as a variation in load voltage across the load resistor.

Amplification is possible because **the grid is much closer to the filament than to the plate**. In this way a small voltage change between grid and filament can result in a large change in current. This large change in current in turn causes a large change in output voltage; that is, **a small change in input voltage results in a large change in output voltage**. The triode is seen to be a voltage amplifier.

Both transistors and triodes can amplify voltage and both are three-element devices. However, transistors and triodes operate on completely different principles. Basically, a transistor operates by transferring current from a low to a high resistance. In a triode there is no input current. **A triode operates by controlling the voltages between elements which are in a vacuum.**

Therefore it is more useful to think of a transistor as basically a current amplifier (although voltage amplification is possible). A vacuum tube, on the other hand, must be considered as a voltage amplifier. Since no input current exists in a triode, current gain is not possible with a triode.

The fact that no current flows in the input of a triode means that the input resistance of a triode is infinite. This is apparent from Ohm's law. A real voltage divided by zero current is infinite resistance. The infinite input resistance of a triode is a distinct advantage in connecting triodes, since an infinite resistance cannot cause any loading effect regardless of the component being connected to it.

On the other hand, transistors require less power (no filament) and lower voltage bias sources, and a filament must eventually burn out whereas a transistor has nothing to burn out. Transistors are also much smaller than triodes.

Most filaments are operated from step-down transformers. Typical filament voltages are 6.3 and 12.6 V_{rms}, because these voltages are the load voltages of the wet-cell batteries which were originally used to operate filaments. When AC is used to heat a filament the voltage and therefore the current emitted will vary over a complete cycle.

This means that there will be a 60-Hz output signal regardless of whether or not an input signal is present. Thus distortion will result due to the filament

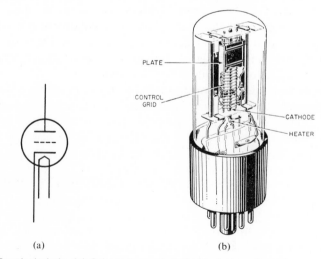

10.17 Practical triode. (a) Schematic symbol. (b) Typical configuration.

being operated from an AC source. To solve this problem a **cathode** is added to triodes. A cathode is a sleeve which is placed in thermal, but not electrical, contact with the filament. The cathode is also a material which can emit electrons. However, the fact that there is a thermal lag between the filament and cathode results in a relatively uniform current being emitted from the cathode over a cycle. Figure 10.17 shows a practical triode.

Roughly speaking (since the operating principles are different), we can compare the elements of a triode and a transistor. The emitter and cathode correspond approximately, the base and grid are both control elements, and the collector and plate correspond. This is the situation for a triode and a *NPN* transistor. There is no vacuum-tube equivalent for a *PNP* transistor.

10.10   Practical Triode Circuits

For the transistor, the principle of transistor action was discussed and then a model was developed using the black-box approach. The same situation applies to the triode. One approach to a triode model would be to copy the transistor equivalent circuit using triode terms.

This method is shown in Fig. 10.18. It consists of three internal resistors (grid, cathode, and plate) and a controlled voltage source. The term μ (mu)

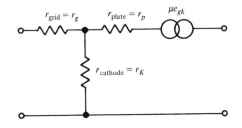

10.18   Possible model of a triode.

is the triode voltage amplification factor (just as β is the transistor current amplification factor),

$$\mu = \frac{e_p}{e_g} \tag{10.8}$$

that is, μ is the ratio of output signal voltage e_p (plate voltage) to input signal voltage e_g (grid voltage).

Actually the triode model shown in Fig. 10.18 is much more complex than is required. We have seen that the triode has an infinite input resistance. Thus r_g can be replaced by an open circuit. Also it turns out that internal cathode resistance is negligible. Thus r_k can be replaced by a short circuit.

This reduces the model of a triode to the rather simple circuit shown in Fig. 10.19.

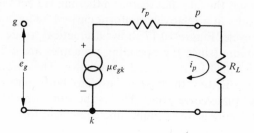

10.19   Triode equivalent circuit.

The realities of the situation have reduced the equivalent triode circuit from a tee which requires two loops for analysis to a single-loop circuit. This greatly simplifies the analysis. For example, to determine the voltage gain of a triode,

$$A_v = \frac{e_{\text{out}}}{e_{\text{in}}} = \frac{i_p R_L}{e_g} \tag{10.9a}$$

Kirchhoff's voltage law for the output circuit is

$$\mu e_g = i_p(r_p + R_L) \tag{10.9b}$$

or

$$i_p = \frac{\mu e_g}{r_p + R_L} \tag{10.9c}$$

Combining Eqs. 10.9a and 10.9c we obtain

$$A_v = \frac{\mu R_L}{r_p + R_L} \tag{10.9d}$$

Example 10.11

A certain triode has an amplification factor of 60 and a plate resistance of 15 kΩ. What value of load resistance is required to achieve a voltage gain of 40?

Solution Step 1. From the given data we have $\mu = 60$, $r_p = 15 \times 10^3\ \Omega$, and $A_v = 40$.

Step 2. Therefore

$$A_v = \frac{\mu R_L}{r_p + R_L}$$

$$40 = \frac{60 R_L}{15 \times 10^3 + R_L}$$

$$R_L = 30 \times 10^3 \, \Omega$$

The configuration which we have been discussing has the cathode common to the input and output circuits. According to transistor terminology this would be called a common-cathode configuration, except that in vacuum-tube terminology the term "grounded" has always been used instead of "common." Thus, Fig. 10.19 is the equivalent circuit of a **grounded-cathode** amplifier. The characteristics of the grounded-cathode triode configuration and the CE transistor configuration are comparable.

Other triode configurations are also possible and are shown in Fig. 10.20. The grounded-grid amplifier shown in Fig. 10.20 (a) has input and output

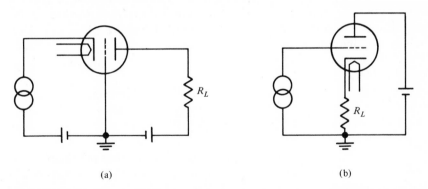

(a)	(b)

10.20 Additional triode configurations. (a) Grounded-grid. (b) Grounded-plate.

resistances which are similar to the CB amplifier. In Fig. 10.20 (b) there is a grounded-plate amplifier. This is roughly equivalent to the common collector. The grounded plate is sometimes called a cathode follower just as the common collector is called an emitter follower.

It is possible to reduce the number of batteries needed to operate a triode just as we did for the transistor. Figure 10.21 shows a practical grounded-cathode amplifier. In this case biasing the triode properly is accomplished with a single battery V_B instead of two batteries as in Fig. 10.16 (V_C and V_B). However, an additional voltage source is still required to operate the filament.

The requirement for proper triode biasing is that the plate be positive with respect to the cathode and that the grid be negative with respect to the

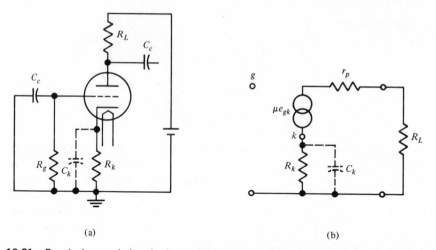

(a)   (b)

10.21   Practical grounded-cathode amplifier. (a) Schematic. (b) Equivalent circuit.

cathode. Plate current flowing through the cathode resistor R_k makes the cathode positive with respect to ground. But no current flows through the grid resistor R_g, and so the grid is at ground. Thus, **the grid is at a lower voltage than the cathode** and proper biasing is achieved with a single battery. The cathode resistor may have a bypass capacitor as was the case with the CE amplifier.

The function of the grid resistor (R_g) is rather interesting. As electrons travel from the cathode toward the plate, occasional electrons will land on the grid even though the grid is negative. When sufficient electrons have been piled up on the grid, the grid will become so negative as to cut the triode off completely. Resistor R_g prevents electrons from piling up on the grid by providing a return path to ground. Resistor R_g is referred to as a **grid-leak resistor.**

The addition of the cathode resistor (R_k) modifies the equivalent circuit as shown in Fig. 10.21 (b). Actually the triode amplifies the signal between the grid to cathode (e_{gk}). With the addition of R_k, e_{in} is no longer equal to e_{gk}:

$$e_{in} = e_{gk} + i_p R_k \qquad \textbf{(10.10a)}$$

and Kirchhoff's voltage law for the output becomes

$$\mu e_{gK} = i_p(r_p + R_L + R_K)$$

or   **(10.10b)**

$$e_{gK} = \frac{i_p}{\mu}(r_p + R_L + R_K)$$

Substituting this into Eq. 10.10a we obtain

$$\mu e_{in} = i_p[r_p + R_L + (\mu + 1)R_K]$$

or   (10.10c)

$$i_p = \frac{\mu e_{in}}{r_p + R_L + (\mu + 1)R_K}$$

If we multiply Eq. 10.10c by R_L and divide by e_{in} we obtain the expression for voltage gain:

$$A_v = \frac{e_{out}}{e_{in}} = \frac{\mu R_L}{r_p + R_L + (\mu + 1)R_K} \qquad \text{(10.10d)}$$

The gain with a cathode resistor is lower than the gain without a cathode resistor (Eq. 10.9d) since the denominator is increased by a factor of $(\mu + 1)R_K$.

Example 10.12
Assume that the same tube and load resistor are used as in Example 10.11. If bias is achieved using a 2500-Ω cathode resistor what will be the voltage gain?

Solution Step 1. From Example 10.11 $\mu = 60$, $r_p = 15\,k\Omega$, and $R_L = 30\,k\Omega$. From this example, $R_k = 2.5\,k\Omega$.

Step 2. Therefore

$$A_v = \frac{\mu R_L}{r_p + R_L + (\mu + 1)R_K}$$

$$= \frac{60 \times 30 \times 10^3}{15 \times 10^3 + 30 \times 10^3 + (60 + 1) \times 2.5 \times 10^3}$$

$$= 9.15$$

The amplification action of the triode increases the effect of the cathode resistor by a factor of $\mu + 1$ just as the amplification action of the transistor increases the emitter resistance by $\beta + 1$ (Eq. 9.19c). In both cases gain is reduced as a result of the effective increase of resistance in the output circuit. However, this decrease in gain is partially compensated for by a decrease in gain variation from unit to unit.

In the case of transistors gain variation was due to manufacturing tolerances which affected β. In the case of triodes the variation of μ from unit to unit is smaller, because dimensions associated with triodes are relatively large and uniformity is thus more readily attainable. However, as the triode ages and the filament becomes weaker μ will drop. Resistor R_K helps keep gain more uniform over the operating life of the triode.

In the transistor case we discussed frequency response, cascading stages, power amplification, and DC amplifiers. All of these concepts apply equally well to triodes. In fact historically the triode came before the transistor. The first triode was announced in 1905 while the transistor was announced in 1948.

On balance the transistor seems to be superior to the triode for most applications. Most new designs employ transistors instead of triodes.

Summary

1. The addition of an emitter bypass capacitor creates separate paths for signal and bias circuits. This stabilizes bias and helps to reduce gain variation due to manufacturing variations in transistor parameters.
2. The value of capacitance used in an amplifier determines which frequencies can be amplified. Coupling and bypass capacitors determine the low-frequency range and shunt capacitance determines the high-frequency range.
3. Amplifier bandwidth is the range between the upper and lower half-power frequencies. Half-power is significant because it is the minimum change which the ear can detect.
4. It is convenient to describe gain in terms of ratio as well as actual value. This is generally expressed in decibels.
5. Amplifier phase shift with frequency is caused by the capacitance in the circuit.
6. Additional gain can be obtained by cascading stages of amplification. Overall amplifier gain is the product of the individual stage gains.
7. Power amplifiers must be considered from an efficiency standpoint. Therefore different bias techniques are used.
8. In power amplifiers transformers are generally used to couple the amplifier to the load. The transformer turns ratio permits maximum power transfer by transforming the load resistance to a different value.
9. Slowly-varying signals cannot use capacitors or transformers as coupling elements. Therefore slowly-varying signals require DC amplifiers.
10. The problems associated with DC amplifiers are in separating the true signal from changes in amplifier performance. Choppers and differential amplifiers are two practical solutions.
11. Triodes operate by controlling the voltage between elements in a vacuum. This results in voltage gain and infinite input resistance.
12. Triodes are basically voltage amplifiers while transistors are basically current amplifiers. Triodes require higher operating voltages than transistors. In addition triodes require filaments which do not exist in transistors.

Questions

1. How does the addition of the emitter bypass capacitor stabilize the emitter bias voltage?

2. How is the value of the emitter bypass capacitor determined?
3. Why do capacitors affect the gain of an amplifier?
4. Which capacitances affect the low-frequency gain and why is this so?
5. Which capacitances affect the high-frequency range and why is this so?
6. What is the significance of half-power with respect to an amplifier?
7. What is a decibel?
8. Why do CE and CC configurations have different phase-shift characteristics?
9. Why do power amplifiers have different bias considerations than signal amplifiers?
10. How is bias obtained in the different types of power amplifiers?
11. Under what circumstances are DC amplifiers required?
12. What is the principle of a chopper amplifier?
13. What is the principle of a differential amplifier?
14. How does a triode amplify?
15. Compare triodes and transistors as to advantages and disadvantages.
16. Explain the function of the cathode resistor.
17. What is the purpose of the grid-leak resistor?

Problems

1. What value of capacitor will effectively bypass a 1-kΩ emitter resistor at 20 Hz?
2. Bypass a 2-kΩ emitter resistor at 100 Hz?
3. A transistor has an equivalent input resistance of 1 kΩ and shunt capacitance which totals 50 pF. What value of capacitance will give an f_l of 10 Hz? What will be the frequency of maximum gain?
4. For Example 3.3 the voltage gain at f_l is 30. What is the maximum voltage gain?
5. A transistor has an R'_{in} of 1.5 kΩ and a total shunt capacitance of 20 pF. How much capacitance should be placed in parallel with C_{sh} to reduce the value of f_h to 100 kHz?
6. An amplifier has a midband gain of 20 dB. What is the gain at the half-power frequencies?
7. An amplifier has a midband power gain of 200. What is the gain in decibels at midband and at the half-power frequency?
8. A single-ended power amplifier drives a 4-Ω load. If the output resistance of the amplifier is 100 Ω, what turns ratio is necessary for matching?
9. Match a 500-Ω load to an amplifier with a 2000-Ω output resistance with a transformer.
10. An amplifier with a 100-kΩ input resistance is to be used to amplify a signal which changes approximately once a minute. Determine if capacitor coupling is realistic.
11. The conditions are the same as in Problem 10 except that the signal changes approximately once a second.
12. A typical incandescent lamp will burn out in approximately 750 hr. How many months of continuous operation is this?
13. A quality triode has a filament which lasts 10,000 hr. How many months of continuous operation are possible?
14. What is the grid-to-cathode voltage in a triode in which the plate current is 5 mA and the cathode resistor is 2 kΩ?

15. A certain triode has a 30-kΩ plate resistance and an amplification factor of 50. What is the voltage gain if a 40-kΩ load is used?

16. For the triode of Problem 15, what value of load resistor is required to achieve a voltage gain of
    (a) 40
    (b) 55

17. A triode with $\mu = 50$, $r_p = 15\ \text{k}\Omega$ is to be used with a 1 kΩ cathode resistor. What value of load resistance is needed for a voltage gain of 25?

18. Assuming the same triode and R_L as determined in Problem 17, determine the gain if $R_k = 2\ \text{k}\Omega$.

19. A certain triode has an r_p of 15 kΩ and a μ of 60. It is used with a 1.5-kΩ R_k. What value of R_L will give a voltage gain of 30?

Chapter 11 Feedback

11.1   Introduction

In this chapter the effect of returning a portion of the output signal to the input of the amplifier is investigated. Such signals can be returned either out of phase or in phase with the output signal. Both methods have advantages and both are investigated to determine applications.

11.2   Distortion in Amplifiers

An ideal amplifier should only increase the magnitude of an input signal. When effects other than an increase in magnitude occur, the amplifier has introduced distortion. Presumably a high-fidelity (hi-fi) amplifier is one which does not produce a distorted output. Several types of distortion have already been discussed.

For example, we have seen that choosing an incorrect bias level or overdriving an amplifier results in a distorted output. In this case the result will be saturation, cutoff, or both; that is, the output will be clipped off at either end or at both the top and bottom.

Another type of distortion which has been discussed is associated with the capacitors or inductors which are present in the amplifier. Amplifiers have a certain specified bandwidth, so input signals of different frequencies will be amplified by different amounts.

Example 11.1

A certain hi-fi amplifier has a bandwidth of 20 Hz to 20 kHz, and the amplifier has a voltage gain of 100. What will be the output for a 20-Hz and a 5-kHz signal if both signals have 0.1-volt input levels?

Solution Step 1.   Five kHz is well within the midband. Therefore

$$A_v = \frac{e_{\text{out}}}{e_{\text{in}}}$$

$$e_{\text{out}} = A_v{}_{\text{in}}$$

$$= 100 \times 0.1$$

$$e_{\text{out}(5\,\text{kHz})} = 10 \text{ volts}$$

Step 2.   Twenty Hz is the 3-dB point or the frequency at which the voltage gain is 0.707 of the midband value. Therefore

$$e_{\text{out}} = 0.707 \, Ae_{\text{in}}$$
$$= 0.707 \times 100 \times 0.1$$
$$e_{\text{out(20 Hz)}} = 7.07 \text{ volts}$$

Of course, signals which have lower frequencies than 20 Hz or higher frequencies than 20 kHz will have gains which are even less. The fact that an amplifier does not amplify all frequencies equally well is referred to as **frequency distortion.** Since phase shift goes hand in hand with frequency response, we can expect **phase distortion** to accompany frequency distortion.

Another type of distortion is shown in Fig. 11.1. This output results because the transistor or triode does not amplify all signal levels equally well; that is, β varies with current level. Since an input signal is itself a variation, the output signal may have different segments amplified by different amounts. This is referred to as **amplitude distortion** or **harmonic distortion.**

It is also possible that certain input frequencies will be mixed within the amplifier in such a manner that sums and differences of existing frequencies will appear at the output. In such cases frequencies appear at the output which did not exist at the input. This is referred to as **intermodulation distortion.** For example, if this type of distortion exists between two input frequencies which are, say, 1000 Hz and 1100 Hz, additional frequencies will appear at the amplifier output. In this case both 2100 Hz (the sum)

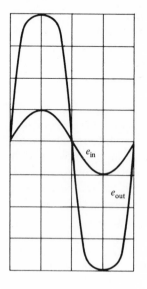

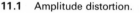

11.1 Amplitude distortion.

and 100 Hz (the difference) are possible frequencies which can appear at the output.

Power-supply ripple is another source of distortion. If any part of the power-supply ripple is amplified it will appear at the output. This is another case of a signal appearing at the output which did not exist at the input.

We have seen that there is a variation of β within transistors of the same type. Also we have noted that the μ of a triode will vary with age. Resistors and capacitors also have manufacturing tolerances. Thus we can expect a variation in gain from amplifier to amplifier.

Example 11.2

An amplifier consists of three stages, each of which has a nominal gain of 10 with a $\pm 20\%$ tolerance. Compute the nominal, maximum, and minimum possible gain.

Solution Step 1.   For the nominal stage gain of 10,

$$A_T = A_1 A_2 A_3$$
$$= 10 \times 10 \times 10$$
$$A_{T(nom)} = 1000$$

Step 2.   Maximum gain occurs if each stage has maximum possible gain. Since 20% of 10 is 2, maximum possible stage gain is 12:

$$A_T = A_1 A_2 A_3$$
$$= 12 \times 12 \times 12$$
$$A_{T(max)} = 1728$$

Step 3.   Similarly, the minimum possible stage gain is 10 minus 2, or 8:

$$A_T = A_1 A_2 A_3$$
$$= 8 \times 8 \times 8$$
$$A_{T(min)} = 512$$

Thus a relatively small stage variation ($\pm 20\%$) results in an overall possible spread of over $3:1$; this would be even worse in an amplifier with additional stages. Strictly speaking, gain variation due to component tolerance is not in itself distortion as long as the output is an accurate replica of the input. However, it is most certainly a problem if identical performance is required as might be the case in, say, replacing a defective unit.

It is rare that technical problems will be pointed out unless solutions are to be presented. Some techniques of reducing distortion are readily apparent. For example, the use of the proper bias point to avoid saturation and cutoff,

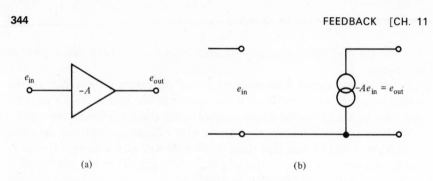

(a)   (b)

11.2   Ideal amplifier. (a) Block diagram. (b) Equivalent circuit.

the appropriate bandwidth to avoid frequency distortion, and lower power-supply ripple, are rather obvious approaches. Other techniques for reducing distortion are more subtle and will require investigation.

11.3   Negative Feedback

In addition to the "common sense" approaches for reducing amplifier distortion, another powerful technique exists. But we must first discuss the properties of an ideal amplifier. Figure 11.2 shows an ideal amplifier. The negative sign indicates that the input and output are 180° out of phase. This property has already been discussed.

What makes the amplifier ideal is shown in Fig. 11.2 (b). The amplifier has infinite input resistance and zero output resistance. This means that regardless of what is connected at either the input or output of the amplifier the signal level will not be affected. That is, the amplifier will not load down. Also, since there are no capacitors or inductors, the ideal amplifier amplifies all frequencies, including DC, equally well. It is not possible to construct an ideal amplifier; however, these properties can be approached and are worth investigation.

Two methods of using an ideal amplifier are of interest. In Fig. 11.3 (a) an ideal amplifier is used in a conventional manner. That is, a signal is applied

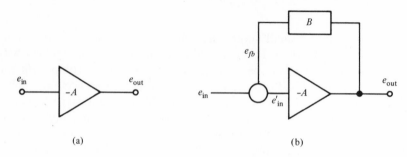

(a)   (b)

11.3   Ideal circuits. (a) Conventional. (b) With negative feedback.

at the input and the amplified signal, which is out of phase, is available at the output. In Fig. 11.3 (b) a portion of the output signal is returned (fed back) to the input. Since the input and output are out of phase, the portion of the output which is returned to the input is out of phase with the input. **Returning a portion of the output out of phase with the input is called negative feedback.**

Without negative feedback [Fig. 11.3 (a)] the gain is

$$A_v = \frac{-e_{out}}{e_{in}} \qquad \text{(11.1a)}$$

The block labeled B [Fig. 11.3 (b)] is the circuit which returns a fraction of the output to the input:

$$B = \frac{e_{fb}}{e_{out}} \qquad \text{(11.1b)}$$

where e_{fb} is the feedback voltage. Since e_{fb} is out of phase with the input, it will buck the input. Thus the input voltage to the amplifier with feedback e'_{in}) will be less than the actual input voltage:

$$e'_{in} = e_{in} + e_{fb} \qquad \text{(11.1c)}$$

Where e_{fb} is negative the gain with negative feedback (A'_v) is given by

$$A'_v = \frac{-e_{out}}{e'_{in}} = \frac{-e_{out}}{e_{in} + e_{fb}} \qquad \text{(11.1d)}$$

We can substitute Eq. 11.1b to obtain

$$A'_v = \frac{-e_{out}}{e_{in} + Be_{out}} \qquad \text{(11.1e)}$$

If we divide the numerator and denominator of Eq. 11.1e by the input voltage a very useful result is obtained:

$$A'_v = \frac{-e_{out}/e_{in}}{e_{in}/e_{in} + Be_{out}/e_{in}}$$

or, since $-e_{out}/e_{in} = A_v$,

$$A'_v = \frac{A_v}{1 - BA_v} \qquad \text{(11.2)}$$

Equation 11.2 shows that the gain with negative feedback is less than the gain without negative feedback.

Example 11.3

An amplifier consists of three stages, each with a gain of -10. Find (a) overall gain; (b) gain with negative feedback if 0.05 of output is returned to the input.

Solution Part (a).

$$A_v = A_1 A_2 A_3 = (-10)(-10)(-10)$$

$$= -1000$$

Part (b). With feedback we have

$$A'_v = \frac{A_v}{1 - BA_v}$$

$$= \frac{-1000}{1 - (0.05)(-1000)}$$

$$= \frac{-1000}{1 + 50}$$

$$A'_v = -19.6$$

Apparently negative feedback reduces gain by an appreciable amount even if only a small portion of the output is returned to the input. One advantage of feedback is illustrated in Example 11.4.

Example 11.4

The gain of each stage in Example 11.3 is reduced by 10%. Find (a) reduced overall gain; (b) reduced overall gain with negative feedback using the same amount (0.05) of negative feedback as in Example 11.3.

Solution Part (a). With the gain reduced by 10% each stage has a gain of -9. Therefore

$$A_{v(\text{reduced})} = A_1 A_2 A_3$$

$$= (-9)(-9)(-9)$$

$$= -729$$

Part (b). With negative feedback the reduced gain is

$$A'_{v(\text{reduced})} = \frac{A_v}{1 - BA_v}$$

$$= \frac{-729}{1 - (0.05)(-729)}$$

$$= \frac{-729}{1 + 36.45}$$

$$\simeq -19.5$$

Without negative feedback the gain in Example 11.4 is reduced by more than 27% while with negative feedback the gain is reduced by less than 1%. **We have traded high gain for gain stability.** Thus one method of compensating for variation of components and for aging of components is to use negative feedback.

In fact if we construct an amplifier which has very high gain (say 10,000 or greater) we are virtually immune to gain variations. This is more apparent if we divide both the numerator and the denominator of Eq. 11.2 by A_v:

$$A'_v = \frac{A_v/A_v}{1/A_v - BA_vA_v}$$

$$= \frac{1}{1/A_v - B}$$

(11.3a)

If A_v is very large then $1/A_v$ approaches zero. Therefore

$$A'_v \simeq -\frac{1}{B}$$

(11.3b)

Equation 11.3 (b) shows that **if the gain without feedback is very large, the gain with feedback depends only on the feedback element and not on the amplifier itself.**

In addition to reducing distortion due to gain variation, high-gain amplifiers with negative feedback are a practical way of designing amplifiers with a specific **constant gain.** For example, with a $B = 0.05$, Eq. 11.3b shows that we shall obtain a gain of -20. Similarly, if we require an accurate gain of -100, a $B = 0.01$ will achieve this. One important application of accurate and constant amplification is in instrumentation, where the actual level needs to be known (e.g., the output of a thermocouple) but is too small to be useful without amplification.

11.4   Advantages of Negative Feedback

We have seen that gain variation due to component tolerance is reduced when negative feedback is used. Other advantages also result when negative feedback is used.

Consider a signal which appears at the output of an amplifier which does not contain negative feedback. As shown in Fig. 11.4, such a signal is a composite signal. It contains an amplified replica of the input signal. This output signal also contains distortion of the types which have been described. Amplitude, intermodulation, power-supply ripple, frequency, and phase distortion, and so on may all be present in addition to the desired output

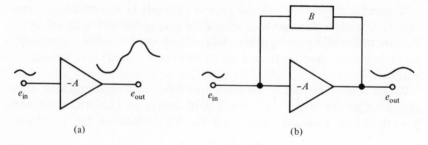

11.4   Distortion in amplifiers. (a) Without feedback. (b) With feedback.

signal. Thus the output signal is the combination of amplified signal plus distortion.

In the previous sections we observed that negative feedback reduces the gain by a factor of $(1 - BA)$. At the same time gain variation is reduced by a factor of $(1 - BA)$. Thus we have traded gain to obtain stability of the remaining gain.

Now consider an amplifier with distortion which uses negative feedback [Fig. 11.4 (b)]. The amplified output which contains both signal and distortion is fed back to the input as a composite signal. The amplifier input cannot distinguish desirable signal from distortion. Both signal and distortion are processed in the same manner. We have seen that gain is reduced by a factor of $(1 - BA)$ when negative feedback is used. Since gain and distortion are indistinguishable to the amplifier, any distortion (D) will also be reduced by a factor of $(1 - BA)$, so the distortion with negative feedback (D') will be

$$D' = \frac{1}{1 - BA} \qquad (11.4)$$

Example 11.5

Power-supply ripple results in 1 volt of distortion at the output of an amplifier which has a gain of -100. If 0.05 of the output signal is returned to the input, what is the resultant distortion?

Solution Step 1.   From the data given, $D = 1$ volt, $A = -100$, and $B = 0.05$.

Step 2.   Therefore

$$D' = \frac{D}{1 - BA}$$

$$= \frac{1}{1 - (0.05)(-100)}$$

$$= \frac{1}{1 + 5}$$

$$= 167 \, \text{mV}$$

It should be emphasized that we are paying a penalty to reduce distortion. We are reducing the gain by the same factor that we are reducing distortion. Therefore if we require additional gain we must add additional stages either prior to or after the stages which have feedback. Presumably this can be done at a signal level where the distortion is less or is a smaller percentage of desired output signal. For example, 1 volt of power-supply ripple is quite significant if the output signal is 1 volt. However, if the output signal is, say, 50 volts, we might not even notice any distortion. That is, if we trade gain for distortion at the appropriate point we can add gain elsewhere.

The factor $(1 - BA)$ also reduces frequency distortion. Bandwidth is increased when negative feedback is used. The lower half-power frequency with feedback (f'_l) will be decreased and the upper half-power frequency with feedback (f'_h) will be increased. Both are improved by the same factor:

$$f'_l = \frac{f_l}{1 - BA} \tag{11.5a}$$

$$f'_h = f_h(1 - BA) \tag{11.5b}$$

Example 11.6

An amplifier without feedback has a gain of -1000 and a bandwidth of 50–5000 Hz. What is the bandwidth if 0.04 of the output is returned to the input?

Solution Step 1. From the given data, $A = -1000$, $B = 0.04$, $f_l = 50$ Hz, and $f_h = 5000$ Hz.

Step 2. Therefore, to find f'_l,

$$f'_l = \frac{f_l}{1 - BA}$$

$$= \frac{50}{1 - (0.04)(-1000)} = \frac{50}{1 + 40}$$

$$= 1.22 \text{ Hz}$$

Step 3. Similarly, to find f'_h,

$$f'_h = f_h(1 - BA)$$

$$= 5000(1 + 40)$$

$$= 205,000 \text{ Hz}$$

Example 11.6 shows that we can greatly improve the bandwidth by using negative feedback. However, we must always keep in mind that all improvements resulting from negative feedback result in reduced gain. In the case of Example 11.6 the gain with feedback is only -24.6 compared to -1000

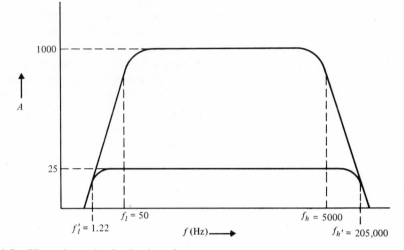

11.5   Effect of negative feedback on frequency response.

without feedback. This is the effect of the $(1 - BA)$ factor. The conditions of Example 11.6 are illustrated in Fig. 11.5.

We have seen that many types of distortion can be reduced if we are willing to trade gain for reduction of distortion. However, one class of distortion is not reduced by negative feedback. Gain variations, power-supply ripple, frequency response, phase shift, and so on are forms of distortion which all have one factor in common: These types of distortion are generated within the amplifier itself. Such internally generated distortion can be reduced with negative feedback. However, **negative feedback will not improve a signal which is already distorted prior to entering the amplifier.** Thus a signal which enters an amplifier with static, or garbled, and so on is not helped by negative feedback. Such effects did not arise within the amplifier and will not be improved through the use of negative feedback.

In connection with this a somewhat interesting situation arises concerning hi-fi amplifiers. Such amplifiers have tone controls (bass for low frequency and treble for high frequency) which permit us to adjust the amplifier frequency response. However, if we assume that the record (or other input signal) was properly recorded we are distorting the signal when we adjust base and treble. In effect we are adding distortion to make the music "sound natural."

11.5   Negative Feedback Circuits

We have seen some of the benefits and some of the penalties which result

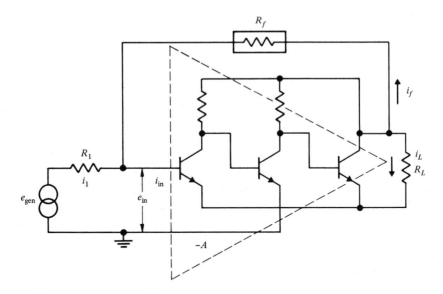

11.6 Simplified shunt-feedback circuit.

from applying negative feedback to an amplifier. We should now investigate actual circuits with negative feedback to determine exactly what is inside the circuit labeled B.

A greatly simplified circuit which uses a resistor (R_f) as the only element in the feedback block B is shown in Fig. 11.6. Since this amplifier contains an odd number (three) of stages the input and output are out of phase. Therefore the current (i_f) which is fed back to the input is out of phase with the input (i_{in}) and we have negative feedback. Equation 11.3b demonstrated that with a high-gain amplifier which uses negative feedback we could obtain precise gain which depends only on B. Since the only component in B is a resistor we can obtain precise gain by using a precision resistor.

Notice that R_f in Fig. 11.6 is connected between the load resistor and the input to the first stage. If the gain of the amplifier is very high, the input signal will be very small; that is, the input signal will be approximately zero. With this approximation R_f and R_L are connected in parallel since they are essentially connected together at both ends. This type of feedback is referred to as parallel or **voltage-shunt feedback.**

The current at the input terminal to the amplifier can be determined using Kirchhoff's current law:

$$i_1 = i_{in} + i_f \qquad\qquad (11.6a)$$

Both i_1 and i_f can be described in terms of a voltage-to-resistance ratio

(Ohm's law). Therefore Eq. 11.6a can be rewritten as

$$\frac{e_{gen} - e_{in}}{R_1} = i_{in} + \frac{e_{in} - e_{out}}{R_f} \tag{11.6b}$$

If the gain of the amplifier is very large e_{in} will be much smaller than either e_{out} or e_{gen}; that is, $e_{in} \simeq 0$. In this case Eq. 11.6b can be written as

$$\frac{e_{gen}}{R_1} \simeq i_{in} - \frac{e_{out}}{R_f} \tag{11.6c}$$

Also, if the input resistance of the amplifier is reasonably high the small input voltage will cause only a very small input current. Therefore

$$i_{in} \simeq 0 \tag{11.6d}$$

In this case Eq. 11.6c becomes

$$\frac{e_{gen}}{R_1} \simeq \frac{-e_{out}}{R_f} \tag{11.7a}$$

or

$$\frac{e_{out}}{e_{gen}} = -\frac{R_f}{R_1} \tag{11.7b}$$

However, e_{out}/e_{gen} is the basic definition of voltage gain (with feedback in this case), so we arrive at

$$A'_{v(shunt)} = -\frac{R_f}{R_1} \tag{11.8}$$

as the voltage gain using voltage-shunt feedback.

Notice that **the gain of the amplifier when shunt feedback is used is determined by the value of two resistors only.** If the gain of the individual stages changes, the overall gain will be unaffected. This is in accordance with our original discussion of negative feedback, which showed that the gain of an amplifier with negative feedback depended only on the B block (Eq. 11.3b).

Also, Eq. 11.8 shows that an amplifier with an accurately specified gain can be achieved by using precision resistors for R_1 and R_f.

Example 11.7

An amplifier has a gain of -200. An accurate gain of -10 is required. Determine R_1 if $R_f = 10 \text{ k}\Omega$.

Solution Step 1.   The given data which are necessary are $A'_v = -10$ and $R_f = 10 \text{ k}\Omega$.

Step 2.   Equation 11.9 is directly applicable:

$$A'_{v(\text{shunt})} = -\frac{R_f}{R_1}$$

$$-10 = \frac{10 \times 10^3}{R_1}$$

$$R_1 = 1\,\text{k}\Omega$$

The input and output resistance with feedback (r'_{in} and r'_{out}) are as important as without feedback. In either case these resistances determine what can be connected at either end of the amplifier. Strictly speaking, we should start with a tee equivalent of the entire amplifier. With the addition of R_f we could determine r'_{in} and r'_{out} using loop equations. This procedure is the same as we used in Chapter 9. Although it is straightforward, the mathematical manipulations are tedious and tend to obscure what is happening. Therefore the results are presented without proof:

$$r'_{in(\text{shunt})} \simeq \frac{R_f}{1 - A_v} \qquad \text{(11.9a)}$$

$$r'_{out(\text{shunt})} \simeq \frac{R_f}{1 - 1/A_v} \qquad \text{(11.9b)}$$

Example 11.8
Determine the input and output resistance of the negative feedback amplifier of Example 11.7.

Solution Step 1.   The data of Example 11.7 are $A_v = -200$ and $R_f = 10\,\text{k}\Omega$.

Step 2.   To find $r'_{in(\text{shunt})}$,

$$r'_{in(\text{shunt})} = \frac{R_f}{1 - A_v}$$

$$= \frac{10 \times 10^3}{1 + 200}$$

$$\simeq 50\,\Omega$$

Step 3.   To find $r'_{out(\text{shunt})}$,

$$r'_{out(\text{shunt})} \simeq \frac{R_f}{1 - 1/A_v}$$

$$\simeq \frac{10 \times 10^3}{1 + 1/200}$$

$$\simeq 9950\,\Omega$$

Typically, an amplifier of the type shown in Fig. 11.6 might have an input resistance of 1500 Ω and an output resistance of 40,000 Ω.

Thus we see that shunt feedback decreases both the input and output resistance. As has already been indicated, typical amplifier applications require high input resistance and low output resistance.

11.6   Series Feedback

Another type of negative feedback circuit is shown in Fig. 11.7. Resistor R_f in this case is essentially in series with R_L. Thus this type of configuration is referred to as **current-series feedback.** In this case we have

$$e_{\text{gen}} = e_{\text{in}} + e_f \qquad \qquad (11.10)$$

where e_f is the voltage across R_f and e_{in} is the base-emitter signal voltage.

As shown in Fig. 11.7 (a), the current-series feedback circuit is the same as a CE amplifier, Fig. 11.7 (b), with the important exception that the emitter resistor does not have a bypass capacitor.

This means that what we are calling R_f in this case is really an emitter-stabilization resistor, and an emitter-stabilization resistor without a bypass capacitor is directly in series with r_e. Therefore, instead of going to the trouble of solving loop equations we can use the CE equations (Eqs. 9.19). Since R_f is in series with r_e, there is only one modification necessary to use Eqs. 9.19. We must add R_f to r_e wherever an r_e term appears. Thus the voltage gain (Eq. 9.19a) with current-series feedback becomes

$$A'_{v(\text{series})} \simeq \frac{\beta R_L}{r_b + (\beta + 1)(r_e + R_f) + R_g} \qquad (11.11)$$

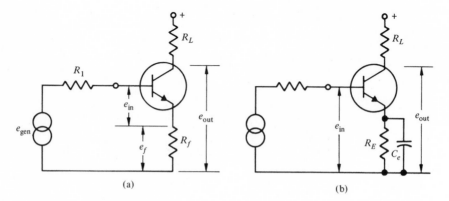

11.7   Comparing series feedback and the common emitter. (a) Series feedback (b) Common emitter.

The input resistance becomes

$$r'_{in(series)} \simeq r_b + (\beta + 1)(r_e + R_f) \qquad (11.12)$$

The output resistance becomes

$$r'_{out(series)} \simeq r_c(1 - \alpha)1 + \frac{\beta(r_e + R_f)}{r_b + r_e + R_f + R_g} \qquad (11.13)$$

Example 11.9

A 100-Ω resistor is to be used in a series-feedback configuration. The other conditions are the same as in Example 9.8. Determine A'_v, r'_{in}, and r'_c.

Solution Step 1.   From these data $R_f = 100\,\Omega$. The conditions of Example 9.8 are $\alpha = 0.98$, $r_b = 200\,\Omega$, $r_e = 20\,\Omega$, $r_c = 900\,k\Omega$, and $R_L = 1\,k\Omega$.

Step 2.   Compute β:

$$\beta = \frac{\alpha}{1 - \alpha}$$

$$= \frac{0.98}{1 - 0.98}$$

$$= 49$$

Step 3.   Determine $A'_{v(series)}$:

$$A'_{v(series)} \simeq \frac{\beta R_L}{r_b + (\beta + 1)(r_e + R_f) + R_g}$$

$$\simeq \frac{49 \times 10^3}{200 + (49 + 1)(20 + 100) + 600}$$

$$\simeq 7.2$$

Step 4.   Determine $r'_{in(series)}$:

$$r'_{in(series)} \simeq r_b + (\beta + 1)(r_e + R_f)$$

$$= 200 + (49 + 1)(20 + 100)$$

$$\simeq 6200\,\Omega$$

Step 5.   Determine $r'_{out(series)}$:

$$r'_{out(series)} = r_c(1 - \alpha)\left[1 + \frac{\beta(r_e + R_f)}{r_b + r_e + R_f + R_g}\right]$$

$$= 900(1 - 0.98)\left[1 + \frac{49(20 + 100)}{200 + 20 + 100 + 600}\right]$$

$$\simeq 147\,k\Omega$$

Table 11.1   Comparing Amplifier Characteristics

	A_v	r_{in} (kΩ)	r_{out} (kΩ)
Common emitter	27.2	1.2	39.5
Series feedback	7.2	6.2	147

We can see that series feedback increases both the input and output resistance. Table 11.1 compares the characteristics of the CE amplifier of Example 9.8 and the amplifier using series-current feedback of Example 11.9.

A more detailed discussion of types of negative feedback would distinguish between various types of shunt and series feedback. As a result, characteristics which are somewhat different from those which have been discussed may occur. However, the principle of returning a portion of the output out of phase to the input will always be present.

An important example of another negative-feedback configuration is shown in Fig. 11.8. In this case we have a voltage-series feedback configuration. This configuration has also been studied in Chapter 9. It is a CC (emitter follower) in which $R_L = R_F$. In Chapter 9 we saw that while an emitter follower does not furnish voltage gain it has high input resistance and low output resistance. High input resistance and low output resistance are exactly the characteristics needed to avoid loading down the circuit. Applying the CC formulas from Chapter 9 we can write

$$r_{in(CC)} = (\beta + 1)(R_f + r_e) \qquad \textbf{(11.14a)}$$

$$r_{out(CC)}: = r_e + \frac{R_g + R_b}{\beta + 1} \qquad \textbf{(11.14b)}$$

Equation 11.14 shows that with a moderate-value feedback resistor (R_f) we can obtain excellent input characteristics.

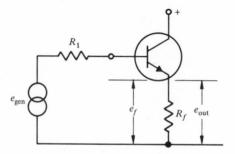

11.8   Emitter follower as a feedback amplifier.

Example 11.10

Using $R_f = 2\,k\Omega$ and the same characteristics as in Example 11.9, determine $r_{in(CC)}$ and $r_{out(CC)}$ in the CC configuration.

Solution Step 1.   The useful data are $R_f = 2\,k\Omega$, $\beta = 49$, $r_e = 20\,\Omega$, $r_b = 200\,\Omega$, and $R_g = 600\,\Omega$.

Step 2.   To find $r_{in(CC)}$:

$$r_{in(CC)} = (\beta + 1)(R_f + r_e)$$

$$= (49 + 1)(2000 + 20)$$

$$= 101\,k\Omega$$

Step 3.   To find $r_{out(CC)}$:

$$r_{out(CC)} = r_e + \frac{R_g + r_b}{\beta + 1}$$

$$= 20 + \frac{600 + 20}{49 + 1}$$

$$= 34.4\,\Omega$$

As in the case of amplifiers without feedback we choose the proper configuration to obtain the desired results.

11.7   Automatic Control Circuits

We have discussed negative feedback principles and circuits. The use of negative feedback to reduce distortion which arises within the amplifier has been covered.

In addition the principle of returning a measure of the output out of phase to the input has broad applications to the entire field of automatic control. As an example we shall take an electromechanical case.

Figure 11.9 is a diagram of a drill press which will bore a hole to a predetermined depth and then stop. We first "set" the desired depth by adjusting a variable resistor to the desired level. For example, our scale might be such that 1 volt represents 1 in. In this case we would adjust the "set depth" resistor to $-3\,v$ to bore a 3-in. hole.

Notice that the drill press motor is operated by the output voltage of an amplifier. Attached to the quill of the drill press there is the wiper of the "measure depth" resistor. Figure 11.9 shows that the wiper of the "measure depth" resistor is returned to the amplifier input. Since the polarities of the "set depth" and "measure depth" resistors are added, the input voltage to

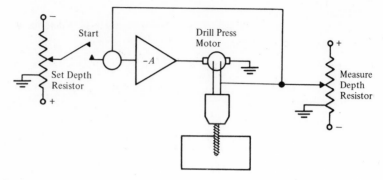

11.9   Automatic-depth drill press.

the amplifier will be

$$e_{in} = e_{set\,depth} + e_{measure\,depth} \tag{11.15}$$

This is similar to Eq. 11.1c.

Initially the "measure depth" resistor is at 0 volts. Thus when the switch is closed the initial input voltage according to Eq. 11.15 will be

$$e_{in} = -3 + 0 = -3\,volts$$

As the drill begins to bore, the "measure depth" voltage becomes positive. For example, at a 1-in. depth there will be 1 v returned from the "measure depth" resistor to the amplifier input. In this case the input voltage according to Eq. 11.15 will be

$$e_{in} = -3 + 1 = -2\,volts$$

Finally, when the 3-in. depth is reached the input voltage will be zero. This means there is no output voltage and the drill press will stop. In fact a more complete diagram would show the drill pulled out when the amplifier input reaches zero volts.

The automatic drill press which we have just discussed uses negative feedback. There are two inputs to the amplifier. One is preset to a desired condition. The other input measures the condition at the output. Since these two signals are in phase there will be an input to the amplifier until the two signals become equal. This is the desired point and operation ceases.

Another automatic control circuit is shown in Fig. 11.10. In this case we see an automatic rudder control for a ship. One resistor "sets" the ship's course. In this case the resistor scale relates volts to degrees of a compass. For example, 1 v might be equivalent to 1°, or some other convenient scale.

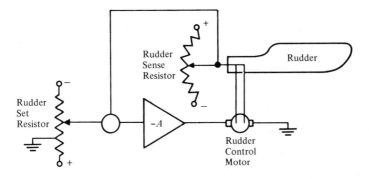

11.10   Automatic rudder control.

The other resistor senses the position of the rudder. The "set" and "sense" resistor signals are combined (out of phase) at the amplifier input. As long as these two signals do not exactly cancel there will be voltage to operate the rudder control motor. Regardless of which direction unbalances the rudder, it will be returned automatically to the desired setting.

Automatic control systems which involve a motor and controlling the motor by comparing a desired input with the condition of the output are called **servosystems.** Motors specially constructed for such application are called **servomotors.**

By combining rudder, elevator, and wing-flap controls, using the principles which have been described we could set the course of an airplane automatically. This is the basis of the automatic pilot (autopilot).

We could use this same principle to keep the temperature in an electrical furnace constant (purifying semiconductor material, for example). In this case we would use a resistor to set the desired temperature. A temperature-sensing resistor in the furnace returns an out-of-phase signal. The difference between the two readings controls the current through the furnace heating coil.

Another application of automatic control is strictly electronic. Due to distance from the transmitter, antenna problems, and so on, the signals we receive on our home televisions and radios vary in intensity as we switch from one station to another. To simplify tuning we would like to keep the TV picture quality constant (or the radio volume constant) as we tune in stations.

A block diagram of how level is kept constant is shown in Fig. 11.11. Using a voltage divider, a portion of the output signal is rectified and filtered. This rectified signal is returned to the input and is out of phase with the input. As the output signal varies in amplitude so will the rectified signal which is returned to the input. The rectified signal is used to control the bias of the low-level amplifier. If, for example, we switch from a weak station to a strong station, the voltage returned to the input will increase (become more

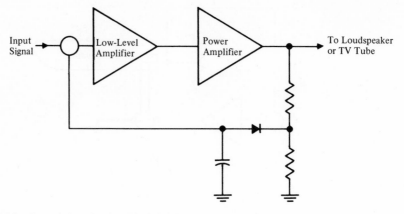

11.11   Automatic volume-control circuit.

negative). This more negative signal reduces the bias and therefore the gain of the low-level amplifier. The more powerful the station the more the bias is lowered.

With a weaker station there is less signal to be returned, so bias is not reduced as much. In this way the output level tends to remain constant as we switch from station to station. This type of circuit is generally referred to as automatic volume control (AVC) or automatic gain control (AGC). Again the principle being used is negative feedback. We are returning a portion of the output out of phase to the input.

11.8   Positive Feedback

The circuits which have been described thus far all involve negative feedback. It is also possible to use **positive feedback.** Negative feedback results when the signal which is returned to the input is out of phase with the input signal. Accordingly, **positive feedback results when the signal which is returned to the input is in phase with the input signal.**

The CE stage has an output which is out of phase with its input. Part of the discussion of negative feedback used a three-stage CE amplifier. Any odd number of CE stages provides phase reversal and three stages provide a large gain.

If we instead build an amplifier which has an even number of CE stages, the input and output will be in phase. Therefore if we return a portion of the output to the input, positive feedback will result. A positive-feedback amplifier is shown in Fig. 11.12.

The derivation of the general feedback equation (Eq. 11.2) does not depend on the fact that the amplifier does or does not have phase reversal. Thus this equation is as valid for the positive-feedback situation as it is for negative

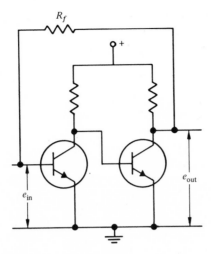

R_f

e_{in}

e_{out}

11.12   Two-stage amplifier with positive feedback.

feedback. The only difference is that we must remember to use a positive value of gain rather than a negative value of gain.

Example 11.11

Each stage of the amplifier shown in Fig. 11.11 has a voltage gain of -10. Determine the voltage gain without feedback and the voltage gain if 0.001 of the output is returned to the input.

Solution Step 1.   Since $A_T = A_1 A_2$ the gain without feedback is $(-10)(-10)$. Therefore

$$A_T = 100$$

Step 2.   From the given data, $B = 0.001$. Therefore

$$A'_v = \frac{A_v}{1 - BA_v}$$

$$= \frac{100}{1 - 0.001(100)}$$

$$= \frac{100}{1 - 0.1}$$

$$= 111$$

Example 11.11 shows that **the gain with positive feedback is greater than the gain without feedback.** This result could have been anticipated. Negative feedback results in reduced gain since the input and output are out of phase. Therefore the signal which enters the amplifier is reduced.

In the positive-feedback situation the input and output are in phase. Therefore the signal which enters the amplifier is increased, and a larger output results. Since positive feedback apparently increases gain we might try for a greater increase than in Example 11.11.

Example 11.12

The conditions are the same as in Example 11.11 except that 0.005 of the output is returned to the input. Determine the voltage gain.

Solution Step 1.   The data are $A_v = 100$ and $B = 0.005$.

Step 2.

$$A'_v = \frac{A_v}{1 - BA_v}$$

$$= \frac{100}{1 - 0.005(100)}$$

$$= \frac{100}{1 - 0.5}$$

$$= 200$$

Under the conditions of Example 11.12 the gain with feedback is exactly twice that without feedback. Of course we are increasing distortion at the same time as we are increasing gain. This may or may not be a severe penalty, depending on the particular situation.

At best, using positive feedback to increase gain is a risky business. This is illustrated in Example 11.13.

Example 11.13

The conditions are the same as in Example 11.11 except that 0.01 of the output is returned to the input. Determine the voltage gain.

Solution Step 1.   The data are $A_v = 100$ and $B = 0.01$.

Step 2.

$$A'_v = \frac{A_v}{1 - BA_v}$$

$$= \frac{100}{1 - 0.05(100)} = \frac{100}{1 - 1} = \frac{100}{0}$$

$$= \text{infinity}$$

The conditions of Example 11.13 result in "infinite gain." Infinite gain actually means that the amplifier is completely unstable; that is, the amplifier does not amplify. Instead **oscillation** results. Oscillators are a very important part of electronics. **When oscillation is required, the proper amount of positive feedback is the method used to obtain it.**

Amplifiers are also important in electronics. However, if we use positive feedback to get "something for nothing" as far as gain is concerned, we are risking the possibility of having an amplifier suddenly break into oscillation. This condition could result from any transient or sudden noise spike since the returned signal would experience a momentary increase.

In the early days of radio, positive feedback was used to increase gain. Such amplifiers, however, never gained popularity since the listener continually had to operate a "regeneration" control whenever the radio broke into oscillation. As a general rule we use positive feedback only when it is our intention to achieve oscillation.

The precise conditions necessary to obtain oscillation can be determined by examining Example 11.13. "Infinite" gain is the requirement for oscillation. This condition will occur when the denominator of the feedback equation is zero. The denominator will become zero when BA is equal to unity and this is the requirement for oscillation:

$$BA = 1 \qquad\qquad (11.16)$$

Example 11.14

A certain amplifier has a gain of 500. What fraction of the output must be returned to the input to obtain oscillation?

Solution Step 1. $A = 500$ and Eq. 11.16 is directly applicable.

Step 2. Since $BA = 1$,

$$B \times 500 = 1$$

$$B = \frac{1}{500}$$

$$= 0.002$$

Equation 11.16, which gives the condition for oscillation, is called the **Barkhausen–Kurz criterion** in honor of these two Germans, who published their findings in 1919. In the next chapter we shall see how this equation is used to determine the frequency at which oscillation occurs.

Summary

1. An amplifier output which is not an exact replica of the input is said to be distorted. Distortion has many causes and good design techniques are a partial solution.
2. Returning a portion of the output signal to the input when it is out of phase is referred to as negative feedback. Negative feedback reduces gain but also reduces gain variation due to component variation.

3. If negative feedback is used with a high-gain amplifier, the gain depends only on the feedback network. This is important in instrumentation and other applications which require accurate and precise gain.
4. Negative feedback can reduce distortion which is generated within the amplifier. It will not improve signals which are distorted prior to entering the amplifier.
5. Reduction of distortion by negative feedback is achieved by a corresponding decrease in gain.
6. Shunt feedback results when the feedback element is placed in parallel with the load.
7. Shunt feedback decreases both r_{in} and r_{out}.
8. Current-series feedback places the feedback element so that it is approximately in series with the load.
9. Series feedback increases both r_{in} and r_{out}.
10. Negative feedback can be used to perform automatic control functions in electro-mechanical systems. Similarly, negative feedback can be used to perform automatic control in purely electronic systems. In both cases automatic control is achieved by returning a portion of the output to the input in an out-of-phase condition.
11. Positive feedback can increase gain, but this tends to produce instability.
12. Positive feedback is used specifically to obtain oscillation. Oscillation occurs when the positive feedback is sufficient to result in infinite gain.

Questions

1. List at least five possible types of amplifier distortion.
2. Discuss possible methods of reducing or eliminating amplifier distortion.
3. What is meant by negative feedback?
4. Discuss at least one application where precise gain is important.
5. Why does negative feedback reduce distortion?
6. Why is a signal which enters an amplifier already distorted unimproved by negative feedback?
7. What is meant by shunt feedback?
8. Why are characteristics altered when shunt feedback is used?
9. What is meant by series feedback?
10. What characteristics are altered when series feedback is used?
11. Describe how negative feedback is used to obtain automatic control in an electro-mechanical system.
12. Describe how negative feedback is used to obtain automatic control in electronic systems.
13. Why does positive feedback result in an increase in gain?
14. What is meant by "infinite" gain?

Problems

1. An amplifier has a bandwidth of 20–100,000 Hz and a voltage gain of 1000. Compute the gain at (a) 2000 Hz; (b) 20 Hz; (c) 0 Hz (i.e., DC).

2. An amplifier with a voltage gain of 100 amplifies a 1-mV signal. Find e_{out} for the signal, assuming that a power-supply ripple of 0.5 mV is also amplified.

3. A three-stage amplifier has a nominal gain of -20 per stage ($\pm 10\%$). Compute the nominal, maximum, and minimum possible gains.

4. The conditions are the same as in Problem 3 except that 0.04 of the output is returned to the input out of phase. Compute the nominal, maximum, and minimum gains with feedback.

5. An amplifier without feedback has an overall gain of -5000. What is the gain if 0.001 of the output is returned to the input?

6. Three different amplifiers have gains of -1000, $-10,000$, and $-100,000$, respectively. Determine the gains in each case if 0.05 of the output is returned to the input and discuss the validity of Eq. 11.3b.

7. An amplifier with a gain of -1000 has 0.5 V of power-supply ripple appearing at the output when the desired output is 1 volt. Determine the desired output and the ripple when 0.05 of the output is returned to the input.

8. For the conditions of Problem 7, (a) what is the input signal level; (b) what would the input level have to be to achieve the same output when negative feedback is used?

9. An amplifier with a lower 3-dB frequency of 100 Hz has a gain of -5000. (a) What fraction of the output should be returned to obtain a lower 3-dB frequency of 20 Hz? (b) What is the resultant amplifier gain at midband?

10. If the original upper 3-dB frequency in Problem 9 is 4000 Hz, what is the upper 3-dB frequency with negative feedback?

11. An amplifier has a voltage gain of $-10,000$. A precise gain of -25 is required. If $R_f = 10\,k\Omega$, how much should R_1 be?

12. The conditions are the same as in Problem 11 except that $R_f = 20\,k\Omega$. Find R_1.

13. Determine $r_{in(shunt)}$ and $r_{out(shunt)}$ for Problem 12.

14. Current-series feedback is used with the same conditions as in Example 11.9, except $R_f = 1\,k\Omega$. Determine A'_v, r'_{in}, and r'_{out}.

15. Repeat Problem 14 for an emitter follower.

16. Repeat Problem 14 for an emitter follower with $R_f = 4\,k\Omega$.

17. Sketch a Wheatstone bridge which uses a motor-driven precision resistor to balance itself automatically.

18. Sketch a temperature-control circuit for an electrical furnace.

19. An amplifier has a gain of $+40$. What gain results if 0.02 of the output is returned to the input?

20. For an amplifier with a gain of $+40$, what fraction of the output should be returned to the input to achieve oscillation?

Chapter 12 Communications

12.1 Introduction

In this chapter concepts which have been discussed previously are combined to describe the operation of communication systems. The basic principles involved in communication are discussed and several practical systems are covered.

12.2 Resonance

In Chapter 7 we extended the concept of resistance by introducing reactance. This in turn led to the concept of impedance. Equation 7.24 gives the impedance of a series network containing resistance, capacitance, and inductance:

$$Z = \sqrt{R^2 + (X_L - X_C)^2} \tag{12.1}$$

It was pointed out that if a circuit contains no capacitance or inductance, then the impedance is a pure resistance. That is, if both X_C and X_L are zero Eq. 12.1 reduces to

$$Z = \sqrt{R^2 + (0 - 0)^2} = R \tag{12.2}$$

It is also possible for a circuit to contain resistance, capacitance, and inductance and yet have an impedance which is purely resistive. Equation 12.1 applies to the series RLC circuit shown in Fig. 12.1.

If the inductive reactance is equal to the capacitive reactance the impedance is a pure resistance. That is, if

$$X_L = X_C$$

then

$$(X_L - X_C) = 0 \tag{12.3a}$$

and again

$$Z = \sqrt{R^2 + 0} = R$$

The circuit will behave as a resistor although L and C are present. We can

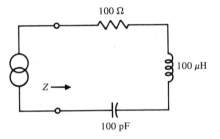

12.1   Series *RLC* circuit.

determine how this occurs by substituting Eq. 7.12b for X_L and Eq. 7.20c for X_C into Eq. 12.3a:

$$\omega L = \frac{1}{\omega C} \qquad\qquad \textbf{(12.3b)}$$

Rearranging we have

$$\omega^2 = \frac{1}{LC} \qquad\qquad \textbf{(12.3c)}$$

and since $\omega = 2\pi f$ (Eq. 6.6) we have

$$(2\pi f)^2 = \frac{1}{LC} \qquad\qquad \textbf{(12.3d)}$$

Finally

$$f_{\text{res}} = \frac{1}{2\pi\sqrt{LC}} \qquad\qquad \textbf{(12.4)}$$

Equation 12.4 gives the frequency at which a series *RLC* circuit is a pure resistance. The frequency at which a circuit which contains resistance, inductance, and capacitance reduces to a resistor is called the **resonant frequency** (f_{res}).

Example 12.1

Determine the resonant frequency of the circuit shown in Fig. 12.1.

Solution Step 1.   From Fig. 12.1 we have $L = 100\,\mu\text{H}$ and $C = 100\,\text{pF}$.

Step 2.   Therefore

$$
\begin{aligned}
f_{\text{res}} &= \frac{1}{2\pi\sqrt{LC}} \\[2mm]
&= \frac{1}{2\pi\sqrt{100 \times 10^{-6} \times 100 \times 10^{-12}}} \\[2mm]
&= 1.59 \times 10^{6}\ \text{Hz}
\end{aligned}
$$

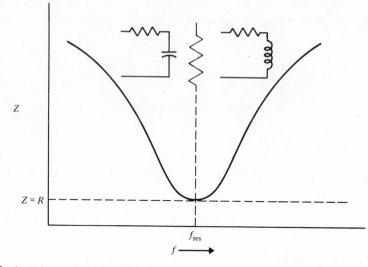

12.2 Impedance of a series *RLC* circuit.

Thus the circuit shown in Fig. 12.1 will act as a purely resistive circuit at a frequency of 1.59 MHz.

Below the resonant frequency the capacitance will have a greater reactance than the inductance. Therefore, below the resonant frequency the circuit appears as a resistor in series with a capacitor; that is, below resonance the applied voltage will lag the current. Above the resonant frequency the inductor will have a greater reactance than the capacitor and thus the circuit will appear as a resistor in series with an inductor. At resonance the circuit is a pure resistance and since it consists only of resistance we see that **the impedance of a series *RLC* circuit is a minimum at the resonant frequency.** This is indicated in Fig. 12.2.

It is interesting to determine the voltage across each of the components at the resonant frequency.

Example 12.2

The generator voltage of the circuit shown in Fig. 12.1 is set at 10 volts and the frequency is adjusted to 1.59 MHz. Find the voltage across *R*, *L*, and *C*.

Solution Step 1.   Since the circuit is resonant,

$$I = \frac{V}{Z} = \frac{V}{R}$$

$$= \frac{10}{100}$$

$$= 0.1 \text{ Amp.}$$

Step 2.

$$V_R = IR$$
$$= 0.1 \times 100$$
$$= 10 \text{ volts}$$

Step 3.   Since this is a series circuit the current is the same through each component. Therefore from Eq. 7.21a,

$$V_L = IX_L = I\omega L = I2\pi f L$$
$$= 0.1 \times 2\pi \times 1.59 \times 10^6 \times 100 \times 10^{-6}$$
$$= 100 \text{ volts}$$

Step 4.   Similarly, from Eq. 7.21b,

$$V_C = IX_C = \frac{I}{\omega C} = \frac{I}{2\pi f C}$$
$$= \frac{0.1}{2\pi \times 1.59 \times 10^{-6} \times 100 \times 10^{-12}}$$
$$= 100 \text{ volts}$$

It may appear at first glance that the results obtained in Example 12.2 violate Kirchhoff's voltage law. The generator is set at only 10 volts and yet 100 volts exists across both the inductor and capacitor. There is no contradiction here. In Section 7.6 it was seen that the voltage across an inductor leads the current through the inductor by 90°. Also, the voltage across a capacitor lags the current through the capacitor by 90°. This means that the voltage across the inductor leads the voltage across the capacitor by 180°. Two quantities which are 180° out of phase and equal in magnitude cancel each other. Thus although there exist 100 volts across both the inductor and capacitor the sum of these two voltages is not 200 volts but zero. The 10 volts across the generator exists across the resistor and thus we see the Kirchhoff's voltage law is applicable to a resonant circuit. Figure 12.3 is a diagram of the relationship between the voltages at resonance.

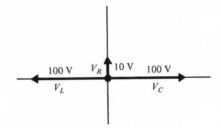

12.3   Voltages across components at resonance.

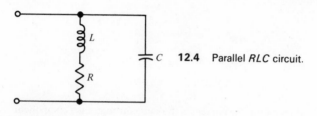

12.4   Parallel *RLC* circuit.

Note that if we make either L or C adjustable then it will be possible to vary the resonant frequency.

A parallel circuit which can also be made resonant is shown in Fig. 12.4. A resistor is shown in series with the inductor since an actual coil is made of wire and therefore there is resistance associated with any inductance. If we extend our discussion of impedance to parallel circuits (product over the sum) we obtain

$$Z = \frac{(\sqrt{R^2 + X_L^2})(\sqrt{X_C^2})}{\sqrt{R^2 + (X_L - X_C)^2}} \tag{12.5}$$

for the impedance of the circuit in Fig. 12.4. With a little manipulation we could show that the resonant frequency of this circuit is given by

$$f_{\text{res}} = \frac{1}{2\pi}\sqrt{\frac{1}{LC} - \left(\frac{R}{L}\right)^2} \tag{12.6}$$

Example 12.3

The components used in Example 12.1 are rearranged to form a parallel resonant circuit. Find the resonant frequency.

Solution Step 1.   From Example 12.1 we have $L = 100\,\mu\text{H}$, $R = 100\,\Omega$, and $C = 100\,\text{pF}$.

Step 2.   Therefore

$$f_{\text{res}} = \frac{1}{2\pi}\sqrt{\frac{1}{LC} - \left(\frac{R}{L}\right)^2}$$

$$= \frac{1}{2\pi}\sqrt{\frac{1}{100 \times 10^{-6} \times 100 \times 10^{-12}} - \left(\frac{100}{100 \times 10^{-6}}\right)^2}$$

$$= \frac{1}{2\pi}\sqrt{10^{14} - 10^{12}}$$

$$\simeq 1.59 \times 10^6 \text{ Hz}$$

Example 12.3 shows that if we have a parallel resonant circuit in which the resistance is small (i.e., a quality inductor) the resonant frequency of a parallel resonant circuit is approximately equal to the resonant frequency of a series circuit. However, **in a parallel resonant circuit the impedance is a maximum at resonance.** This is the exact opposite of a series resonant circuit.

12.3   Oscillators

In Chapter 11 we saw that positive feedback could be used to create oscillation. If we use a resonant circuit as the feedback element (instead of a resistor) we can obtain a circuit which oscillates at the resonant frequency. Actually if the Barkhausen–Kurz condition is investigated in greater detail it provides two pieces of information:

1. The frequency of oscillation as given by Eq. 12.4 or Eq. 12.6.
2. The minimum amplification necessary to achieve oscillation. That is, if we use a transistor with insufficient β or a triode with insufficient μ there will not be enough positive feedback to maintain oscillation. Both the resonant frequency and minimum gain condition must be satisfied simultaneously to achieve oscillation.

One form of a practical oscillator is shown in Fig. 12.5. Components R_L, R_B, and C_C perform the same functions as they do for amplifiers. L, C_1, and C_2 form a parallel resonant circuit which is quite similar to that shown in Fig. 12.4. The resistance of the inductor is neglected and two capacitors in series are used instead of a single capacitor. Capacitors C_1 and C_2 also form a voltage divider and the voltage across C_2 is fed back to the input.

The formula for the resonant frequency is applicable in this case except that we must use the total capacitance of the two capacitors in series (Eq.

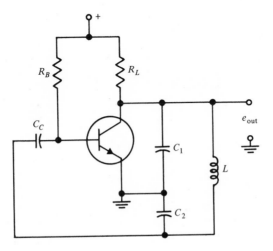

12.5   Colpitts oscillator.

7.3c). Therefore the frequency of oscillation is given by

$$f = \frac{1}{2\pi\sqrt{L\dfrac{C_1 C_2}{C_1 + C_2}}} \tag{12.7a}$$

The minimum β necessary to achieve oscillation is determined by the two capacitors in the resonant circuit:

$$\beta \geq \frac{C_2}{C_1} \tag{12.7b}$$

The Barkhausen–Kurz criterion indicates that both conditions (Eq. 12.7a and Eq. 12.7b) must be satisfied simultaneously.

Example 12.4

For an oscillator of the type shown in Fig. 12.5, calculate the minimum β transistor and the value of inductance. The required frequency of oscillation is 1 MHz, $C_1 = 50\,\text{pF}$, and $C_2 = 500\,\text{pF}$.

Solution Step 1.   To determine the minimum β,

$$\beta \geq \frac{C_2}{C_1}$$

$$\geq \frac{500 \times 10^{-12}}{50 \times 10^{-12}}$$

$$\beta_{min} = 10$$

Step 2.   To determine the required value of L,

$$f = \frac{1}{2\pi\sqrt{L\dfrac{C_1 C_2}{C_1 + C_2}}}$$

$$1 \times 10^6 = \frac{1}{2\pi\sqrt{L\dfrac{50 \times 10^{-12} \times 500 \times 10^{-12}}{550 \times 10^{-12}}}}$$

$$L = 550\,\mu\text{H}$$

An oscillator of the type shown in Fig. 12.5, which uses two capacitors as a voltage divider for feedback, is referred to as a **Colpitts oscillator.**

We have previously stressed that a CE stage such as is used in Fig. 12.5 has an input and output which are out of phase. However, we have also seen that positive feedback is required to obtain oscillation. Since the CE stage provides 180° of phase shift there must exist another 180° of phase shift to obtain positive feedback. **This additional phase shift comes from the resonant circuit itself.** In the discussion of resonance we saw that in a circuit which contains both L and C 180° of phase difference did indeed exist. Therefore we see that the amplifier performs one phase inversion and the resonant circuit performs the additional phase inversion which results in positive feedback.

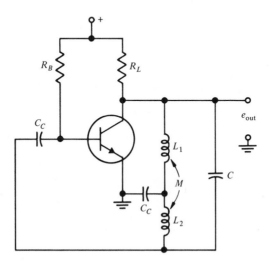

12.6   Hartley oscillator.

There is an interesting question about oscillators that did not arise with amplifiers. Where is the input coming from? The only input to the oscillator is that portion of the output which is being fed back. But the output is supposed to result from an input. We appear to have a "did the chicken or the egg come first?" situation.

Actually this is not the case. In Chapter 1 we saw that electrons are always in random motion even when no voltage is being applied. When the oscillator power supply is first turned on, the random electron motions are amplified. A portion of these amplified random motions is returned in phase to the input. Very quickly the only random motions which can be returned are at the frequency of the resonant circuit. From this point on sustained oscillation occurs.

Another type of oscillator which is quite similar to the Colpitts type is shown in Fig. 12.6. This type of oscillator is called a **Hartley oscillator.** Notice that the difference is that in the Hartley oscillator feedback is provided by an inductive voltage divider, rather than by a capacitive voltage divider. The frequency of oscillation is again given by the formula for resonance except that we must now use the total inductance including mutual inductance (if any) of two inductors in series (Eq. 7.8c):

$$f = \frac{1}{2\pi\sqrt{(L_1 + L_2 + 2M)C}} \qquad (12.8a)$$

The minimum β in a Hartley oscillator depends on the inductance:

$$\beta \geq \frac{L_1 + M}{L_2 + M} \qquad (12.8b)$$

Example 12.5

A single inductor is tapped for use in a Hartley oscillator in such a way that $L_1 = 80\,\mu H$, $L_2 = 20\,\mu H$, and $M = 10\,\mu H$. Calculate the minimum β transistor and the value of C required for a 1-MHz oscillator.

Solution Step 1.   Determine the minimum β for a Hartley oscillator:

$$\beta \geq \frac{L_1 + M}{L_2 + M}$$

$$\geq \frac{80 + 10}{20 + 10}$$

$$\beta_{min} = 3$$

Step 2.   Determine the required value of C

$$f = \frac{1}{2\pi\sqrt{(L_1 + L_2 + 2M)C}} = \frac{1}{2\pi\sqrt{(80 \times 10^{-6} + 20 \times 10^{-6} + 20 \times 10^{-6})C}}$$

$$C = 210\,pF$$

In addition to using L and C there are other methods of obtaining the additional 180° of phase shift required to obtain positive feedback. A combination which consists of a resistor and capacitor or a combination of a resistor and an inductor can furnish something under 90° of phase shift. Therefore three sections of RC or RL can provide 180° of phase shift. One possibility is 60° per section with a three-section RC network. Such an oscillator is called a **phase-shift oscillator.** An RC phase-shift oscillator is shown in Fig. 12.7.

We have seen that transistors, triodes, and passive components are subject to variation due to temperature and aging. In Chapter 7 it was indicated that values of inductance and capacitance depend on the physical dimensions of these components. Changes in temperature result in expansion or contraction and thus the actual values of inductance and capacitance fluctuate with temperature changes. Since it is the actual values of inductance and

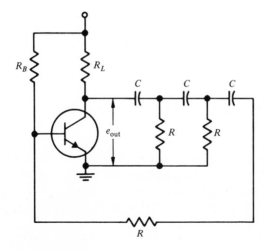

12.7   An *RC* phase-shift oscillator.

capacitance which determine the frequency of oscillation, changes in temperature result in changes in frequency.

In certain cases, such as radio and television systems, fluctuations in frequency of oscillation are unacceptable. Several possibilities exist to stabilize frequency. One is an application of negative feedback which is similar to the automatic volume-control system described in Chapter 11. **Automatic frequency control** (AFC) also rectifies a portion of the output signal, which in this case is the oscillator output. The rectified signal is used to adjust the bias level of the oscillator and this helps to stabilize the oscillator frequency.

Another approach to stabilizing oscillator frequency is the use of a **quartz crystal.** It has been found that a properly manufactured quartz crystal is electrically equivalent to a stable series-parallel combination of inductance and capacitance. Thus using a quartz crystal as the resonant circuit greatly

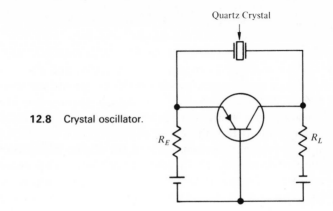

12.8   Crystal oscillator.

improves frequency stability. A further improvement is to place the crystal in a temperature-controlled oven. Figure 12.8 shows an oscillator in which the crystal constitutes the entire resonant circuit. Other forms of crystal oscillator use the crystal in combination with actual capacitors or inductors.

12.4   Communications Principles

When we wish to talk to someone a few hundred feet away, it may be possible to use a megaphone. In a sports stadium this process is improved by using a public address system. Basically, a public address system consists of a microphone, an amplifier, and a loudspeaker. The public address system is an improvement over the megaphone but we are still limited in range to the order of hundreds of yards.

The telephone is an electronic communications system which uses microphones, amplifiers, earphones, and conductors to transmit a message from one location to another. Distance is not a serious problem with the telephone. Any place that has telephone cables can be contacted. However, talking to many different people at different locations is not efficiently accomplished by telephone.

Fortunately, high-frequency radio waves can travel many miles through air and even through vacuum. If the outputs of the oscillators discussed in Section 12.3 are connected to suitable **antennas** they will transmit radio waves. Radio waves travel at the speed of light, which is 3×10^8 m/sec (approximately 186,000 miles/sec).

Example 12.6

How long does it take a message to reach an astronaut standing on the moon?

Solution Step 1.   The distance to the moon is approximately 248,000 miles.

Step 2.   Since distance = rate × time, we have

$$248,000 = 186,000 \times \text{time}$$

$$\text{time} = 1.33 \text{ sec}$$

If we combine an oscillator, an antenna, and a key (which is a form of switch) we can transmit information over great distances merely by turning the oscillator on and off in an agreed-upon manner. This is a basic radio telegraph transmitter for sending Morse code and is shown in Fig. 12.9. Using 10-watt transmitters of this type, radio amateurs (hams) have been able to communicate anywhere in the world. At the receiving end we also require an antenna and a resonant circuit which is tuned to the same frequency as the transmitter. The receiver operator selects the proper frequency by varying either the inductance or the capacitance of a resonant circuit.

If we wish to transmit voice, music, pictures, and so on using radio waves the process is an extension of the radio telegraph system. We must now combine the speech, music, or whatever with the radio wave. Combining two waveforms in this manner is called **modulation.** Modulation is a mixing of two signals of different frequencies.

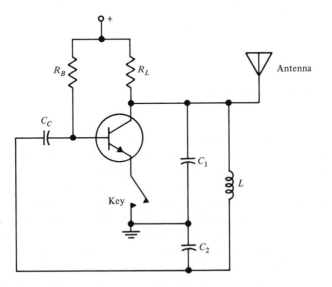

12.9   Basic Morse code transmitter

For example, we may wish to transmit a news broadcast. But the radio announcer's voice has a very limited range. On the other hand, radio waves have great range. Therefore we combine the information we wish to send with the radio wave. In this case we amplify the announcer's voice and use this signal (audio range) to modulate the radio-frequency **carrier.** The carrier is needed since the signal itself cannot be transmitted with a realistic antenna. It is not realistic to transmit the modulation without a carrier. An efficient antenna must be at least one fourth of a wavelength long. Thus the minimum-size antenna to transmit, say, a 1000-Hz signal would have to be at least 300 kilometers (approximately 50 miles). On the other hand, a ¼-wavelength antenna for 1 MHz is only 75 meters (approximately 225 feet) long.

With a modulated wave the receiver must also be more complex. There must still be a tuned resonant circuit which separates the desired frequency from all the other stations. But with a modulated wave we must be able to separate the desired message from the carrier. Separating signals at two different frequencies is called **demodulation.** After demodulation the audio signal is amplified and used to drive a loudspeaker. A basic radio system is shown in Fig. 12.10.

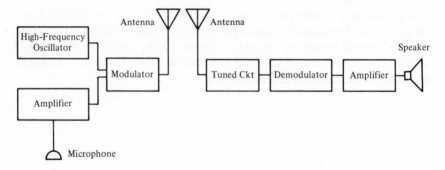

12.10   Radio communication system.

Television transmission requires a device which can translate optical signals into electrical signals. In turn these electrical signals are amplified and used to modulate a radio wave. In Chapter 1 we discussed the fact that light energy affects the free-electron density and therefore the resistance of various materials. Using a substance which is especially sensitive to changes in light (such as selenium) is the basis of converting an optical signal which is seen by a lens into an electrical signal. The selenium is scanned in sequence. That is, an electrical spot is moved horizontally across each line. This spot determines the level of light. Thus the transmitted video signal consists of a sequence of electrical signals which, if properly reassembled at the receiver, will permit the picture to be seen. This is accomplished by forcing the receiver to scan its screen at the same position as the selenium is scanned at the studio. That is, the scan at both the transmitter and receiver must be at the same rate and initiate at the same time. If this is not the case we get either an unstable picture or no picture at all. Thus our receiver must be **synchronized** to the scanning at the transmitter. In addition to sending video information a television station must also send audio information.

12.5   Amplitude Modulation

One type of modulation is shown in Fig. 12.11. In this case the carrier wave is injected into the base and the signal is injected into the emitter. The modulated wave which is the combination of the carrier and signal waveforms appears at the collector. The **envelope** is the shape of the combination.

It is the envelope of the modulated signal which contains the information to be transmitted. As the amplitude of the information increases so does the amplitude of the modulated signal. This type of modulation is called **amplitude modulation** (AM). When the signal frequency changes the frequency of the envelope changes accordingly. If a modulated AM wave is

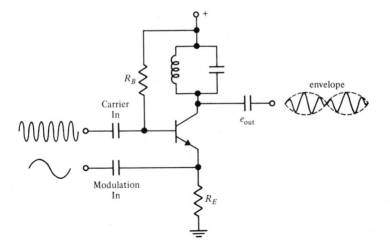

12.11   An AM modulator.

analyzed mathematically it is found to contain three components:
1. Carrier frequency
2. Carrier frequency + modulation frequency **(upper sideband)**
3. Carrier frequency − modulation frequency **(lower sideband)**

Example 12.7

An AM station operating at 1-MHz carrier frequency transmits a 1-kHz tone. Determine the frequency components of this broadcast.

Solution Step 1.   The carrier frequency is 1 MHz or 1000 kHz.

Step 2.   The upper sideband is 1000 kHz + 1 kHz or 1001 kKz.

Step 3.   The lower sideband is 1000 kHz − 1 kHz or 999 kHz.

Presumably "high-fidelity" sound reproduction requires frequencies up to 20 kHz. This would mean that an AM station would need 40 kHz to broadcast high-fidelity sound. The entire AM frequency range is from 535 kHz to 1605 kHz. As a compromise between fidelity and allowing a large number of stations to broadcast simultaneously, each AM station is limited by law to a 10-kHz bandwidth.

Example 12.8

Determine the highest frequency which an AM station can broadcast and also the possible number of AM stations.

Solution Step 1.   The upper sideband minus the lower sideband is 10 kHz.

Step 2.   Therefore

$$f_{max} = \frac{10\,kHz}{2} = 5\,kHz$$

Step 3.   The frequency range between the highest and lowest broadcast frequency is

$$
\begin{array}{r}
1605 \\
-535 \\
\hline
1070\,kHz
\end{array}
$$

Step 4.   At 10 kHz per station,

$$\frac{1070\,kHz}{10\,kHz/station} = 107\,stations$$

Actually a larger number of stations is possible. By limiting the range of each station and by locating stations with the same carrier frequency in different parts of the country, the total possible number of AM stations is increased.

At the receiver the appropriate station must be selected and the modulated wave must be demodulated to receive the information being transmitted. Figure 12.12 shows the simplest AM receiver.

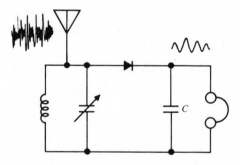

12.12   An AM crystal receiver.

The antenna receives all stations which are transmitting. The tuned circuit selects the desired station. In this case tuning is accomplished by adjusting the capacitor. The purpose of the diode is to rectify the radio-frequency signal. If this were not done the average signal through the earphones would be zero and we would not hear anything. When a diode is used to rectify a radio-frequency signal it is called a **detector.** The capacitor across the earphones acts as a bypass for the carrier frequency (see Example 10.1). Therefore only audio signal appears at the earphones.

The type of receiver shown in Fig. 12.12 is called a **crystal set** because originally lead sulphide crystals were used as diodes. Notice that a crystal set does not require a power supply. However, if we wish to operate a loud-speaker, a complete amplifier with power supply must be attached to the detector. In this case it is possible to detect and amplify at the same time. This is accomplished by biasing the base-emitter junction so that either the positive or negative half of the modulated signal is cut off. In this way we rectify and simultaneously amplify the rectified portion.

12.6   Heterodyning

From Fig. 12.12 we see that the desired station is selected by adjusting a parallel resonant circuit of the type shown in Fig. 12.4. At resonance the impedance of such a circuit is a pure resistance and is given by

$$Z_{res} = \frac{L}{RC} \tag{12.9}$$

Equation 12.9 indicates that as we tune for different stations the impedance of the resonant circuit will change.

Example 12.9
A 230-μH coil has 5 Ω of resistance. It is connected in parallel with a variable capacitor to tune the AM broadcast band. Determine the impedance when it is set to receive a station at (a) 600 kHz; (b) 1200 kHz.

Solution Part (a) Step 1.   Find the required value of C for 600 kHz:

$$f = \frac{1}{2\pi\sqrt{LC}}$$

$$600 \times 10^3 = \frac{1}{2\pi\sqrt{230 \times 10^{-6}C}}$$

$$C = 307 \text{ pF}$$

Step 2.   Using Eq. 12.9 find the impedance at this frequency:

$$Z_{res} = \frac{L}{RC}$$

$$= \frac{230 \times 10^{-6}}{5 \times 307 \times 10^{-12}}$$

$$= 150,000 \ \Omega$$

Part (b) Step 1.   Find the required value of C for 1200 kHz:

$$f = \frac{1}{2\pi\sqrt{LC}}$$

$$1200 \times 10^3 = \frac{1}{2\pi\sqrt{230 \times 10^{-6}C}}$$

$$C = 76 \text{ pF}$$

Step 2.   Find the impedance at this frequency:

$$Z_{res} = \frac{L}{RC}$$

$$= \frac{230 \times 10^{-6}}{5 \times 76 \times 10^{-12}}$$

$$= 600,000 \, \Omega$$

Example 12.9 shows that the differences in impedance of the resonant circuit which selects the desired station are quite large. The impedance of this resonant circuit determines the strength of the signal with which the receiver begins. This in turn means that even if two stations are transmitting with the same power one station (the lower-frequency one) will have less volume when amplified. Therefore we must adjust volume at the same time as we tune for stations. In the early days of radio this was the case.

Figure 12.13 shows a diagram of such a tuned radio-frequency (TRF) receiver. The first few stages are circuits which are resonant at the radio-frequency carrier. These are simultaneously adjusted by varying capacitors which are mechanically "ganged" together. After sufficient amplification the radio-frequency signal is detected and then amplified to operate a loudspeaker.

It is inconvenient to have to adjust volume at the same time that a station is being selected. In addition there is difficulty in tracking all tuned circuits simultaneously, and many tuned circuits tend to supply positive feedback, with oscillation resulting. The solution to this is the **heterodyne** receiver.

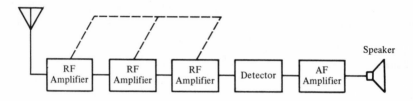

12.13   Block diagram of a TRF receiver.

A heterodyne receiver amplifies all signals at the same frequency. A block diagram of a heterodyne receiver is shown in Fig. 12.14.

The heterodyne receiver has its own oscillator (local oscillator). The capacitor of the local oscillator is mechanically coupled to the capacitor of the radio-frequency amplifier. Therefore as we adjust for a different station the local-oscillator frequency adjusts simultaneously. The local-oscillator frequency is always a constant amount (typically 455 kHz for AM receivers) higher than the station being received.

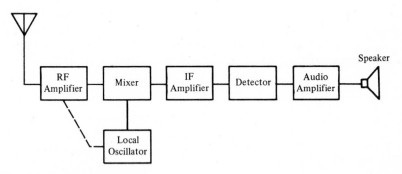

12.14   Heterodyne AM receiver.

Signals from both the radio-frequency amplifier and the local oscillator are combined in the **mixer,** which is tuned for this difference in frequency between the station being received and the local oscillator (455 kHz in this case). The output of the mixer is fed into an **intermediate-frequency** (IF) amplifier. The intermediate-frequency stages perform most of the amplification. Since this intermediate frequency is the same regardless of which station is being received, all stations receive approximately the same amplification in the receiver.

Example 12.10

Determine the local-oscillator frequency for stations at 700 kHz and 1400 kHz.

Solution Step 1. From the discussion the local oscillator is 455 kHz above the frequency of the station being received. Therefore for a station at 700 kHz,

$$f_{osc} = 700 + 455 = 1155 \, kHz$$

Step 2. Similarly, for a station at 1400 kHz,

$$f_{osc} = 1400 + 455 = 1855 \, kHz$$

The heterodyne principle is used in all radio-frequency communications systems, including television.

12.7   Frequency Modulation

From our own experience we know that AM is a practical system. However, certain problems are associated with AM. For one thing, AM is extremely susceptible to both natural and man-made static. Lightning, arcing motors, faulty fluorescent lights, and so on, cause static to appear on AM broadcasts.

In addition we have all experienced interference from other AM stations which operate at the same or nearby carrier frequencies to the station we are listening to. This effect is known as adjacent-channel interference.

Both static and adjacent-channel interference are greatly reduced if we use a modulation method which is quite different from AM. In Fig. 12.15 we

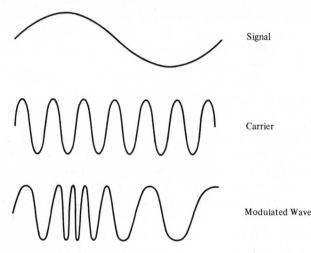

12.15   Frequency modulation waveforms.

see a signal, a carrier, and a modulated waveform in which the amplitude is kept constant. Notice that when the signal is at its maximum value the modulated waveform contains many sine waves. As the amplitude of the signal decreases the number of sine waves in the modulated waveform also decreases. This type of modulation is called **frequency modulation** (FM).

Thus for an FM station **the instantaneous frequency varies but the amplitude is intentionally kept constant.** The rate at which the modulation frequency varies contains the signal information. The total frequency variation contains the amplitude information.

As in the case of AM, the frequency allocation of the FM band is determined by law. The entire FM band is between 88 MHz and 108 MHz. Consider an FM station operating at 100 MHz. If we wish to transmit, say, a 500-Hz note we might do this by varying the carrier between 100.04 MHz and 99.96 MHz (i.e., ± 40 kHz) 500 times per second. Similarly, to transmit a 1000-Hz note we could still vary the carrier between 100.04 MHz and 99.96 MHz but at the rate of 1000 times a second. If we wish to change the volume we have to change the total frequency shift from the center frequency. To double the volume we have to double the frequency shift. In FM frequency shift is referred to as **frequency deviation.** Thus in either the 500-Hz or the 1000-Hz case, doubling the volume means shifting the carrier between 100.08 MHz and 99.92 MHz (i.e. ± 80 kHz).

Frequency modulation seems to be more complex and quite different from amplitude modulation. This is true and it is this difference which accounts for the superior performance of FM with respect to static and adjacent-channel interference. Static appears largely as noise spikes which alter the amplitude of an AM wave. Since the amplitude is intentionally kept constant in FM the effect of static is greatly reduced. Moreover, it is unlikely that an adjacent FM station will deviate in exactly the same manner (unless it is transmitting the identical program). Therefore FM also reduces adjacent-channel interference.

The superior performance of FM over AM is not without penalty. FM stations can and do transmit frequencies up to 20 kHz. However, to achieve this each FM station must be permitted a frequency deviation of 200 kHz (± 100 kHz). Thus the enhanced performance of FM is achieved at the expense of limiting the total number of FM stations. A single FM station occupies as large a frequency range as 20 AM stations.

Example 12.11

How many different FM stations are possible in the band allocated for FM?

Solution Step 1.   The FM band is between 88 and 108 MHz. Therefore the FM band is 20 MHz wide.

Step 2.   At 200 kHz per station,

$$\frac{20\,\text{MHz}}{200\,\text{kHz/station}} = 100 \text{ stations}$$

In order to obtain FM a different modulation technique must be used. A basic form of FM circuit is shown in Fig. 12.16.

Transistor Q_1 and its associated components constitute a Colpitts oscillator. Transistor Q_2 is chosen from a type whose output capacitance is especially voltage sensitive. As the microphone is used the change in input signal level produces a change in the output capacitance of Q_2. This output capacitance is in parallel with capacitor C_1 of the Colpitts oscillator. Thus changes in microphone level result in a variation of the parallel capacitance combination of C_1 and the output capacitance of C_2. This variation in capacit-

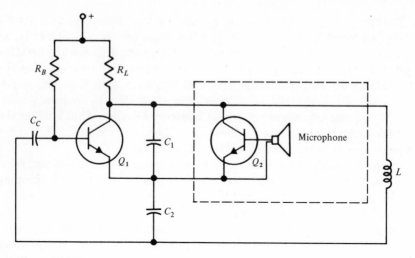

12.16 An FM circuit.

ance causes the frequency of the oscillator to deviate and frequency modulation results.

An FM receiver must be different in certain respects from an AM receiver. Figure 12.17 shows a block diagram of an FM receiver. If we compare this with the AM receiver block diagram shown in Fig. 12.14, we see that both AM and FM receivers contain radio frequency amplifiers, local oscillators, mixers, audio amplifiers, and speakers. The difference is that while an AM receiver contains a detector, an FM receiver contains a limiter and a discriminator.

The purpose of the **limiter** is to remove any incidental AM (such as static) which may have combined with the FM signal. The limiter is connected to the output of the intermediate-frequency amplifier (IF for FM is 10.7 MHz). As shown in Fig. 12.18, limiting is accomplished by providing additional gain which should be sufficient to drive the limiter into saturation and cutoff.

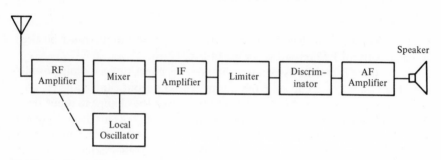

12.17 An FM receiver.

12.18 Limiter action.

(See Section 9.7.) This removes the AM by "squaring off" the bottom and top of the signal. The result is a pure FM signal.

In the case of AM we discussed the advantage of AVC. Automatic volume control is of little use in an FM receiver. We either have enough signal to achieve limiting or some AM will appear at the output. AVC will not remedy this situation. When there is insufficient signal to obtain limiting a steady "hissing" sound appears at the output.

The AM receiver accomplishes demodulation by rectifying the modulated wave and removing the carrier. That is, in the AM case the information is contained in the envelope of the carrier. With FM there is no envelope. Thus a scheme which converts a varying frequency into an audio signal is required. The circuit which accomplishes this is called a **frequency discriminator.**

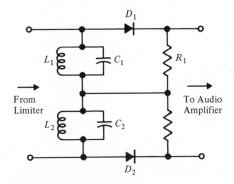

12.19 Frequency discriminator circuit.

A basic discriminator is shown in Fig. 12.19. Circuit $L_1 C_1$ is adjusted so that it is resonant above the 10.7-MHz intermediate frequency. Circuit $L_2 C_2$ is adjusted so that it is resonant below the 10.7-MHz frequency. The output of the discriminator is the difference between the voltage across R_1 and R_2.

If only the carrier frequency is being received the current through D_1 is the same as the current through D_2 and there is no output. If the frequency being received is above the 10.7 MHz resonant frequency, more current flows through D_1 than through D_2 and the discriminator output is positive. If the frequency being received is below resonance more current flows through

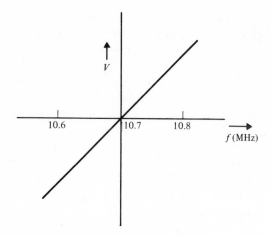

12.20   Ideal discriminator output.

D_2 than through D_1 and the output is negative. An ideal discriminator output should be linear and is shown in Fig. 12.20.

In addition to the FM band, frequency modulation is the audio system used for television broadcasting. It is interesting to note that both the heterodyne receiver and FM were invented by the same man. Edwin H. Armstrong, a professor of electrical engineering at Columbia University, is credited with both of these major achievements.

12.8   Radar

Earlier in this chapter it was indicated that radio waves travel at the speed of light. This fact can be exploited to measure distance.

Example 12.12

How far does a radio-frequency wave go in 1 μsec (microsecond)?

Solution Step 1.   The speed of light is 186,000 miles/sec. Convert this into feet per second.

$$1.86 \times 10^5 \frac{\text{miles}}{\text{sec}} \times 5.28 \times 10^3 \frac{\text{feet}}{\text{mile}} = 9.84 \times 10^8 \text{ feet/sec}$$

Step 2.   Therefore in 1 μsec a radio-frequency wave will travel

$$\frac{9.84 \times 10^8}{10^6} = 984 \text{ feet/}\mu\text{sec}$$

Thus if we send out a short pulse of radio frequency, it will travel until it strikes some object (airplane, ship, mountain, etc.). After striking this object some of the energy will be reflected back to the source. By measuring the time between sending the pulse and receiving the echo we know twice the distance (a complete round trip) to the object. That is, it takes the same time for the radio wave to reach the object as it does for the reflected radio wave to return.

Example 12.13

Ten μsec after a radio-frequency pulse is transmitted its echo is received. Find the distance to the object.

Solution Step 1.   From Example 12.12 we know that 1 μsec is equivalent to 984 ft. Therefore 10 μsec is equivalent to 9840 feet.

Step 2.   But this is twice the distance to the object since the echo must return.

$$2d = 9840 \text{ feet}$$
$$d = 4970 \text{ feet} \quad \text{(slightly less than 1 mile)}$$

The system which uses the speed of radio waves to measure distance is called **radar**. The word radar comes from *r*adio *d*etection *a*nd *r*anging. Radar was first used in a practical application by Great Britain early in World War II. By locating German planes before they actually arrived the greatly outnumbered Royal Air Force was able to use its planes efficiently. Figure 12.21 shows a block diagram of a radar system which uses the same antenna for both transmitting and receiving the echo.

A pulse is used to modulate an oscillator. These radio-frequency pulses are amplified and fed to the antenna.

The advantage of using the same antenna to transmit and receive is that direction as well as distance can be accurately determined. Since the reflected echo is very weak a high-gain receiver is required. The purpose of the

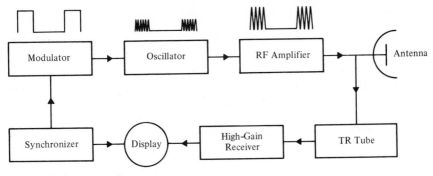

12.21   Radar system diagram.

TR (transmit-receive) tube is to short the receiver during the time that the pulse is being transmitted. This protects the receiver from damage. The output of the receiver is used to display the transmitted and received echo on a cathode-ray tube similar to that used in an oscilloscope. The chief difference is that range markers are used instead of time cm divisions. Figure 12.22 shows an ideal radar display. In a real display there would be noise.

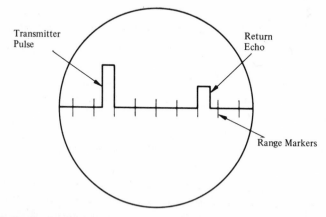

12.22   Idealized radar display.

The synchronizer shown in Fig. 12.21 is required to start the display at the same time as the pulse is being transmitted. Otherwise the position of the echo is meaningless. This is similar to the synchronization required for a television system.

By allowing the radar antenna to rotate we determine direction. Similarly, by allowing the antenna to move up and down we can determine the angle at which the echo is received. Knowing the distance and the angle of elevation of, say, an airplane permits determination of altitude by triangulation as shown in Fig. 12.23.

This technique is the basis of ground-controlled approach (GCA) radar in which an airport operator "talks" an airplane down during foggy weather. Similarly, by mounting a smaller radar system aboard an aircraft we can determine true elevation. This is a **radar altimeter.** A barometric altimeter reads height above sea level, but under poor visibility knowing the height above sea level is not as useful as knowing the height above the peak of a mountain.

Example 12.14

If the time between transmitting a pulse and receiving an echo on a radar altimeter is 3 μsec, what is the height between the airplane and the "obstacle".

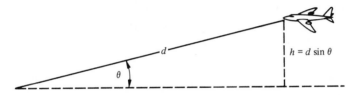

12.23   Using radar to determine altitude.

Solution Step 1.   Since 1 μsec corresponds to 984 feet, 3 μsec corresponds to 3 × 984 = 2852 ft.

Step 2.   Therefore

$$2d = 2852 \text{ feet}$$
$$d = 1426 \text{ feet}$$

Depending on the particular application, ground-based radar systems may transmit pulses which are in the megawatt range. This is a power range where (at present) semiconductors do not exist. Specially designed vacuum tubes are used for such applications.

Summary

1. The frequency at which an *RLC* circuit acts as a pure resistance is the resonant frequency. Series and parallel *RLC* circuits have approximately the same resonant frequency.
2. At series resonance the voltage across both the inductor and the capacitor can exceed the input voltage. The impedance of a series resonant circuit is a minimum and the impedance of a parallel resonant circuit is a maximum at resonance.
3. Oscillators combine a frequency-determining network and positive feedback to achieve oscillation. All forms of oscillators have these in common.
4. The frequency-determining network of an oscillator must provide 180° of phase shift. This can be accomplished by *LC*, *RC*, *RL* components or quartz crystals. Crystal oscillators improve frequency stability.
5. Radio communication increases the range of message transmission. Radio waves travel at the speed of light.
6. At the transmitter the message to be sent is used to modulate the carrier. At the receiver the message must be demodulated.
7. Amplitude modulation varies amplitude to adjust level and frequency to alter frequency. Government restrictions limit frequency variation to ±5 kHz.
8. At the receiver an AM signal can be demodulated using a diode.
9. Since the impedance of a parallel resonant circuit varies with frequency, a TRF receiver will not amplify all stations equally well. A heterodyne receiver amplifies all signals at the same frequency.

10. In frequency modulation the rate at which the carrier frequency is varied determines the tone being transmitted and the total frequency excursion determines the volume.
11. Frequency modulation is less susceptible to static and adjacent-channel interference than amplitude modulation.
12. A frequency discriminator is used to demodulate an FM signal.
13. Radar is based on the principle that radio waves travel at the speed of light.
14. By using an antenna which rotates and also moves up and down, bearing and elevation can be determined in addition to range.

Questions

1. What is meant by resonance?
2. In a series RLC circuit, how can the voltage across the inductor exceed the input voltage?
3. Under what condition is the parallel resonant frequency equal to the series resonant frequency?
4. What are the similarities in all oscillators?
5. What is the difference between a Colpitts and a Hartley oscillator?
6. How can RC or RL circuits furnish 180° of phase shift?
7. Why must an audio signal be modulated for radio transmission?
8. What is the purpose of demodulation?
9. What takes place when a radio receiver is tuned to a specific frequency?
10. What is meant by amplitude modulation?
11. How is amplitude modulation accomplished?
12. What is meant by detecting an AM signal?
13. How does a TRF receiver operate?
14. How does a heterodyne receiver operate?
15. What is the advantage of a heterodyne receiver?
16. What is the principle of FM?
17. What are the advantages of FM?
18. How does a discriminator work?
19. How does radar operate?
20. How can radar determine direction and elevation?

Problems

1. A series RLC circuit consists of a 10-Ω resistor, a 200-pF capacitor, and a 50-μH inductor. Find the resonant frequency.
2. The same components as in Problem 1 are connected as a parallel circuit. Find f_{res}.
3. A 50-μH inductor is connected to a variable capacitor. What value of C will result in an f_{res} of 1 MHz?
4. Repeat Problem 3, except that the required f_{res} is 2 MHz.

5. For a Colpitts oscillator which oscillates at 500 kHz, $C_1 = 0.003\,\mu F$ and $L = 900\,\mu Hz$. Determine C_2 and the minimum possible transistor β.

6. A transistor with a β of 10 and a 500-μHz inductor are to be used in a 2-MHz Colpitts oscillator. Determine C_1 and C_2.

7. Assume that in both Problem 6 and Problem 7 a germanium transistor is used with a 10-volt power supply. If the required base current is 200 μA, find R_B. (Hint: See Example 9.10.)

8. Find C and β for a Hartley oscillator which is to operate at 500 kHz, if $L_1 = 200$ μH, $L_2 = 40\,\mu H$, and $M = 15\,\mu H$.

9. The conditions are the same as in Problem 8 except that there is no mutual inductance between L_1 and L_2. Find β and C.

10. A 1-MHz Hartley oscillator is to be built using a transistor with $\beta = 4$. If $L_1 = 110$ μH and $L_2 = 20\,\mu H$, find M and C.

11. Most commercial radio stations have a range of approximately 50 miles. How long does it take for a radio wave to travel this distance?

12. How long does it take to communicate with an astronaut on the moon and receive a reply?

13. An AM station has a carrier frequency of 1600 kHz. Determine the extreme upper and lower sidebands.

14. Assuming that 20 kHz is required for hi-fi reception, how many AM stations are possible?

15. A 200-μH inductor with 10 Ω of resistance is used with a variable capacitor to tune the AM band. Determine the impedance of the tuning circuit at (a) 1000 kHz; (b) 1500 kHz.

16. An FM carrier is deviated 8 kHz to send a 500-Hz tone at a given volume. What deviation is needed to send a 1-kHz note at (a) the same volume; (b) half the given volume.

17. If the FM band were moved into the present AM band, how many different FM stations would be possible?

18. If the AM band were moved up to the FM band, how many different AM stations would be possible?

19. A shipboard radar receives a radar echo from another ship 15 μsec after a pulse is transmitted. How far apart are the ships?

20. If the time between transmitting pulses of a radar is 30 μsec, what is the maximum range at which objects can be detected?

Chapter 13 Digital Circuits

13.1 Introduction

In addition to amplification, transistors can also perform switching functions. The ability of transistors to switch at very high speeds is the basis of modern digital computers. In this chapter some important switching techniques and their circuits are discussed.

13.2 Switches

Although frequently taken for granted, a switch is an electronic component. As shown in Fig. 13.1, a switch usually has two states: Switches can be either open [Fig. 13.1 (a)] or closed [Fig. 13.1 (b)].

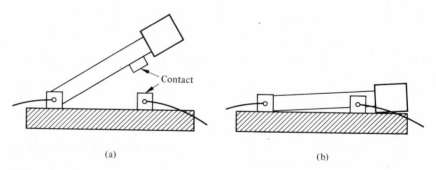

(a)   (b)

13.1 Switch conditions. (a) Open. (b) Closed.

Typically, a switch consists of two metal contacts mounted on an insulator. When the contacts are separated there should be an open circuit, and no current is supposed to flow. Actually some current will flow when the switch is open since there is no perfect insulator. That is, the mechanical support on which the contacts are mounted contains some free electrons. Thus when a voltage is applied current can flow through this insulator. We would like an open switch ("off" position) to present an infinite resistance. However, we must accept a very high resistance instead.

When a switch is closed ("on" position) we would like the switch to have zero resistance. This is not possible since the contacts are made of a real and

394

not an ideal conductor. However, it is quite possible to have switch contacts with very low resistance.

Example 13.1

A switch with an "off" resistance of $10^{12}\ \Omega$ and an "on" resistance of 30 milliohms connects a 100-volt battery to a 500-Ω resistor. Find the voltage across the resistor when the switch is (a) open; (b) closed.

Solution Step 1.   As shown in Fig. 13.2, the equivalent circuit is a voltage divider consisting of the switch resistance and the 500-Ω load.

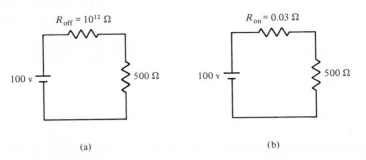

(a)   (b)

13.2   Circuit for Example 13.1. (a) Switch open. (b) Switch closed.

Step 2.   Therefore for the "off" condition, in accordance with Eq. 2.14,

$$V_{L(off)} = V_{in} \frac{R_L}{R_L + R_{off}}$$

$$= 100 \frac{500}{500 \times 10^{12}} \simeq \frac{5 \times 10^4}{10^{12}}$$

$$\simeq 0.05\ \mu V$$

Step 3.   Similarly, for the "on" condition,

$$V_{L(on)} = V_{in} \frac{R_L}{R_L + R_{on}}$$

$$= 100 \frac{500}{500 + 0.03}$$

$$\simeq 99.994\ volts$$

Example 13.1 indicates the conditions encountered in a realistic situation. For example, if we are using a wall switch to operate a light we can say that, for all practical purposes, no voltage exists across the light when the switch is off and full voltage exists across the light when the switch is on.

In addition to an on and off resistance, the time to operate is an important characteristic in many applications involving switches. **An ideal switch would have infinite off resistance and operate in zero time.**

The electromechanical **relay** is an example of a switch which can control circuits remotely. As shown in Fig. 13.3 the relay contains a coil of wire,

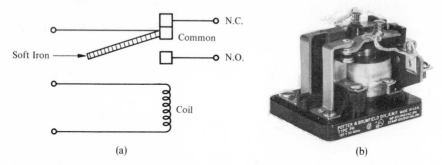

13.3 Basic relay. (a) Principle. (b) Photograph. (*Courtesy of Potter and Brumfield.*)

a piece of soft iron, and at least one set of contacts which contain normally open and normally closed configurations. When current flows through the coil it becomes a magnet. This magnet attracts the soft piece of iron to which the movable contact is attached. In this way we can switch from an open to a closed condition or vice versa, depending on how we wire our circuit. The relay contacts will remain in the "down" position as long as current flows through the coil of the relay. Many relays have several sets of contacts. This permits operating several circuits which are electrically isolated at the same time. For example, we may wish to operate a public address system and a scoreboard simultaneously.

Typically, the off and on resistance of a relay is about the same as the values used in Example 13.1. The operating time of a relay is about 40 msec. This is the time required for the contact to move after the coil is energized. Manual switches have about the same resistance characteristics as relays, but the relay operates in less time than a manual switch.

13.3 Transistor Switches

In addition to manual and electromechanical switches it is also possible to construct a switch which has no moving parts. **The transistor can be used as a switch.**

Up to this point we have discussed the use of a transistor as an amplifier. The bias conditions for using a transistor as an amplifier are forward biasing of the base-emitter junction and reverse biasing of the collector-base junction.

If we intentionally violate the forward-bias base-emitter junction condition we cut the transistor off. This is shown in Fig. 13.4. Thus by making the

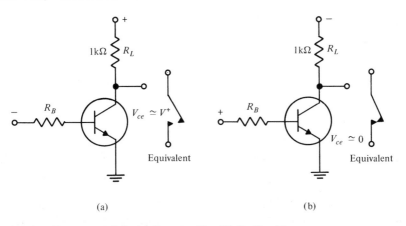

13.4   Transistor as a switch. (a) Negative V_{be}. (b) Positive V_{be}.

base of an NPN transistor negative with respect to the emitter we inject no base current. Since there is no base current, there is no collector current, there is no voltage drop across R_L, and the battery voltage is the same as the collector-to-emitter voltage.

We can make a transistor act as an open circuit by reverse biasing the base-emitter junction. The transistor is not an ideal open circuit because I_{co} flows as long as the collector-base junction is reverse biased. Since silicon transistors have lower collector leakage currents than germanium transistors, silicon transistors will more closely approximate an ideal open circuit.

Example 13.2

Assuming that the transistor shown in Fig. 13.4 has an $I_{co} = 1\ \mu A$, find the transistor off resistance if a 5-volt power supply is used.

Solution Step 1.   Since the transistor is cut off the only collector current is I_{co}.

Step 2.   Therefore

$$V_{R_L} = I_{co}R_L$$

$$= 10^{-6} \times 10^3$$

$$= 10^{-3}\ \text{volts} = 1\ \text{mV}$$

Step 3.   From Kirchhoff's voltage law,

$$V(+) = V_{R_L} + V_{ce}$$

$$5 = 10^{-3} + V_{ce}$$

$$V_{ce} = 4.999 \simeq 5\ \text{volts}$$

Step 4.   Therefore

$$R_{\text{off}} = \frac{V_{ce}}{I_{co}}$$

$$= \frac{5}{10^{-6}}$$

$$\simeq 5 \times 10^{6} \, \Omega$$

Example 13.2, which uses fairly realistic numbers, shows that the off resistance of a transistor is much lower than either a manual or an electro-mechanical switch.

If we heavily forward bias the base-emitter junction we saturate the transistor (see Section 9.7). That is, with a heavily forward-biased base-emitter junction so much collector current will flow that a further increase in base current will not result in a further increase in collector current. For a typical silicon transistor the collector-to-emitter voltage V when the transistor is saturated (called $V_{ce(\text{sat})}$) is about 0.1 volts.

Example 13.3

Assuming that the collector saturation current of the transistor shown in Fig. 13.4 is 5 mA, find the transistor on resistance.

Solution Step 1.   From the preceding discussion

$$V_{ce(\text{sat})} \simeq 0.1 \text{ volts}$$

Step 2.   Therefore

$$R_{\text{on}} = \frac{V_{ce(\text{sat})}}{I_{c(\text{sat})}}$$

$$= \frac{0.1}{5 \times 10^{-3}}$$

$$= 20 \, \Omega$$

Example 13.3 shows that the on resistance of a transistor is considerably higher than for either a manual or an electro-mechanical switch.

Thus although a transistor is a poorer switch in both the on and off states than other switches, we shall have no trouble distinguishing whether the transistor is on or off. If

$$V_{ce} \simeq V(+) \qquad \text{the transistor is off}$$

$$V_{ce} \simeq V_{ce(\text{sat})} \qquad \text{the transistor is on}$$

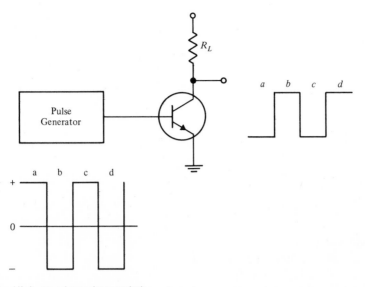

13.5   High-speed transistor switch.

Clearly it is not the actual values of on and off resistance which make transistors attractive as switching elements. However, transistors can switch in much faster times than any mechanical device. As this book is being written, transistors are readily available which will switch in less than 10^{-9} sec (nanosecond). This is about 10 million times faster than a relay can switch. An idea of how fast a nanosecond is can be gained from the British term for nanosecond: The British refer to a nanosecond as a light-foot. This is because in 10^{-9} sec light travels approximately 1 foot (0.984 ft).

Switching speed is particularly important in digital computers. The speed at which transistors switch determines how fast a computer can perform computations. Thus by using voltage waveforms which rise very rapidly from negative to positive and vice versa (i.e., AC pulses) we can switch a transistor very rapidly from on to off to on. This is shown in Fig. 13.5.

Table 13.1 compares the resistance and operating times of several types of switches. It should be emphasized that while the resistance characteristics of the transistor are inferior to other switches, the switching time of the transistor is far superior.

Table 13.1   Switch Characteristics

Type	R_{off} (Ω)	R_{on} (Ω)	T_{switch} (sec)
Manual	10^{12}	0.02	0.3
Mechanical	10^{12}	0.02	0.03
Transistor	10^{6}	20.0	0.000000001

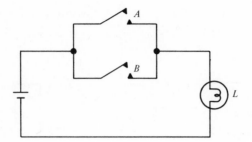

13.8   One type of four-input gate.

13.4   Logic Gates

In addition to the important function of completing circuits by applying voltage sources, switches are also used as gates. A **gate** is a circuit which may have many switches as inputs but only one output. One example of a gate is shown in Fig. 13.6. This gate circuit consists of a battery, two switches (inputs) and a single lamp (output). When either switch A or switch B is closed the lamp (L) will be on. This type of gate is called an **OR gate.** If we call the closed switch position true (T) and the open switch position false (F) we can construct a "truth" table of all the possible switch combinations, as shown in Table 13.2 (a). For example, as shown in Table 13.2, if A is false (off) and B is true (on) the lamp will be true (on). If A is true and B is false the lamp will be true, and so on.

Table 13.2   Two-Input OR Gate Truth Table. (a) True-False. (b) 1-0.

A	B	L		A	B	L
F	F	F		0	0	0
F	T	T		0	1	1
T	F	T		1	0	1
T	T	T		1	1	1
	(a)				(b)	

Instead of using the symbols true and false we could assign other symbols: Table 13.2 (b) uses a truth table in which 1 replaces true and 0 replaces false. Notice that in terms of 1's and 0's the truth table looks very similar to the arithmetic process of addition.

It is useful to describe the operation of gates using a system of equations. Because of the similarity of the OR gate to addition the symbol for OR is $+$. Thus

$$A + B = L \qquad\qquad (13.1)$$

is the equation for a two-input OR gate. Equation 13.1 is read "*A* **or** *B* is (equals) *L*." Since *A* and *B* are only symbols, Eq. 13.1 could mean

John (*A*) OR Fred (*B*) is home (*L*).

Door #305 OR door #306 is closed, etc.

Another type of input gate is shown in Fig. 13.7. Notice that for this gate both switches must be closed for the lamp to be on. A gate in which all the inputs must be true for an output to exist is called an **AND** gate. Table 13.3 shows truth tables for an input AND gate in terms of both true–false and 1–0.

Table 13.3   Input AND Gate Truth Tables. (a) True-False. (b) 1-0.

A	B	L		A	B	L
F	F	F		0	0	0
F	T	F		0	1	0
T	F	F		1	0	0
T	T	T		1	1	1
(a)				(b)		

Table 13.3 (b) shows that the logic AND operation is similar to the arithmetic operation of multiplication. The logic equation for a two-input AND gate is written

$$A \cdot B = L \tag{13.2}$$

In terms of the previous examples Eq. 13.2 would mean

Both John AND Fred are home.

Both door #305 AND #306 are closed, etc.

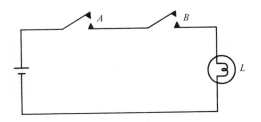

13.7   Manual AND gate.

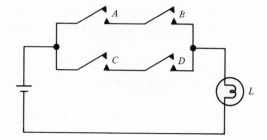

13.8   One type of four-input gate.

If we think in terms of **AND as meaning every** and **OR as meaning any,** it will simplify matters. It is possible to have gates with more than two inputs and it is also possible to have gates with additional complexity. An example of a four-input gate is shown in Fig. 13.8.

For this particular gate the logic equation is

$$(A \cdot B) + (C \cdot D) = L \tag{13.3}$$

At this point it would be useful to fit statements to Eq. 13.3:

If either (A AND B) or (C AND D) . . . .

In addition to having switches operate on an input we may want to operate on the negative of an input. That is, we may wish to operate on not $A(\overline{A})$ rather than on A. Such an operation can be conveniently accomplished by using a relay which has both a normally open and a normally closed contact. As shown in Fig. 13.9, we can assign A to the normally open contact. In this way operation is possible on either A [Fig. 13.9 (a)] or $\overline{A}$ [Fig. 13.9 (b)], depending on how the circuit is connected.

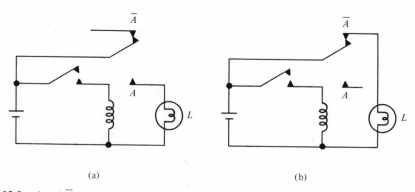

(a)   (b)

13.9 A and $\overline{A}$ circuits. (a) Lamp operates on A. (b) Lamp operates on $\overline{A}$.

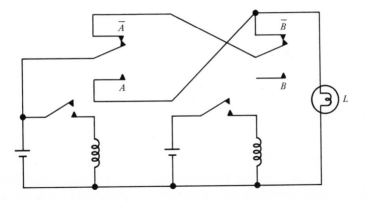

13.10 Two-input NAND gate.

This enables us to combine the negatives of statements as well as the statements themselves. For example, the circuit shown in Fig. 13.10 operates only when both $\bar{A}$ and $\bar{B}$ are the conditions. The logical equation for this circuit is

$$\overline{A{\cdot}B} = L \tag{13.4}$$

an AND gate which functions only on the negatives is called a **NAND** (Not AND) gate. In terms of the previous cases Eq. 13.4 would indicate

> Both John and Fred are not home (out).
>
> Both door #305 and door #306 are not closed (open).

Table 13.4 shows the truth tables for NAND gates in terms of True–False and 1–0. Comparing this NAND-gate truth table with the AND-gate truth table (Table 13.3) we see that they are opposites. Actually it does not matter initially whether we assign true as closed and false as open or vice versa. This is quite arbitrary. The important point is to be consistent once a particular convention has been selected. These remarks apply also to NOR gates (Not OR) as well as to combinations of various types of gates.

Table 13.4 Two-Input NAND Gate Truth Tables. (a) True-False. (b) 1-0.

A	B	L
F	F	T
F	T	T
T	F	T
T	T	F

(a)

A	B	L
0	0	1
0	1	1
1	0	1
1	1	0

(b)

13.5   Transistor Gates

Since transistors switch much faster than any type of mechanical switch it is useful to investigate transistor switches. The circuit shown in Fig. 13.11 could be either a two-input CC amplifier or a two-input OR gate. Resistors R_A and R_B prevent the inputs from affecting each other. For operation as a CC amplifier we must restrict the input current to the base to levels which do not result in distortion. On the other hand, if we inject either no base current at A and B, or else sufficient base current to cause saturation, a two-input OR gate results.

Consider what happens if no input is applied to both A and B. Under this condition the transistor is cut off since the base-emitter junction is not forward biased. On the other hand, if either A or B has sufficient base current to saturate the transistor, almost the entire battery voltage will appear across the load resistor (which could be a lamp).

Regardless of the particular base-current value, Kirchhoff's voltage law must apply to the output loop of the circuit shown in Fig. 13.11:

$$V_{\text{battery}} = V_{ce} + V_{R_L} \tag{13.5a}$$

When there is no base current the only collector current is leakage current. Under this condition there is very little voltage across R_L:

$$\text{cutoff} \qquad V_{R_L} \simeq 0 \text{ volts} \tag{13.5b}$$

When the transistor is saturated maximum collector current flows and almost the entire battery voltage appears across the load resistor:

$$\text{saturation} \qquad V_{R_L} \simeq V_{\text{battery}} \tag{13.5c}$$

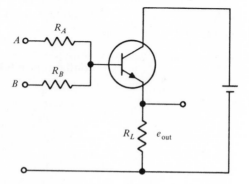

13.11   Two-input transistor OR gate.

If both A and B have sufficient current to cause saturation the output voltage cannot change appreciably since **either input is sufficient to cause saturation.**

Thus by assigning $e_{out} \simeq 0$ as false and $e_{out} \simeq$ battery as true, the circuit shown in Fig. 13.11 makes a very fast OR gate. This circuit can be converted into a three- or four-input OR gate by adding additional input resistors to the base.

Example 13.4

Assume that the transistor shown in Fig. 13.11 is silicon, and has $I_{co} = 10\,\mu A$, $R_L = 1\,k\Omega$, and $V_{battery} = 5$ volts. Determine e_{out} for (a) cutoff; (b) saturation.

Solution Part (a) Step 1.   When the transistor is cut off,

$$I_e \simeq I_{co} \qquad \text{Kirchhoff's current law}$$

Therefore

$$I_e = 10\,\mu A$$

Step 2.   Since

$$V_{R_L} = I_e R_L$$
$$= 10 \times 10^{-6} \times 10^3$$
$$= 0.01 \text{ volts} \qquad \text{cutoff}$$

Part (b) Step 1.   When a silicon transistor is saturated $V_{ce} \simeq 0.1$ volts. Therefore, using Eq. 13.5a,

$$V_{battery} = V_{ce} + V_{R_L}$$
$$5 = 0.1 + V_{R_L}$$
$$V_{R_L} = 4.9 \text{ volts} \qquad \text{saturation}$$

We can convert a transistor OR gate into a transistor NOR gate by placing the load resistor in the collector leg rather than in the emitter leg, as shown in Fig. 13.12.

In effect we have converted from a CC configuration (OR gate) in which the input and output are in phase to a CE configuration (NOR gate) in which the input and output are out of phase.

By adding an additional resistor to the base (R_{neg}) which is connected to a negative voltage the OR gate shown in Fig. 13.11 is converted into the AND gate shown in Fig. 13.12. From Kirchhoff's current law we know that the base current is the sum of the currents which enter the base:

$$I_b = I_A + I_B + I_{neg} \qquad (13.6)$$

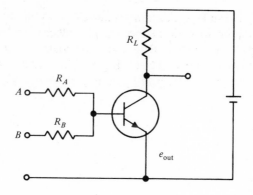

13.12 Two-input transistor NOR gate.

Assume that the current flowing through R_{neg} is $-5\,\text{mA}$. If $+3\,\text{mA}$ is an input to either A or B, the total base current is $-2\,\text{mA}$ (Eq. 13.6) and the transistor is still cut off. But if $3\,\text{mA}$ is an input to R_A and an additional $3\,\text{mA}$ is an input to R_B the total base current is $+1\,\text{mA}$. With positive base current there will be a voltage drop across R_L since the transistor will conduct.

Therefore the only condition under which current flows through R_L is if and only if inputs exist at every input. This is an AND gate. It can be extended to include additional inputs by adding resistors to the base. We must select the values of input currents so that all the inputs are required to permit the transistor to conduct. In particular the current when all transistors conduct should cause saturation. Saturation is desirable since it is as different from cutoff as possible. Therefore noise and temperature fluctuations will still permit a large difference between the on and off states of the transistor.

Example 13.5

For the AND gate shown in Fig. 13.13, assume that $I_{neg} = -0.3\,\text{mA}$ and that $\beta = 50$. The other values are the same as in Example 13.4. Determine realistic values for I_A and I_B.

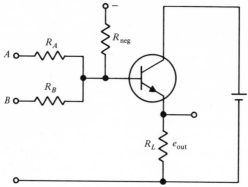

13.13 Transistor AND gate.

Solution Step 1.   With no inputs at both A and B we have

$$I_b = I_A + I_B + I_{neg}$$
$$= 0 + 0 - 0.3 \, mA$$
$$= -0.3 \, mA$$

and the transistor is cut off.

Step 2.   From Example 13.4, $V_{R_L} = 4.9$ volts when saturation occurs. Therefore

$$I_{sat} = \frac{V_{R_L(sat)}}{R_L}$$

$$= \frac{4.9}{1 \times 10^3}$$

$$= 4.2 \, mA$$

Step 3. $\beta = I_c/I_b \simeq I_e/I_b$, we can determine the minimum value of base current required to cause saturation:

$$I_{b(min)} \simeq \frac{I_e}{I_b}$$

$$= \frac{4.9 \times 10^{-3}}{50}$$

$$= 0.098 \, mA$$

Step 4.   Assuming equal currents for I_A and I_B we have

$$I_b = I_A + I_B + I_{neg}$$
$$= 2I_A + I_{neg}$$
$$0.098 = 2I_A - 0.3$$
$$2I_A = 0.398$$
$$I_A = I_B = 0.199 \, mA$$

as minimum values to result in AND-gate operation.

As in the OR–NOR situation, AND gates can be converted into NAND gates by moving the load resistor from the emitter to the collector. This is shown in Fig. 13.14.

There are many other circuits which can be and are used to perform OR–NOR, AND–NAND gating. In fact, the types which have been discussed should be considered as possible approaches (and not necessarily the best for all applications). It is possible to construct gates which use only

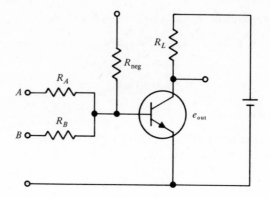

13.14   Transistor NAND gate.

diodes. It is also possible to construct gates which use diodes in combination with transistors, and so on. Since many gate circuits are possible, it is convenient to have general symbols for these gates which do not depend on the actual details of the circuit. Figure 13.15 shows the symbols for the gates which have been discussed. A circle at the gate output converts a gate to its negative. In Fig. 13.16 we see how Eq. 13.3 looks when drawn using these logical gate symbols.

13.6   Binary Numbers

Since man has 10 fingers a number system based on 10 (0, 1, 2, ... , 9) is logical. When we write a number such as 456 we mean that each figure is

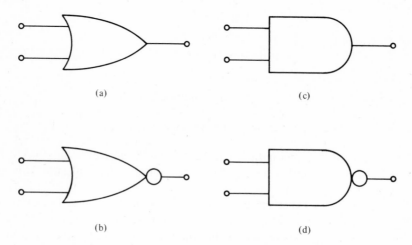

13.15   Gate symbols. (a) OR. (b) NOR. (c) AND. (d) NAND.

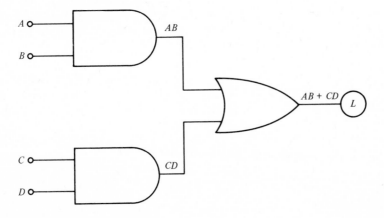

13.16   Logic diagram for $AB + CD = L$.

multiplied by the next higher power of 10. In this case the **least significant digit** (LSD) is multiplied by 10 raised to the zero power and the **most significant digit** (MSD) is to the second power:

$$\begin{aligned} \text{LSD} \qquad 6 \times 10^0 &= 6 \\ 5 \times 10^1 &= 50 \\ \text{MSD} \qquad \underline{4 \times 10^2} &= \underline{400} \\ &\ 456 \end{aligned}$$

The highest digit in the decimal system is 9. The next higher number requires moving to the next higher power of 10 column.

Typically switches have two "fingers" (on and off). This indicates that while people like the 10-number system, switches "like" the 2-number system. A number based on 2 is called a **binary system. The only numbers in the binary system are 0 and 1.** In the binary system each position is multiplied by 2 to the appropriate power, rather than by 10 to the appropriate power.

Example 13.6

Find the decimal number which is equivalent to the binary number 1011.

Solution Step 1.   This number has four figures. Thus the LSD is multiplied by 2^0 and the MSD is multiplied by 2^3.

Step 2.   Therefore

$$\begin{aligned} \text{LSD} \qquad 1 \times 2^0 &= 1 \\ 1 \times 2^1 &= 2 \\ 0 \times 2^2 &= 0 \\ \text{MSD} \qquad \underline{1 \times 2^3} &= \underline{8} \\ &\ 11 \quad \text{is the decimal equivalent} \end{aligned}$$

The binary number 1011 is equivalent to the decimal number 11. In comparing numbers from different systems it is convenient to indicate the base of the number by subscripts in parenthesis. Thus,

$$1011_{(2)} = 11_{(10)}$$

If this were not done it would be difficult to tell exactly which number system were being used. Notice that both 1011 and 11 could pass as either decimal or binary numbers.

Addition in binary is quite simple:

$$0 + 0 = 0$$

$$0 + 1 = 1$$

$$1 + 0 = 1$$

$$1 + 1 = 0 \text{ and carry } 1$$

With the exception of the "carry 1" operation we see that binary addition is the same as the truth table for an OR gate [Table 13.2 (b)]. In modern computers, addition is performed in a circuit which is basically a combination of an OR gate with an AND gate used to perform the carry operation. Such a circuit is called a **half-adder.** Two half-adders make an adder, which can add, carry in, and carry out.

While binary multiplication can be implemented using the AND-gate truth table it has been found more convenient to obtain multiplication by repeated addition. Similarly, subtraction and division also involve adders. Thus, **the basic operation used to perform calculations in modern computers is binary addition.**

In Table 13.5 the first few decimal and binary numbers are compared. The binary number system is seen to be as logical as the decimal system. Binary numbers increase in sequence by adding 1 (in binary) to the previous

Table 13.5   Decimal and Binary Numbers

Decimal	Binary
0	0
1	1
2	10
3	11
4	100
5	101
6	110
7	111

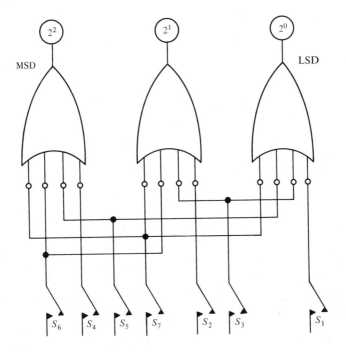

13.17 Decimal-to-binary encoding.

number just as decimal numbers increase by adding 1 (in decimal) to the previous number.

Since people operate more conveniently in decimal and computers operate more conveniently in binary it is necessary to convert **(encode)** decimal inputs to binary prior to computation in a computer. A very convenient method of encoding from decimal to binary uses OR gates, as shown in Fig. 13.17.

The decimal numbers are shown as switches. In an actual computer, manual switches would not be used although the principle is the same. Since any input to an OR gate results in an output we run a lead from the appropriate decimal number to the appropriate gates. For example, a lead from decimal 1 (S_1) goes to the LSD OR gate only. Similarly, a lead from S_2 runs to the second OR gate only, and so on. Actually, Fig. 13.17 is the implementation of Table 13.5 if we consider 1 as connecting a lead to the OR gate and zero as not connecting a lead. This takes care of encoding from decimal to binary.

At the computer output we must **decode** from binary back to decimal. This is conveniently accomplished by using AND gates, as shown in Fig. 13.18.

In this case we require switch closures as well as switch openers; that is, we need a function as well as its negative. If we consider S as 1 and $\bar{S}$ as zero,

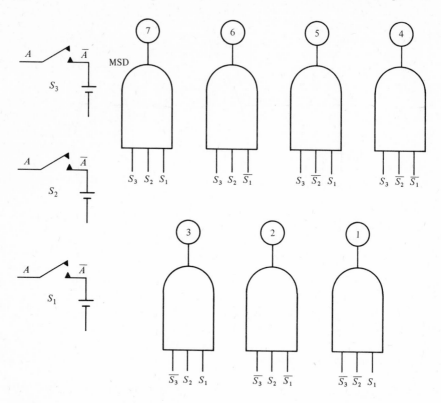

13.18 Binary-to-decimal decoding.

binary-to-decimal encoding corresponds to Table 13.5. For example, the decimal 4 light will be on only when we have $S_3, \bar{S}_2, \bar{S}_1$. This corresponds to binary 100, which is decimal 4, and so on.

Thus we see that logic gates are the basis of computation in a computer as well as the basis of encoding and decoding.

13.7 Bistable Switches

In addition to gates which perform logical functions, a computer needs information in the form of numbers on which to operate. This means that a computer must also have a **memory.** Memory is required to store the results of intermediate computation which will be updated at a later time.

A basic memory unit should have two stable states which can be "read out" when necessary. A single transistor switch has two stable states which can be read out by determining if the output is cut off or saturated. Also, the state of the output can be reversed by reversing the input voltage to the transitor. But a single transistor does not have a memory; if we remove the input, the output will change.

By adding a second transistor to a basic transistor switch, we can create a switch which has a memory as well as having two stable states. Such a switch is called a **bistable** switch. The form of a bistable switch is shown in Fig. 13.19.

If transistor Q_2 is saturated e_{out} is very low. This means that the voltage across the base-emitter junction of Q_1 ($V_{R_{D_1}}$) will be even lower since R_{B_1} and R_{D_1} act as a voltage divider. Therefore Q_1 is cut off when Q_2 is saturated. It is also possible that Q_2 is cut off. If Q_2 is cut off e_{out} is approximately equal to the power-supply voltage. This means that the voltage across R_{D_1} due to

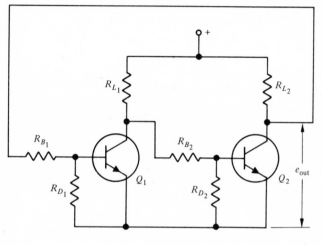

(a)

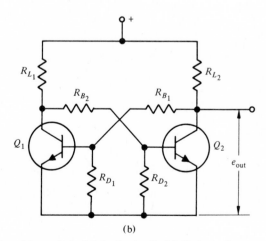

(b)

13.19   Bistable transistor switch. (a) Basic circuit. (b) Redrawn for symmetry.

voltage divider action of R_{D_1} and R_{B_1} will be high. This voltage should be sufficient to drive Q_1 into saturation. Thus we see that when Q_2 is saturated Q_1 is cut off and when Q_2 is cut off Q_1 is saturated. If we called cut off 1 we could call saturation 0. Instead we could use A and $\bar{A}$ or some other con- venient system to describe the two states of the bistable switch. Since only two states are possible in a bistable switch this type of circuit is often called a **flip-flop.**

Example 13.7

Determine the minimum value of β necessary for the flip-flop shown in Fig. 13.20.

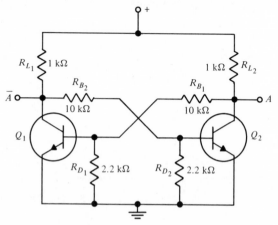

13.20   Transistor flip-flop.

Solution Step 1.   For germanium transistors the saturation voltage is approximately 0.4 volts. Assume that Q_1 is saturated. Therefore $\bar{A} \simeq 0.4$ volts.

Step 2.   Since Q_1 is saturated, R_{B_2} and R_{D_2} constitute a voltage divider. Therefore

$$V_{be(Q_2)} = \bar{A}\frac{R_{D_2}}{R_{B_2} + R_{D_2}}$$

$$= 0.4\frac{2.2 \times 10^3}{10 \times 10^3 + 2.2 \times 10^3}$$

$$\simeq 0.07 \text{ volts}$$

This voltage is low enough so the Q_2 is cut off.

Step 3.   When Q_2 is cut off the current through R_{L_2} is essentially determined by the base current of Q_1. (This condition is redrawn in Fig. 13.21.) From Kirchhoff's current law we know that

$$I_L = I_{2.2 k\Omega} + I_b$$

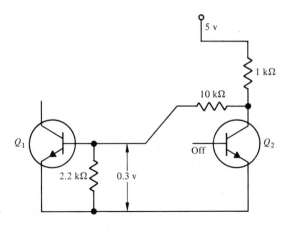

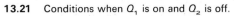

13.21   Conditions when Q_1 is on and Q_2 is off.

Step 4.   The voltage drop across a heavily forward-biased germanium base-emitter diode is about 0.3 volts. Therefore

$$I_L = \frac{5 - 0.3}{1 + 10}$$

$$= 0.428 \text{ mA}$$

Step 5.

$$I_{2.2\,k\Omega} = \frac{0.3}{2.2 \times 10^3}$$

$$= 0.137 \text{ mA}$$

Step 6.   Therefore

$$I_b = I_L - I_{2.2k\Omega}$$

$$= 0.428 \text{ mA} - 0.137 \text{ mA}$$

$$= 0.291 \text{ mA}$$

Step 7.   Since

$$V_{R_L(\text{sat})} = 5 - 0.4$$

$$= 4.6 \text{ volts}$$

$$I_{C(\text{sat})} = \frac{4.6}{10^3}$$

$$= 4.6 \text{ mA}$$

Step 8.   Therefore since

$$\beta = \frac{I_c}{I_b}$$

$$= \frac{4.6 \text{ mA}}{0.291 \text{ mA}} = 21$$

$\beta = 21$ is the minimum for saturated flip-flop action.

Referring again to the basic bistable circuit we see that a flip-flop is really a symmetrical two-stage amplifier with positive feedback. Therefore internal capacitances must be considered in a real design situation so that we avoid oscillation and obtain flip-flop action as required.

Prior to use flip-flops should be in the zero state. For example, in the circuit shown in Fig. 13.20 we may choose Q_2 cut off to be our $A = 1$ case. In this event Q_2 should be saturated ($e_{\text{out}} \simeq 0$) prior to use. By attaching set and reset leads as shown in Fig. 13.22 we accomplish this.

Assume that as a result of the last operation Q_2 is cut off. If a sufficiently positive pulse is applied to the reset lead the base of Q_2 will be driven positive and Q_2 will saturate. Notice that after the reset pulse is removed this condition will remain. The flip-flop has a memory. If, on the other hand, Q_2 is already saturated application of a reset pulse will not take Q_2 out of saturation. Thus if all the flip-flops of a computer receive a reset pulse simultaneously we are assured that all Q_2's are saturated.

Observe that we can reset at most only once. While the first reset may take Q_2 from cutoff to saturation, additional reset pulses will not change anything.

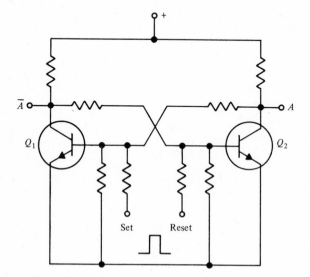

13.22   Flip-flop with set-reset provisions.

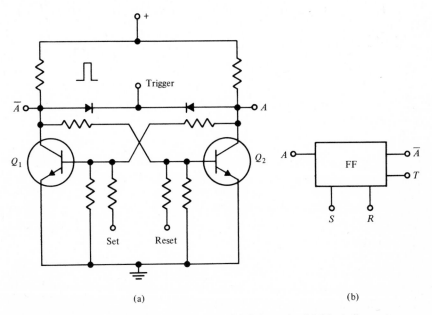

13.23   Flip-flop with triggering and set-reset. (a) Schematic. (b) Block diagram.

A similar set of remarks apply to the set lead which is connected to the base of Q_1.

Instead of a guaranteed reset or set we might require that each incoming pulse reverse the state of the flip-flop. One possible circuit for accomplishing alternate triggering is shown in Fig. 13.23.

The triggering circuit consists of two diodes with their anodes connected to the collectors. Assume that initially Q_2 is saturated and Q_1 is cut off. Under this condition if a negative pulse is applied to the trigger terminal D_1 is forward biased and D_2 is reverse biased. Since D_1 is forward biased R_{L_1} can conduct. This conduction lowers the voltage at the base of Q_2 until Q_2 cuts off, at which time Q_1 is saturated. When the next negative incoming pulse occurs D_2 will be forward biased and D_1 will be reverse biased. Each incoming pulse reverses the state of the flip-flop as well as appropriately biasing the diodes for the next pulse. Diodes used in this manner are called **steering diodes.**

A **binary counter** can be constructed using flip-flops. As shown in Fig. 13.24, all the reset leads are connected together. Counter operation begins with a reset pulse which places all the A outputs in the zero state. Then all three indicator lights are off and this is the binary number 000.

The first pulse which is applied to the trigger input of the LSD flip-flop switches this flip-flop to the $A = 1$ state. This turns on the 2^0 lamp so that the counter now reads 001. The next trigger pulse returns the LSD flip-flop to the $A = 0$ state, which turns the 2^0 lamp off.

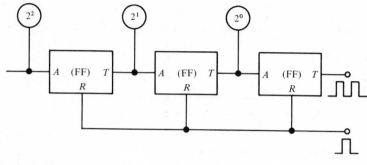

13.24   Basic binary counter.

Since the A of the LSD flip-flop is also connected to the trigger of the 2^1 flip-flop, the 2^1 flip-flop goes on as the 2^0 flip-flop goes off. Thus after two input pulses the lamps indicate 010, which is 2 in binary.

The third trigger pulse again turns the LSD flip-flop on but does not advance the 2^1 count. The lamps now indicate 011, which is 3 in binary. A fourth pulse will return the LSD and 2^1 flip-flops to the zero state and triggers the 2^2 flip-flop on. The lamps now indicate 100, which is binary 4.

Thus a binary counter continues to count in sequence until the highest possible count is reached (111 in this case). The next pulse resets the counter to 000.

By connecting the counter using the $\bar{A}$ outputs instead, a **down counter** is created. A down counter starts with the highest number and subtracts 1 for each input pulse. Notice that either a binary up counter or a down counter can have its outputs connected directly to a binary-to-decimal encoder of the same basic type as shown in Fig. 13.18. The only difference is that the manual switches would be replaced by the outputs of the counter flip-flops.

An important part of any computer is the **registers.** Registers store and shift numbers as required. Basically a **shift register** consists of two chains of flip-flops. One chain is a counter and the other chain stores the count.

13.8   Astable Multivibrators

Pulses are the fundamental units on which computers operate. Therefore methods of generating pulses should be investigated. One method of pulse

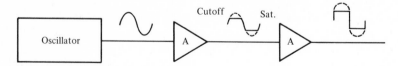

13.25   Sinusoidal square-wave generator.

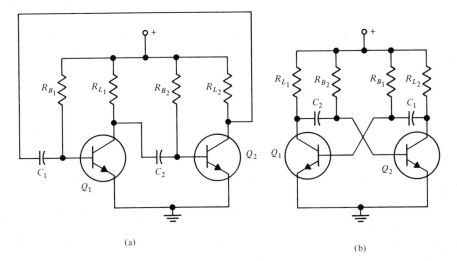

13.26 Astable multivibrator. (a) Basic circuit. (b) Redrawn.

generation starts with a sinusoidal oscillator. The sine wave is intentionally amplified to such a point that cutoff and saturation result. Saturation and cutoff "square off" the tops and bottoms of the sine wave. Several stages of such amplification result in waveforms that are essentially square. This is illustrated in Fig. 13.25. Such a system is quite practical. Laboratory generators which can deliver both sine waves and square waves utilize this method.

Another method of generating square waves is to use a two-stage *RC*-coupled amplifier with positive feedback. Such a circuit is called an **astable multivibrator.** The term multivibrator indicates that square waves rather than sine waves are involved. Astable means not stable; that is, an astable multivibrator is free running. An astable multivibrator continually switches

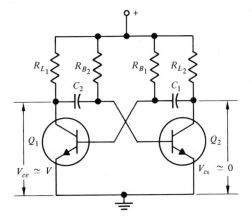

13.27 Operation of an astable multivibrator.

between turning on one transistor and turning off the other as long as a power supply is connected. As shown in Fig. 13.26, an astable multivibrator is similar to a flip-flop.

Basically, the difference between an astable multivibrator and a flip-flop is that the astable multivibrator is RC coupled while the flip-flop is DC coupled. Since a flip-flop also involves square waves and switching from one transistor to the other, a flip-flop is sometimes referred to as a bistable multivibrator. Bistable indicates that both states are stable.

Operation of the astable multivibrator may be understood by "freezing" action at a specific instant and describing a complete cycle of operation. In Fig. 13.27 we see the situation when Q_1 is cut off and Q_2 is saturated.

At the instant that Q_2 becomes saturated the voltage across the base-emitter junction of Q_1 is negative, because there was a drop in voltage when Q_2 went from cutoff into saturation. The negative voltage across C_1 does not remain. C_1 discharges through R_{B_1} in a time-constant situation as discussed in Section 7.5. As C_1 discharges the base-emitter voltage of Q_1 begins to rise.

When $V_{be(Q_1)}$ becomes sufficiently positive (approximately 0.25 volts for germanium or 0.6 volts for silicon) Q_1 begins to conduct and the voltage across Q_2 begins to fall until $V_{be(Q_2)}$ is negative and Q_2 shuts off. This is not a

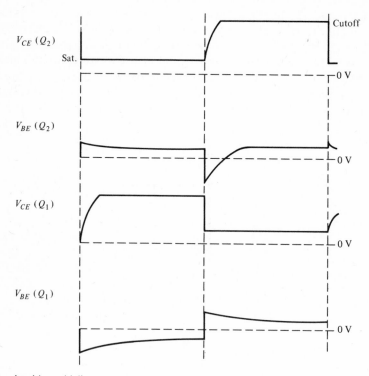

13.28   Astable multivibrator waveforms.

stable situation either, and C_2 begins to discharge through R_{B_2}. In this way an astable multivibrator continues to function. Voltage waveforms for the collectors and bases are shown in Fig. 13.28.

Assuming that the load resistors of an astable multivibrator are much smaller than the base resistors, the period of a complete waveform is given by

$$T \simeq 0.69\,(R_{B_1}C_1 + R_{B_2}C_2) \qquad\qquad (13.7a)$$

Since frequency is equal to $1/T$,

$$\text{PRF} \simeq \frac{1.45}{R_{B_1}C_1 + R_{B_2}C_2} \qquad\qquad (13.7b)$$

Example 13.8

Assume that for the astable multivibrator shown in Fig. 13.27, $R_{L_1} = R_{L_2} = 1\,\text{k}\Omega$, $R_{B_1} = R_{B_2} = 10\,\text{k}\Omega$, and $C_1 = C_2 = 0.01\,\mu\text{F}$. Determine the period and the PRF.

Solution Step 1.   Since the load resistors are much less than the base resistors Eq. 13.7 is applicable.

Step 2.   Therefore

$$T \simeq 0.69\,(R_{B_1}C_1 + R_{B_2}C_2)$$
$$\simeq 0.69\,(10^4 \times 10^{-8} + 10^4 \times 10^{-8})$$
$$\simeq 1.38 \times 10^{-4}\;\text{sec}$$

Step 3.

$$\text{PRF} = \frac{1}{T}$$
$$= \frac{1}{1.38 \times 10^{-4}}$$
$$\simeq 7.25 \times 10^3\;\text{pps}$$

Depending on the particular values of base resistors and coupling capacitors we can adjust the PRF to suit our requirements. In addition, if we use unequal values of $R_{B_1}C_1$ and $R_{B_2}C_2$ we obtain waveforms which are not symmetrical. In this manner narrow pulses can be generated. That is, for unequal R_BC one transistor will be on for a short time and off for a long time.

The rectangular waveform oscilloscope photographs shown in Chapter 6 were made using a pulse generator which works on this principle. Both the PRF and the duty cycle are adjustable.

Astable multivibrators are the source of pulses for computers. In fact, in many computers astable multivibrators are the "power supply" for the gates and the flip-flops. In this way it is easy to control when an operation must end. Otherwise the last bit of a number would be difficult to determine and operations would overlap. Therefore the astable multivibrator is used to activate gates and flip-flops and to cut them off at appropriate intervals.

Summary

1. Switches are characterized by off resistance, on resistance, and operating time. Ideal switches would have infinite off resistance, zero on resistance, and operate in zero time.
2. Transistors are operated as switches by driving from cutoff to saturation (off to on). Transistors have poorer resistance characteristics but better switching speeds than mechanical devices.
3. A gate is a logic circuit which has several inputs and a single output. The inputs are switch closures and the output is some indication of the switch conditions, such as a lamp.
4. An OR gate operates if any of the inputs exist.
5. An AND gate operates only if every input exists.
6. NOR gates are the negatives of OR gates.
7. NAND gates are the negatives of AND gates
8. Transistors can be used as high-speed gates. Generally, conditions are arranged so that cutoff represents one state and saturation represents the other.
9. OR and AND gates generally have load resistors in their emitter legs. These can be converted into NOR and NAND gates by shifting the load resistors to the collector legs.
10. The on-off nature of switches makes the binary number system particularly useful; 1 can represent on and 0 can represent off or vice versa.
11. Gates are used to convert from decimal to binary as well as from binary back to decimal. Gates are also the basis of performing arithmetic operations within the computer.
12. Flip-flops are switches which have two stable states with a memory. The basic flip-flop is a two-stage, DC-coupled, CE amplifier with positive feedback.
13. Flip-flops can be cascaded to form binary up counters, down counters, and registers. Such circuits are important parts of computers and other instruments.
14. Astable multivibrators are used to generate square waves. Square waves may be either symmetrical or unbalanced.
15. An astable multivibrator is a two-stage, RC-coupled amplifier with positive feedback.

Questions

1. Describe why a real switch does not have infinite off resistance.
2. How does a relay operate?
3. How is a transistor used as a switch in the off position?
4. How is a transistor used as a switch in the on position?

5. In what respect is a transistor switch superior to mechanical switches?
6. What is meant by the term logic gate?
7. What are the conditions for an OR gate to operate?
8. What are the conditions for an AND gate to operate?
9. Describe how one form of transistor OR gate operates.
10. Describe how one form of transistor AND gate operates.
11. How can these gates be converted into their inverse gates?
12. As far as switches are concerned, what is the advantage of the binary number system?
13. How can numbers be encoded using gates?
14. How does a transistor flip-flop operate?
15. What is the difference between reset and trigger pulses.
16. What are two methods of generating square waves?
17. How does an astable multivibrator operate?

Problems

1. A certain switch has $10^{11}\,\Omega$ off resistance and $10\,m\Omega$ on resistance. It connects a 50-volt battery to a 200-Ω load. What current flows through the load when the switch is (a) open; (b) closed?
2. A 200-watt lamp is operated from a 115-V_{rms} source through a switch with 20 mΩ on resistance. Find the approximate voltage across the closed switch.
3. A silicon transistor has a 0.5-μA collector leakage current, 0.1-volt saturation voltage, and a 20-mA collector current when operated from a 4-volt supply. Find R_{off} and R_{on}.
4. A germanium transistor with a 10-μA collector leakage current has a 0.4-volt saturation voltage and a 20-mA collector current. The supply voltage is the same as in Problem 3. Find R_{off} and R_{on}.
5. A three-input AND gate has eight possible input states.
   (a) Show a manual three-input AND gate.
   (b) Show a truth table in terms of 1–0.
6. Repeat Problem 5 for a three-input OR gate.
7. Sketch a two-input NOR gate and show a truth table.
8. Sketch an OR circuit which operates on any of three fire alarm locations.
9. Sketch an AND circuit which indicates if all three gates of a factory are closed.
10. Sketch a three-input OR gate. A silicon transistor with $\beta = 100$ and $I_{co} = 1\,\mu$A is used. $R_L = 1\,k\Omega$ and $V_{battery} = 5$ volts. Calculate minimum base currents to result in saturation.
11. Using $e_{out} \simeq V_{battery}$ as 1 and $e_{out} \simeq 0$ as 0 construct the truth table for Problem 10. Use $0\,\mu$A and I_b required for saturation as inputs to the gate.
12. Repeat Problem 11 for a NOR gate.
13. Convert the circuit of Problem 10 into a three-input AND gate. Assuming $I_{neg(base)} = 500\,\mu$A and equal gate inputs, calculate the minimum required gate inputs to cause saturation.
14. Using gate symbols, construct $ABC + DE + FG = L$.
15. Convert the decimal number 10 into binary.
16. What is the decimal number equivalent to (a) $1010_{(2)}$; (b) $101010_{(2)}$?

17. How can odd and even binary numbers be distinguished in terms of their LSD's?
18. The conditions are the same as in Example 13.7, except that 20-kΩ resistors replace the 10-kΩ base resistors. Determine the minimum β transistors which are required.
19. (a) What is the highest decimal number which a four-flip-flop binary counter can reach?

    (b) Using block diagrams, show such a counter which will reset after reaching maximum count.
20. The conditions are the same as in Example 13.8, except $C_2 = 0.001$ μF. Determine (a) the period; (b) the PRF. (c) Sketch approximate collector waveforms.

Chapter 14 Instrumentation and Transducers

14.1 Introduction

In this chapter the principles of electronics are combined to describe the operation of several basic electronic instruments. Methods of measuring certain physical quantities using electronic principles are also described.

14.2 Vacuum-Tube Voltmeters

In Chapter 4 VOM's were described. The voltmeter section of a VOM was seen to consist of a basic ammeter movement with appropriate resistors for each voltage range. As was indicated, the chief problem with such a voltmeter is that the input resistance of the voltmeter loaded down the circuit being measured.

A voltmeter which has a much higher input resistance is shown in Fig. 14.1. This voltmeter uses a triode. Voltmeters which use vacuum tubes are referred to as **vacuum-tube voltmeters** (VTVM).

The meter leads are shorted together and the voltmeter is zeroed after a sufficient warm-up time. Then the meter leads are connected across the terminals of the voltage to be measured. Notice that the unknown voltage is always connected across the entire string of resistors. The appropriate scale is selected by the range switch. In Section 10.9 it was pointed out that a triode has infinite input resistance. Thus the input resistance of a VTVM is the total resistance of a string of series resistors. By using large resistors in the string a high input resistance is obtained. By adding the resistances shown in Fig. 14.1 we see that this particular VTVM has an input resistance of 10 MΩ. Moreover, since the triode has an infinite input resistance we shall have 10 MΩ for all ranges. This is far superior to VOM's and can be increased by using larger resistors.

The range switch selects the appropriate portion of the total input voltage for each particular scale. This is a voltage divider; voltage dividers were described in Chapter 2. To stay within the linear range of the triode the voltage presented to the tube must be approximately the same for all ranges. When lower voltages are to be measured more of the total input voltage will be used. When higher voltages are to be measured less of the

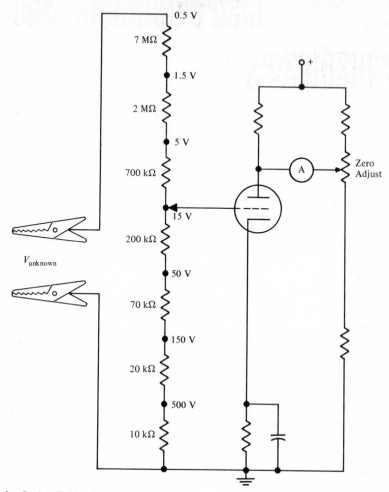

14.1   Basic VTVM schematic.

total input voltage will be used. This keeps the voltage presented to the tube within the same range.

Example 14.1

Calculate the maximum voltage between grid and ground when the voltmeter is in the 500-, 1.5-, and 0.5-V ranges and the input to the VTVM is 500, 1.5, and 0.5 V, respectively.

Solution Step 1. In accordance with Eq. 2.14, the maximum voltage between grid and ground for the 500-V range is

$$V_{500(\text{max})} = V_{\text{in}}\frac{10k}{R_T} = 500\frac{10 \times 10^3}{10 \times 10^6}$$

$$= 0.5 \text{ volts}$$

Step 2. Similarly, for the 1.5-volt range,

$$V_{1.5(max)} = V_{in}\frac{3 \times 10^6}{10 \times 10^6} = 1.5\frac{3 \times 10^6}{10 \times 10^6}$$

$$= 0.45 \text{ volts}$$

Step 3. For the 0.5-v range the entire input voltage is used:

$$V_{0.5(max)} = 0.5 \text{ volts}$$

The input voltages are amplified and read on the ammeter movement. Thus in both the VOM and VTVM cases the actual reading is a current which is proportional to the voltage being measured.

To read AC on a VTVM we rectify using a diode and filter as shown in Fig. 14.2. This resultant DC is connected to the basic DC portion of the VTVM.

Most VTVM's are calibrated in terms of the root-mean-square value of a sine wave. If other waveforms are measured, the readings will be incorrect. Thus it is necessary to know the nature of the waveform before we can consider an AC reading to be valid.

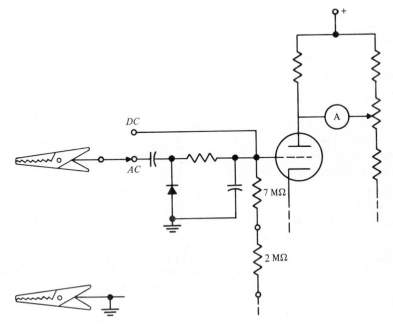

14.2   AC-DC VTVM schematic.

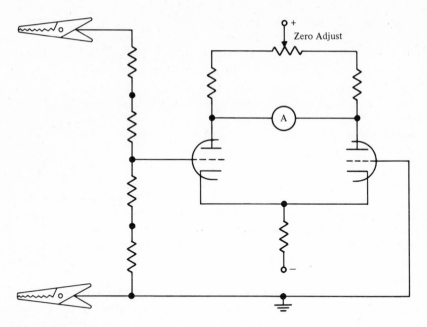

14.3   Differential VTVM schematic.

In Section 10.8 the differential amplifier was introduced. VTVM performance can be improved by using the differential configuration shown in
Fig. 14.3.

The voltage to be measured is connected between the grids of the two
tubes. Using a differential VTVM reduces 60-Hz pick-up and makes zeroing
the meter easier. Accuracy of any VTVM depends on the μ of the tube.
Since μ decreases with age the VTVM accuracy will become degraded.
This fact is less critical for the differential configuration since the output
depends on the difference between the two tubes. Thus if the tubes were
initially matched and age uniformly, aging will be less of a problem than
with single-ended VTVMs.

When ohmmeters were described in Chapter 4 it was pointed out that
to get zero ohms on the left and infinite ohms on the right required a shunt-
type ohmmeter. A shunt-type ohmmeter requires a meter with very high
input resistance. Thus VTVM's make it convenient to have all meter scales
read from left to right. Many but not all VTVM's use regulated voltage
supplies instead of batteries for the ohmmeter section.

Since tubes can amplify, VTVM's can be constructed using several stages
of gain. This permits lower voltage ranges than are possible with VOM's.
VTVM's are available with millivolt and microvolt ranges. Regardless of the
type of VTVM, a regulated power supply as discussed in Chapter 8 is
required to obtain accuracy.

14.3   Strip Chart Recorders

There are applications in electronics where a permanent record of voltage versus time is required. Electrocardiograms, thermocouple measurements, powerline voltage measurements at a generator, and so on are examples of such applications.

A **strip chart recorder** is a machine which creates a graph of the voltage to be measured versus time. The principal components of a strip chart recorder are shown in Fig. 14.4.

The amplifier and pen motor are basically a vacuum tube (or transistor) voltmeter. The pen motor is a rugged version of an ammeter movement. This permits a writing device to be attached to the tip of the meter needle.

One type of writing device uses an ink-type pen. Another type of pen uses an electrically heated stylus. In this case "writing" is accomplished by having the stylus make contact with paper which is impregnated with wax.

As the graph paper passes under the pen a permanent recording of voltage is generated. The speed at which the paper travels can be adjusted by means of a gear train.

Example 14.2

A certain strip chart recorder has paper speeds of 0.1, 1.0, and 10.0 in./sec. How much paper will be used at each of these speeds to record one cycle of a sine wave which has a frequency of 20 Hz?

Solution Step 1. Since $f = 1/T$ the time required to complete a 20-Hz sine wave is

$$T = \frac{1}{f}$$

$$= \frac{1}{20}$$

$$= 0.05 \text{ sec}$$

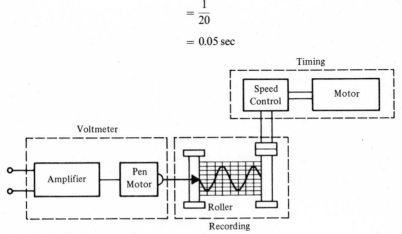

14.4   Basic strip chart recorder.

Step 2. Using distance = rate × time,

$$distance = 0.1 \frac{in.}{sec} \times 0.05 \, sec$$

$$= 0.005 \text{ in. of paper}$$

Step 3. For 1 in./sec,

$$distance = 1 \times 0.05$$

$$= 0.05 \text{ in. of paper}$$

Step 4. Similarly, for 10 in./sec,

$$distance = 10 \times 0.05$$

$$= 0.5 \text{ in. of paper}$$

Example 14.2 indicates that the paper speed should be adjusted to be compatible with the particular waveform. However, for tests of extended duration this is not always realistic.

Example 14.3

A 24-hr record of a thermocouple reading is to be made at 0.1 in/sec. How much paper will be required?

Solution Step 1. Convert 24 hr into seconds:

$$24 \, hr \times 60 \frac{min}{hr} \times 60 \frac{sec}{min} = 8.64 \times 10^4 \text{ sec}$$

Step 2. At a rate of 0.1 in./sec,

$$distance = 0.1 \times 8.64 \times 10^4$$

$$= 8.64 \times 10^3 \text{ in.} = 72 \text{ ft}$$

In cases where such very large amounts of paper are required it may be preferable to sample at specific intervals (e.g., 1 min out of 10) rather than to make a continuous recording.

Both ink and heated-stylus strip chart recorders involve physical contact between pen and paper. This places a rather low limit on the frequency response. Typically, the upper 3-dB frequency of such recorders is about 200 Hz.

A variation of the strip chart recorder which has a higher frequency response uses a mirror and light beam to "write" on photographically sensitive paper. The principle is illustrated in Fig. 14.5. Since no contact is involved between the writing device and the paper in this type of recorder

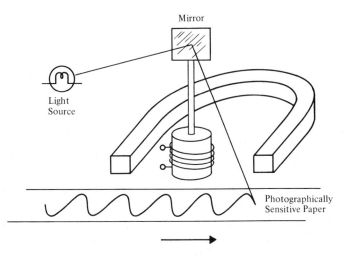

Mirror

Light
Source

Photographically
Sensitive Paper

14.5   Light-writing strip chart recorder.

the frequency response is much higher. Light-writing strip chart recorders
have an upper 3-dB frequency of 5 kHz. Figure 14.6 shows an eight-channel
light-writing recorder.

For higher frequencies **magnetic-tape recorders** can be used. Magnetic-tape
recorders operate by passing a strip of magnetically sensitive tape between
the poles of a magnet. The strength of this magnet is determined by the
amplified voltage which is being measured. In this way the permanent record
consists of fluctuations in the magnetization of the tape. In a broad sense a

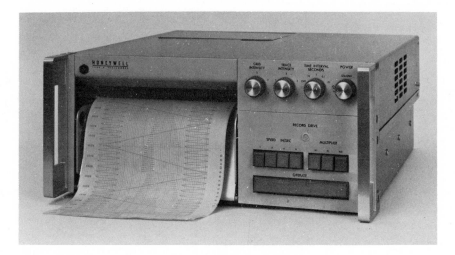

14.6   Eight-channel light-writing recorder. (*Courtesy of Honeywell Co.*)

home entertainment magnetic-tape recorder preserves a permanent record of the artist's voice and music.

14.4 Cathode-Ray Tubes

Another method of observing and obtaining a permanent record of voltages versus time is the cathode-ray oscilloscope (CRO). Oscilloscope photographs have appeared in several places in this text.

The heart of a CRO is the cathode-ray tube (CRT), which is a type of vacuum tube. Figure 14.7 shows a sketch of a CRT. Electrons which are emitted from the cathode are accelerated by a series of grids which have successively higher voltages. The electrons then pass between the plates of two capacitors: vertical deflection plates and horizontal deflection plates. If no voltage is applied to these plates, the accelerated electrons strike the center of the face of the CRT. This face is coated with a fluorescent material. Thus, when the electrons strike this fluorescent material a spot which glows is created.

Since like charges repel and unlike charges attract we can cause the spot to strike anywhere on the CRT face. For example, if the top vertical deflection plate is made positive while the bottom plate is negative the electrons passing between the plates will be deflected upward. In this case the glowing spot will be above the center. If the vertical plate polarities are reversed the spot will be below the center.

Similarly, if the right-hand deflection plate is positive while the left-hand plate is negative the spot will be to the right of center. If the reverse is true

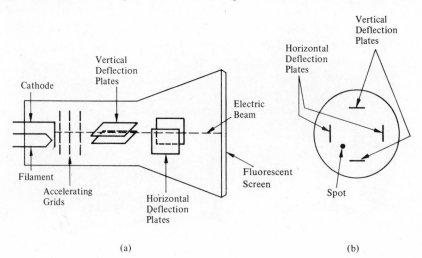

(a)   (b)

14.7   Cathode-ray tube. (a) Side view. (b) Front view.

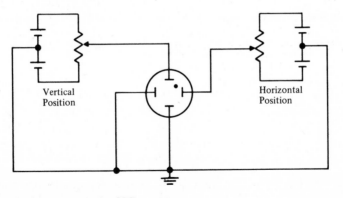

14.8   Positioning a spot on the CRT.

the spot will be to the left of center. By using adjustable voltage sources for both the vertical and horizontal plates, the spot can be positioned anywhere on the face of the CRT. This is shown in Fig. 14.8.

The precise voltage required to deflect the spot on the CRT face by a given amount depends on the tube geometry and on the voltage on the acceleration grids. A typical figure is that 25 volts will deflect the spot 1 cm. If a repetitive voltage waveform is applied across the vertical deflection plates we shall see a continuous bright line rather than a spot. The peak-to-peak amplitude of this waveform can be determined if the deflection sensitivity is known.

Example 14.4

A certain CRT has a deflection sensitivity of 25 V/cm. When a repetitive voltage is applied across the vertical plates a line which is 2 cm long results. Determine the peak-to-peak voltage of this waveform.

Solution Step 1. The given data are sensitivity = 25 V/cm and deflection = 2 cm.

Step 2. Therefore

$$V_{p-p} = \text{sensitivity} \times \text{deflection}$$

$$= 25\frac{\text{volt}}{\text{cm}} \times 2\ \text{cm}$$

$$= 50\ \text{volts}$$

In addition we can apply a small input signal to a high-gain amplifier and connect the amplifier output to the vertical deflection plates. This permits observing a small voltage at an expanded scale.

Example 14.5

It is desired that a 1-millivolt signal result in a deflection of 1 cm on a CRT. If the deflection sensitivity is 25 volts/cm, what amplifier gain is required?

Solution Step 1. The given data requires that an input of 1 mV result in an output of 25 V.

Step 2. Therefore the required amplifier gain is

$$A_v = \frac{e_{out}}{e_{in}}$$

$$= \frac{25}{1 \times 10^{-3}}$$

$$= 25,000$$

Once a stable high-gain amplifier is used a voltage divider similar to that described in Section 14.2 can be connected to the amplifier input. This permits selecting an appropriate range to observe various input voltages. In addition, since a capacitor blocks DC, by switching a capacitor in or out we can select either AC or DC waveforms (assuming that a DC amplifier is used). Such a system consistutes the vertical deflection circuit of a CRO and is illustrated in Fig. 14.9.

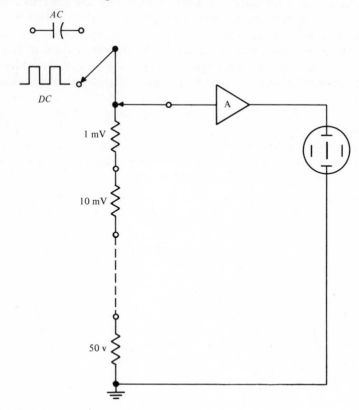

14.9 Vertical deflection system for a CRO.

A method of moving the spot across the CRT with respect to a time base is still required. Otherwise only peak-to-peak voltage, not the shape of the voltage, can be determined. A complete CRO system displays voltage versus time. The time-base signal is applied across the horizontal deflection plates. Suppose that the voltage on the right-hand horizontal deflection plate is increased at a uniform rate. This means that the spot will travel equal horizontal distances in equal time periods.

For example, if the screen has a horizontal distance of 10 cm and the same deflection sensitivity is used, a voltage which increases from 0 to 250 volts will deflect the spot 10 cm. If this voltage increases linearly from 0 to 250 volts in, say, 1 sec, it will take the spot 0.1 sec (100 nsec) to traverse each centimeter. This is illustrated in Fig. 14.10.

When the spot reaches the right-hand plate it can be returned by decreasing the voltage at this plate to zero. If different times are used to reach 250 volts on the right-hand plate each horizontal centimeter will represent some other time period. For example, if the 250 volts is reached in 0.5 sec, each centimeter represents 0.05 sec (50 msec) instead of 100 msec, and so on.

The time required to return the spot is usually much faster. If the speeds are chosen correctly the spot going from left to right appears as a solid line and the time required to return is not visible.

One method of generating the sawtooth voltage required to move the spot across the CRT uses a multivibrator with an unsymmetrical output and another transistor as a switch to charge a capacitor from a constant current source. This is shown in Fig. 14.11.

During the time that the output of Q_2 is negative Q_3 is cut off. C_1 will charge through R_1. If R_1 is very large the charging current will be almost constant. A constant current will cause the voltage across C_1 to increase linearly as described in Section 7.3. When the output of Q_2 is positive Q_3 will saturate and C_1 will discharge through Q_3 much faster than it charged

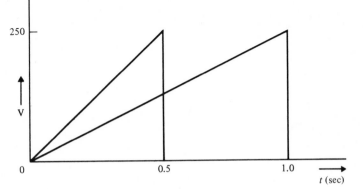

14.10   Horizontal deflection voltages.

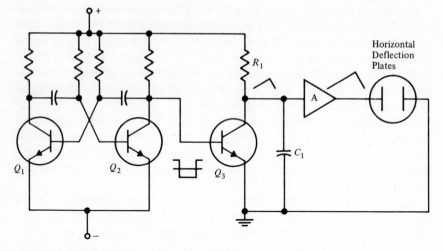

14.11   Horizontal deflection system for a CRO.

through R_1. Thus an unsymmetrical square wave and switch can be used to generate the voltage waveform required to move the spot across the CRO at a linear rate. By changing C_1 or R_1 (i.e., the time constant) we can obtain different sweep times. The voltage across C_1 is amplified to the value required to deflect the spot across the CRT (typically 250 volts).

A block diagram of a CRO is shown in Fig. 14.12. The vertical amplifier and the horizontal deflection system have just been described. The synchronization circuit is used to keep the waveform stable. One method is to take a voltage from the input signal (such as the zero crossing or the maximum

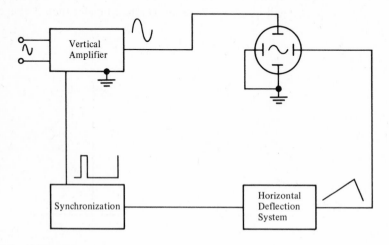

14.12   Block diagram of a CRO.

voltage), and use this to trigger the multivibrator which controls the charging. This will "freeze" the waveform being displayed since it will always begin at the same portion of the signal being observed. By attaching a camera to the CRO a photograph can be made. Since using a CRO requires no mechanical motion, the frequency response is much greater than for strip chart recorders. CRO's with 50-MHz bandwidths are common and much greater bandwidths are readily available. A laboratory oscilloscope is shown in Fig. 14.13.

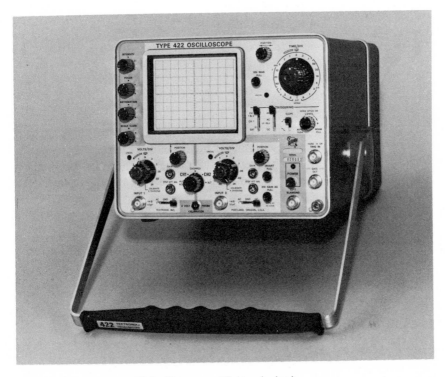

14.13   Laboratory-type CRO. (*Courtesy of Tektronix, Inc.*)

14.5   Digital Voltmeters

Another important laboratory instrument is the **digital voltmeter** (DVM), which displays voltage as a number rather than as the deviation of a pointer. The advantage of a DVM is that more significant figures can be read; this is useful when high accuracy is required. A DVM also simplifies reading the voltage since parallax is not a problem.

There are several methods of measuring voltage using digital techniques. All of these methods depend on comparing the voltage to be measured with an accurately known voltage. This is the same principle as was used in describing the potentiometric voltmeter of Section 5.7.

All of the circuits required to construct a DVM have already been described. One of these circuits requires a little additional discussion. A **comparator** is a high-gain DC amplifier with a differential input and a single-ended output. A block diagram is shown in Fig. 14.14.

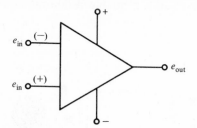

14.14 Comparator block diagram.

One input has a negative sign. This is the **inverting input.** That is, if a signal is applied to the inverting input the amplified output will be out of phase with the input. The input with the positive sign is the **noninverting input.** If a signal is applied to the noninverting input the amplified output will be in phase with the input.

Example 14.6

A certain comparator has a gain of 25,000. Determine the output if a 1-mV signal is applied to (a) the inverting input; (b) the noninverting input.

Solution Part (a). Since $A_v = -e_{out}/e_{in}$, for the inverting input we obtain

$$e_{out} = -Ae_{in}$$

$$= -25,000 \times 0.001$$

$$= -25 \text{ volts}$$

Part (b). For the noninverting input,

$$e_{out} = Ae_{in}$$

$$= 25,000 \times 0.001$$

$$= 25 \text{ volts}$$

As in other differential amplifiers, if signals are applied to both inputs it is the difference between the two signals which will be amplified (Eq. 10.7c). For example, if a 4-mV signal is applied to the noninverting input and a 3.5-mV signal is applied to the inverting input the signal which will be amplified is 0.5 mV. On the other hand, if the voltage at the inverting input is greater than the voltage at the noninverting input the output will be inverted. If the signals at both inputs are exactly equal the output will be zero.

This is the basis of a comparator. Unequal signals will result in an output which is either positive or negative. However, equal signals will result in zero output. Having described the comparator we can now discuss the DVM shown in Fig. 14.15. All the components have previously been described. In addition to the comparator there is a linear ramp generator, a voltage divider, a multivibrator, a crystal oscillator, an AND gate, a binary counter, a binary-to-decimal encoder, and a numerical display.

The crystal-controlled oscillator furnishes a series of positive peaks to one input of the AND gate. The other input to the AND gate is the comparator output. For the connection shown the output of the comparator will be positive as long as the ramp voltage is greater than the voltage being measured. Under these circumstances the AND gate is on and the binary counter continues to count the number of positive sine wave peaks.

When the voltage being measured reaches the ramp voltage the comparator output drops to zero. This turns the AND gate off, thereby stopping the binary counter. For example, assume a 1-MHz oscillator and a ramp that rises linearly from 0 to 1 volt in 1 sec. If it takes exactly 0.5743 sec for the ramp voltage to equal the voltage being measured, then the voltage being measured is exactly 0.5743 volts.

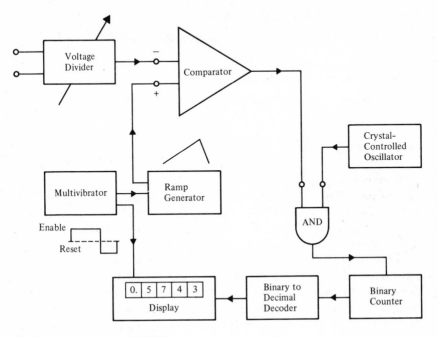

14.15   Block diagram of a DVM.

Figure 14.15 shows a manual range switch on the voltage divider. Automatic range switching which simultaneously moves the decimal point is also possible.

The purpose of the multivibrator is to enable the ramp generator to reset both the ramp and the display at the end on 1 sec. It is also interesting to note that by using only the multivibrator and counter sections of the DVM a digital frequency-measuring circuit can be constructed. Figure 14.16 shows an actual DVM.

14.16   Laboratory-type DVM. (*Courtesy of Hewlett-Packard Co.*)

14.6   Transducers

An important property of electronics is the ability to amplify extremely small signals. This ability can be exploited to measure and control non-electrical quantities provided that some means of converting a nonelectrical quantity into an electrical quantity is available. **A device which converts a signal from one form to another is called a transducer.**

Several types of transducers have already been discussed. A loudspeaker converts a varying electrical signal into a varying pressure, and a microphone does the opposite. A motor converts mechanical energy to electrical energy and a generator does the opposite. From the standpoint of measurement and control we are interested in methods of converting the quantities to be measured into electrical signals.

In Chapter 1 the dependence of resistance on geometry, temperature, and light intensity was indicated. Such dependence is a problem in terms of designing stable circuits. However, in terms of obtaining transducers such dependence is an asset. In fact, we seek materials which are extremely sensitive to the quantity to be measured in obtaining transducers.

Since geometry affects resistance (Eq. 1.4) a change in the length and cross-sectional area of a piece of wire will result in a change in resistance. Thus, if a weight is attached to a piece of wire the resultant change in resistance can be used to indicate the change in length. This is particularly useful since resistance can be measured very accurately using a bridge.

Provided that the wire is not stretched beyond its elastic limit we can calibrate the wire length in terms of resistance, as shown in Fig. 14.17.

A transducer which uses the change in resistance resulting from a change in length is called a **strain gauge.** The gauge factor (G) relates length and resistance:

$$G = \frac{(R_{final} - R_{initial})/R_{initial}}{(L_{final} - L_{initial})/L_{initial}} \tag{14.1}$$

Most metals have a gauge factor of 2, and typically strain gauge resistances will be in the 100–1000-Ω range.

Example 14.7

A strain gauge with $G = 2$ has an initial length of 10 cm and an initial resistance of 200 Ω. When a 2-lb weight is attached to the gauge the final resistance is 201 Ω. Determine the final length.

Solution Step 1. The given data are $G = 2$, $L_{initial} = 10$ cm, $R_{initial} = 200\,\Omega$, and $R_{final} = 201\,\Omega$.

Step 2.

$$G = \frac{(R_{final} - R_{initial})/R_{initial}}{(L_{final} - L_{initial})/L_{initial}}$$

$$2 = \frac{(201 - 200)/200}{(L_{final} - 10)/10}$$

$$L_{final} = 10.025 \text{ in.}$$

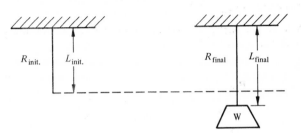

$R_{init.}$ $L_{init.}$ R_{final} L_{final}

W

14.17   Basis of the strain gauge.

If a 4-lb weight replaces the 2-lb weight in Example 14.6, the elongation of the wire doubles and so does the change in resistance. The relationship between elongation and weight makes the strain gauge extremely useful for measuring pressure.

Typically, strain gauges are made zigzag or some other form which permits a long wire in a small area. The strain gauge is then mounted where the pressure is to be measured. Strain gauges have been used to measure pressures up to thousands of pounds per square inch. Instead of just measuring the pressure the strain gauge can be incorporated into an automatic control system to actually control pressure.

In Section 1.3 it was pointed out that the resistance of most conductors increases with increasing temperature. This temperature dependence can be used to measure or as a basis for controlling temperature. The resistance of a piece of wire in terms of temperature is given by

$$R_{final} = R_{ref}[1 + \alpha(T_{final} - T_{ref})] \qquad \text{(14.2)}$$

where α is the temperature coefficient at the reference temperature. Table 14.1 lists the temperature coefficients of some important materials. A platinum wire thermometer is the internationally agreed upon standard for comparing all other thermometers.

Table 14.1   Certain Temperature Coefficients

Material	α (20°C)
Aluminum	0.00427
Copper	0.00383
Gold	0.00340
Platinum	0.00300
Silver	0.00380

Example 14.8

The resistance of a length of platinum wire is 60 Ω at 20°C. What is the temperature when the resistance measures 80 Ω?

Solution Step 1. The given data are $R_{initial} = 60\,\Omega$, $R_{final} = 80\,\Omega$, $T_{initial} = 20°C$, and, from Table 14.1, $\alpha_{Platinum} = 0.003$.

Step 2.

$$R_{final} = R_{initial}[1 + \alpha(T_{final} - T_{initial})]$$
$$80 = 60[1 + 0.003(T_{final} - 20)]$$
$$T_{final} = 130°C$$

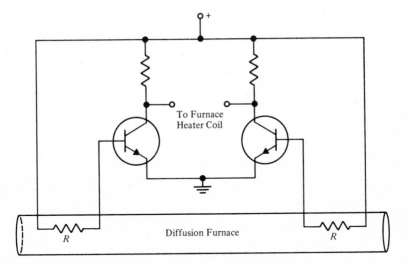

14.18   Temperature-control system.

An important application which uses resistance thermometers for control is the diffusion furnace used in doping semiconductor material. Such furnaces require maintaining a temperature of about $1000°C$ within $\frac{1}{2}°C$. This is accomplished by using a differential amplifier and two resistance thermometers, as shown in Fig. 14.18.

Assume that the proper temperature has been reached. At this point the differential amplifier is balanced and the output is zero. If the temperature of either thermometer changes there will be an output from the differential amplifier which can be used to increase the current through the furnace heater coils.

There are other materials which are especially sensitive to temperature changes. **Thermistors** are *therm*ally sensitive res*istors* which are semiconductors which will decrease resistance by about 5 % per degree ($\alpha \simeq -5.0$).

In Chapter 1 the dependence of certain resistors to light intensity was indicated. Such transducers are called **photoconductors** and are used in light-level applications such as automatic exposure control of cameras.

14.7   Other Transducers

All of the transducers described in the previous section rely on a change in resistance due to a change either in geometry or resistivity. It is also possible to use an ordinary potentiometer such as described in Chapter 2 as part of a position-sensing transducer.

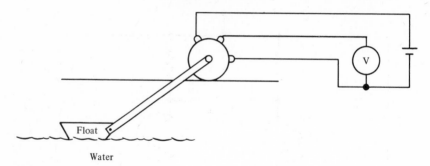

14.19   Measuring water level.

One of the earliest instances of this involves sensing the water level in a canal which is at a remote location. It involves attaching a float to the shaft of the potentiometer as illustrated in Fig. 14.19.

As the water level rises and falls the float will rotate the wiper shaft accordingly. Thus if a voltage source is connected across the entire potentiometer, the float will provide voltage divider action which relates to the water level. For example, a particular float-potentiometer combination might indicate upon calibration that a change of $100\,\Omega$ corresponds to a change of 1 ft in water level. In this case a change of $50\,\Omega$ would mean that the water level had changed by 6.0 in. Figure 14.19 shows a voltmeter as the readout. A bridge circuit could be used just as easily. In either case the resistance of the wires between the potentiometer and the point of measurement would have to be accounted for in a practical situation.

Measuring data from a distance is called **telemetry.** The system just described is an example of wire telemetry; that is, there is a direct connection between the measurement and the point where the data are recorded. Wire telemetry is not always possible. Weather balloons, rockets, space probes, and so on use radio telemetry. In radio telemetry the transducer output is used to modulate a radio-frequency carrier.

Using either wire or radio telemetry we might attach the shaft of a potentiometer to a weather vane. This would give us the direction of the wind in terms of a change in resistance.

Although changes in resistance provide very useful transducers, other methods are also available. In Section 7.2 we saw that capacitance was determined by geometry and dielectric constant. By keeping geometry constant we can use variation in dielectric constant as a means of obtaining a signal.

For example, if the plates of an air dielectric capacitor are insulated with, say, glass we can use the change in capacitance to determine the level of water in a canal. This is illustrated in Fig. 14.20.

When the water level just reaches the bottom of the capacitor, air accounts for the entire dielectric. When the water level reaches the top of the capacitor

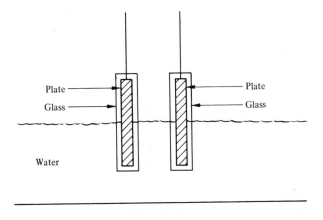

14.20   Capacitive water-level transducer.

the entire dielectric is water. For intermediate water levels, capitance will be determined partially by air and partially by water. The precise value of capacitance which can be measured on a bridge is a measure of the water level.

Similarly, by placing metal plates on opposite sides of a mercury or alcohol thermometer we can use the height of the liquid to translate a temperature variation into a capacitance variation. By turning the capacitor plates sideways as shown in Fig. 14.21 we can use capacitance as a thickness

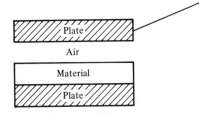

14.21   Capacitive thickness gauge.

gauge. In this case the capacitance is determined by the relative amounts of air and the material being measured. Since different materials have different dielectric constants, such a transducer must be calibrated for each particular material. Equation 7.2 must be modified in terms of average dielectric constant:

$$C = \kappa_{Av}\frac{A}{d} \tag{14.3}$$

Example 14.9

A parallel-plate capacitor is to be used as a thickness gauge for Teflon. The plates are 10 cm on a side and are separated by 1 cm. What will be the capacitance when (a) there is no Teflon; (b) the Teflon is 1 cm thick; (c) the Teflon is 0.5 cm thick?

Solution Step 1. From Table 7.1, $\kappa_{air} = 8.85 \times 10^{-14}$ F/cm, $\kappa_{Teflon} = 1.77 \times 10^{-13}$ F/cm.

Step 2. From the given data, the plate area is $10 \times 10 = 100$ cm^2.

Step 3. Since $d = 1$ cm we have

$$C = \kappa_{Av} \frac{A}{d}$$

$$= \kappa_{Av} \frac{100}{1}$$

$$= 100\kappa_{Av}$$

Part (a). When there is no Teflon the dielectric is air:

$$C_{0\,cm} = 100\kappa_{air}$$

$$= 100 \times 8.85 \times 10^{-14}$$

$$= 8.85 \text{ pF}$$

Part (b). When there is only Teflon:

$$C_{1\,cm} = 100\kappa_{Teflon}$$

$$= 100 \times 1.77 \times 10^{-13}$$

$$= 17.7 \text{ pF}$$

Part (c). When there is half air and half Teflon:

$$\kappa_{Av} = \frac{\kappa_{air} + \kappa_{Teflon}}{2}$$

$$= \frac{8.85 \times 10^{-14} + 17.7 \times 10^{-14}}{2} = 13.28 \times 10^{-14} \text{ F/cm}$$

$$C_{0.5\,cm} = 100 \times 13.28 \times 10^{-14}$$

$$= 13.28 \text{ pF}$$

Such a thickness gauge can also be made part of the manufacturing process rather than the inspection process. By now it should be apparent that our own ingenuity is the only limit to obtaining electrical signals by using transducers.

Variations in inductance can also be used to obtain electrical signals which are a measure of a nonelectrical quantity. As discussed in Section 7.4, inductance is determined by the geometry and permeability of the core material. Thus variation in permeability can be used to produce variation in inductance. One method which has been found useful is illustrated in Fig. 14.22.

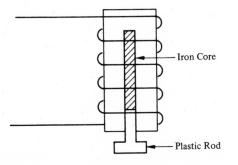

14.22   Inductive transducer.

The iron core is attached to a plastic rod. As the plastic rod is moved deeper in and out of the inductor the average permeability changes accordingly. This principle can be used to measure thickness, position, pressure, or any other physical quantity in which movement is involved.

Transformers are also inductors and a very practical transducer is the **linear voltage differential transformer** (LVDT). The LVDT is another example of moving the core in and out, and is illustrated in Fig. 14.23. The transformer consists of a primary and a secondary which have two windings connected together. These two windings are wound in opposite directions.

An oscillator is connected to the primary side. When the core is in the neutral position equal portions of the iron core are in each section of the secondary. In this case the inductances of both sections are equal and there is no output voltage.

When the core is moved above the neutral position the inductance of the upper section of the secondary increases and the inductance of the lower

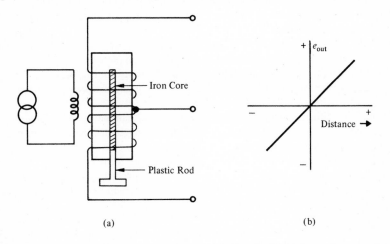

14.23   Linear voltage differential transformer. (a) Sketch. (b) Voltage-distance characteristic.

section decreases. This results in a positive output voltage which increases linearly as the core is moved upward.

When the core is moved below the neutral position the inductance of the lower section increases while the inductance of the upper section decreases. This results in an output voltage which becomes more negative as the core moves downward. The voltage-position characteristic of a LVDT is shown in Fig. 14.23 (b). LVDT's are available which can measure movements as small as tens of microinches.

Several transducers which use resistance, capacitance, and inductance have been mentioned. These were only a brief introduction of what is possible. Other transducers, such as thermocouples and photovoltaic cells, generate a voltage as an output signal rather than requiring application of a voltage to derive a signal.

With transducers, as in most fields of electronics, the only limitations are experience and ingenuity.

Summary

1. Since vacuum tubes have infinite input resistance, vacuum-tube voltmeters have higher input resistance than VOM's. Also, VTVM's have the same high input resistance on all ranges.

2. Differential VTVM's reduce 60-Hz pick-up problems and have superior accuracy with respect to tube aging.

3. Strip chart recorders are used to make a permanent record of voltage versus time. The amplified signal drives a pen motor which makes a record on paper as it passes under the pen.

4. Recorder pens which actually contact the paper have lower frequency response than noncontacting writing schemes. In addition, the paper speeds are adjustable for particular requirements.

5. A CRT displays a spot on a fluorescent screen. This spot can be positioned by applying voltages to horizontal and vertical deflection plates.

6. A CRO uses a calibrated amplifier to display voltage and a linearly increasing voltage to obtain accurate time data. CRO's have higher frequency response than chart recorders since there are no moving parts.

7. A digital voltmeter permits greater accuracy and eliminates the parallax error associated with pointer-type meters. Digital voltmeters are based on comparing the voltage being measured against a standard.

8. Transducers are used to convert a signal from one form to another. Electrical transducers can be used to measure and control nonelectrical quantities.

9. Strain gauges use the relationship between geometry and resistance to measure pressure. Resistance thermometers use the relationship between resistance and temperature.

10. By making the wiper of a potentiometer move with respect to a physical motion, transducer action can result. The technique can be used to measure height, thickness, direction, and so on.

11. Capacitive transducers generally operate by using a change in the dielectric to produce a change in capacitance. Inductive transducers operate by using a change in permeability to produce a change in inductance.

Questions

1. Why does a VTVM have higher input resistance than a VOM?
2. What are the advantages of a differential VTVM over a single-stage VTVM?
3. How does a strip chart recorder operate?
4. Why does a light-sensitive recorder have a higher frequency response than a pen-type recorder?
5. How do the deflection plates in a CRT function?
6. Why is a linearly increasing voltage required for the horizontal deflection system?
7. Why can a CRO have a higher frequency response than a strip chart recorder?
8. What advantages does a DVM have compared to a VTVM?
9. How does a comparator operate?
10. Describe the operation of one form of DVM.
11. Describe the operation of a strain gauge.
12. Describe the operation of a resistance thermometer.
13. Describe how a capacitive transducer might be used to measure the density of samples of wool.
14. How might an inductive transducer be used to measure vibration?

Problems

1. Each resistor in Example 14.1 is doubled. Determine the new input resistance. Assume that the same voltage scales can be maintained by readjusting the load resistor. How do the old and new grid-to-ground voltages compare?
2. Design the voltage divider for a VTVM which is to have 1-, 5-, 10-volt ranges. Input resistance is to be 20 MΩ and maximum grid-to-ground voltage is to be 0.5 volts for all ranges. (*Hint*: Four resistors are required.)
3. What additional range is possible for the conditions of Problem 2?
4. How much paper is required to reproduce one waveform of a 1-Hz signal at 0.1 in./sec, 1 in./sec, and 10 in./sec?
5. The conditions are the same as in Example 14.3 except that the recorder is operated for only 1 min out of every 10 min. How much paper is required?
6. A CRO has sufficient gain to deflect a 1-millivolt signal 1 cm. Determine the resistance ratio for a voltage divider which will deflect a 10-millivolt signal 1 cm.
7. If the input resistance to the CRO in Problem 6 is 1 MΩ determine the actual values for the voltage divider.
8. Assume that the sawtooth across C_1 in Fig. 14.11 is 0.5 volt. What should be the gain of the amplifier if 250 volts are required for a full deflection across the CRT?
9. How can both the DC voltage and the ripple of a power supply be measured accurately using a CRO?
10. A comparator with a gain of 1000 has a 6-mV signal applied to the noninverting input and a 4-mV signal applied to the inverting input. What is the output?

11. What will be the output if the input connections in Problem 10 are reversed?

12. A certain DVM uses a ramp which goes from 0 to 10 volts in 0.1 sec, and a 1-MHz clock. What is the count and the voltage if the ramp equals the measured voltage in 0.07 sec?

13. A strain gauge has a gauge factor of 2. It is 10 cm long and has a resistance of 500 Ω in the unstressed condition. The gauge is placed in a pressure vessel and the stressed length is 10.01 cm. What is the new value of resistance?

14. If a 5-volt source is used for the conditions in Problem 14, what is the difference in current between the stressed and unstressed case?

15. At 20°C the resistance of a gold wire thermometer is 50 Ω. Determine the resistance at 40°C.

16. At 20°C the resistance of a platinum wire thermometer is 100 Ω. What is the temperature when the measured resistance is 95 Ω?

17. For the conditions of Example 14.9, what will be the capacitance if the Teflon is 0.25 cm thick?

18. For the conditions of Example 14.9, what will be the capacitance if the Teflon is $\frac{3}{4}$ cm thick?

19. A certain LVDT has a 1-mV output when the core is moved up 20 μin. What will be the output if the core is moved up 30 μin?

20. For the same LVDT as in Problem 19, what will be the output if the core is moved 40 μin. below the neutral position?

Index

A

Ammeter, 30–32, 95–105
  no-load, 142–145
Ampere, 10, 100
Anode, 252
Amplifier, 290
  current, 291
  ideal, 344
  multistage, 319
  power, 282, 323–326
  push pull, 326
  voltage, 290–292
Antenna, 376
Armature, 182–185
Atom, 4, 8, 11
  acceptor, 22, 242
  donor, 21, 242
Automatic control, 154, 357–360
  of frequency, 375
  of gain, 360
Autopilot, 359
Avalanche, 272–275

B

Bandwidth, 316
Barkhausen-Kurz criterion, 363, 371
Barrier potential, 242–244, 246
Base, 284
  common, 294–301
Battery, 10, 14, 25
Bel, 317
Bias, 243
  fixed, 302–303
  forward, 243–250
  reverse, 244–250
  stabilization, 304–307
Bilateral, 249
Binary number, 409–412
Black box, 128–142, 164

C

Capacitance, 193
Capacitor, 192–198, 261–269
  by pass, 311, 380
  electrolytic, 269
Carrier, 377
Cascading, 319–323
Cathode, 252, 333
  follower, 335
  grounded, 335
  ray tube, 432–433
Choke, 226, 266
Chopper, 328–329
Circuit, 30, 66
  closed, 30
  equivalent, 69, 123–126, 133–138
  open, 30, 64–65
  short, 70, 84, 115
Collector, 284
  common, 298–301
  leakage current, 304–307
Color code, 17, 118
Commutator, 184
Conductor, 11–12, 14–15
Continuity, 115–116
Controlled source, 288
Coulomb, 5, 10, 34
Coulomb's law, 5–6, 11
Counter, 417
  binary, 417, 439
  down, 418

NOTES

NOTES

NOTES

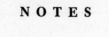

NOTES

NOTES

NOTES

NOTES

NOTES

NOTES